C0-AYP-847

Surviving University

First Year Chemistry

Second Edition

Maria Sokolova

NELSON / EDUCATION

NELSON / EDUCATION

COPYRIGHT © 2012 by Nelson Education Ltd.

Printed and bound in Canada
4 5 6 7   16 15 14 13

For more information contact Nelson Education Ltd., 1120 Birchmount Road, Toronto, Ontario, M1K 5G4. Or you can visit our Internet site at http://www.nelson.com

ALL RIGHTS RESERVED. No part of this work covered by the copyright herein may be reproduced, transcribed, or used in any form or by any means—graphic, electronic, or mechanical, including photocopying, recording, taping, Web distribution, or information storage and retrieval systems—without the written permission of the publisher.

For permission to use material from this text or product, submit all requests online at www.cengage.com/permissions. Further questions about permissions can be emailed to permissionrequest@cengage.com

Every effort has been made to trace ownership of all copyrighted material and to secure permission from copyright holders. In the event of any question arising as to the use of any material, we will be pleased to make the necessary corrections in future printings.

This textbook is a Nelson custom publication. Because your instructor has chosen to produce a custom publication, you pay only for material that you will use in your course.

ISBN-13: 978-0-17-662438-5
ISBN-10: 0-17-662438-4

Cover Credit:
Sebastian Duda/Shutterstock

Dr. François Caron

B.Sc. (Chicoutimi), M.Sc. (INRS-Eau), Ph.D. (McMaster)
Associate Professor, Department of Chemistry and Biochemistry, Laurentian University, Sudbury, Ontario

Dr. Sabine Montaut

D.E.A., M.Sc., Ph.D. (France)
Assistant Professor, Department of Chemistry and Biochemistry, Laurentian University, Sudbury, Ontario

"We often write books and give lectures about how a student should learn. We never know if we hit their interest. This book represents what a student thinks and other students might relate to the content of this work. It is written by a student who has done this material, for students who will follow the same path."

"It is a concise and useful book for anyone studying and reviewing chemistry at the first-year university level. Its question and step-by-step answer format will help you to understand the basic chemical concepts and teach you how to solve the problems on your own."

John Breau

B.Sc, M.Sc. (Laurentian)
Sessional Professor, Department of
Chemistry and Biochemistry,
Laurentian University, Sudbury,
Ontario

"This book offers the students a student's view on how to solve many first year General Chemistry type problems. It can serve also as a quick reference to anyone who has previously taken Chemistry and requires a quick refresher on selected topics."

Surviving University: First Year Chemistry

First Year Students' Comments

Laurentian University, Sudbury, Ontario

Laurentian university students using the first edition of this study guide

"It had all useful concepts easily accessible when I needed it"

"The information was more "how to" than the textbook. It had answers to basic questions"

"[It] makes the textbook easier to understand. [It] only contains the needed info"

"It simplified things into words I can comprehend"

"Simple and easy to learn from"

"How I would make notes"

"[It had] step by step examples that are useful for assignments and studying"

Surviving University: First Year Chemistry

First Year Students' Comments

Laurentian University, Sudbury, Ontario

"Great side help for the class"

"It helped me understand formulas"

"I liked how it was organized and I could always find what I was looking for in the index"

"It summarizes the material. Its examples are great"

"Loved the book and it helped a lot"

"No joke- it saved my life"

"Overall, it is a great book"

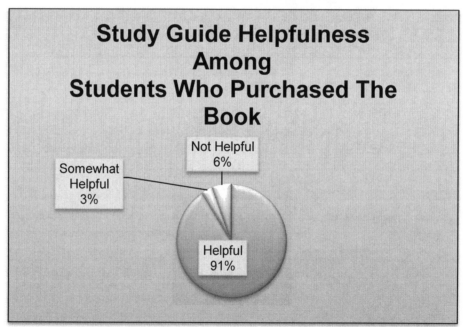

Study Guide Helpfulness Among Students Who Purchased The Book

Not Helpful 6%

Somewhat Helpful 3%

Helpful 91%

* From 103 students (2010)

I would like to thank Dr. Francois Caron and Dr. Sabine Montaut at Laurentian University for reviewing this book.

I would like to thank Dr. Francois Caron at Laurentian University for his contribution towards the nuclear chemistry section of this book.

I would like to thank Bernard Shami at Laurentian University for preparing the IR spectrum image.

I would like to thank Dr. Francois Caron, Dr. Sabine Montaut, Dr. Joy Gray-Munro, and Dr. John Breau at Laurentian University for their dedication, support, and encouragement.

I would like to thank the first year students enrolled in CHMI-1006 at Laurentian University for their feedback.

A Word From The Author

Welcome to first year chemistry! My name is Maria Sokolova and I am a 4th year biomedical biology student at Laurentian University. 3 years ago I was in your position. I saw first year students struggle with chemistry. I believe that the biggest part of the problem is the transition between high school and university. Just like me, many first year students come from high school. In high school, teachers gave us simple explanations and simple examples. Many examples which were given in class appeared on tests. Students did not necessarily need to understand the concepts in order to do well. I saw students who memorized the examples, regurgitated them on tests, and received high marks. Once we entered university, we were overwhelmed by 5 courses and 4-5 labs. We needed to understand concepts in order to apply them and do well. We also needed to develop work ethic and time management skills. I struggled during my first year of university, spent every weekday and weekend at the library, attended tutorials, asked my professors for explanations, and called my friends in the middle of the night with cries for help. All of the sweat and hard work paid off and resulted in being on the Dean's list and receiving an enhanced scholarship.

I thought that I could do something to ease the transition between high school and university. I wanted to decrease the amount of time you would spend understanding the concepts and to increase the time that you would have to practice the problems and write lab reports.

In the summer between my first and second years, I wrote this study guide. The book was reviewed by Dr. Montaut, who is a professor at Laurentian University. I also gave a copy to Dr. Caron. He thought that the study guide was an excellent idea for his course. As a result, the study guide was published by Nelson Education and became mandatory for all students enrolled in General Chemistry 1 and General Chemistry 2 courses at Laurentian University.

Students began to use the first edition of this study guide in September of 2010. Ninety-one percent of the surveyed students taking first year chemistry at Laurentian University found this study guide to be helpful. In the summer of 2011, I decided to incorporate students' suggestions and to expand the book by adding more concepts and examples. This edition has been reviewed by Dr. Caron. I hope you find this book to be helpful. If you have any comments or feedback or would like to order more copies of this book, please contact the publisher.

Surviving University: First Year Chemistry

Table of Contents

Surviving University: First Year Chemistry

Part 1

Basic Concepts of Chemistry

Types of matter

States

Properties

Kinetic molecular theory

Density

Measurements

Converting units

Temperature scales

Precision and accuracy

Significant figures

Basic Concepts of Chemistry

Quantitative information- numerical data (ex. mass)
Qualitative information- non-numerical data (ex. appearance)

Types of matter

Matter- anything that has mass and volume

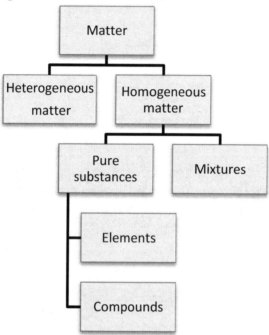

Heterogeneous matter- has nonuniform composition
Homogeneous matter- has uniform composition
Pure substance- has a fixed composition and its own properties
Mixture- consists of 2 or more pure substances
Element- cannot be broken down into 2 or more pure substances
Compound- consists of 2 or more elements

States

- Solid (s), liquid (l), gas (g), or aqueous (aq)
  - Aqueous (aq) means that the substance has been dissolved in water

Surviving University: First Year Chemistry

Physical and chemical changes

Physical change- does not result in production of a new chemical substance (ex. water turns into ice)
Chemical change- reactants are transformed into products (ex. hydrogen and oxygen gases combine to produce water)

Properties

Physical property- is observed or measured without changing the chemical composition of a substance (ex. solution colour)
Chemical property- is observed when a substance to undergo a chemical reaction (ex. iron combines with oxygen and water to produce rust)
Extensive property- depends on the amount of substance present (ex. mass of a substance can be changed by adding/removing the substance)
Intensive property- does not depend on the amount of substance present (ex. the boiling point of water is always 100°C)

Kinetic molecular theory

- All matter consists of tiny particles that are in constant motion
- Increasing temperature results in faster motion of particles
- In solids- particles are packed close together, vibrate back and forth
- In liquids- particles are arranged randomly, move past each other, can collide with each other
- In gases- particles are far apart, move very fast past each other, can collide with each other

Density

Density- mass of a substance per unit volume

$$\rho = \frac{m}{V}$$
$$\rho_{H_2O} = 1g/mL$$

Note: ρ= density (g/mL or g/L or mg/mL or mg/L or kg/mL or kg/L), m= mass (g or mg or kg), V= volume (mL or L), ρ_{H2O}= density of water (g/mL)

Example 1
The density of carbon monoxide is 1.25g/L. What is the mass of carbon monoxide in a 2L container?
m= ?g
V= 2L
ρ= 1.25g/L

Surviving University: First Year Chemistry

Rearranging $\rho = \frac{m}{V}$ for mass,

$m = \rho \times V$
$m = 1.25 g/L \times 2L$
$m = 2.50 g$

The mass of carbon monoxide in a 2L container was 2.50g.

Measurements

- These units are conventionally used for measurements

Used to measure	Unit	Abbreviation
Length	meter	m
Mass	kilogram	kg
Time	second	s
Amount of a substance	mole	mol
Temperature	Kelvin	K

- These are some common power-of-ten prefixes

Prefix	Abbreviation	Power
giga	G	10^{9}
mega	M	10^{6}
kilo	k	10^{3}
deci	d	10^{-1}
centi	c	10^{-2}
milli	m	10^{-3}
micro	μ	10^{-6}
nano	n	10^{-9}

- It is important to know that

$$1L = 1000 cm^3$$
$$1mL = 1cm^3 = 1cc$$
$$1 \, angstrom = 1\text{Å} = 10^{-10} m$$

Converting between units

$$New \, Units = original \, units \times \frac{new \, units}{original \, units}$$

Example 1
How many L are in 55.1mL?
Volume in L= ?L

Volume in mL= 55.1mL

$$Volume\ in\ L = 55.1\cancel{mL} \times \frac{1L}{1000\cancel{mL}}$$

$Volume\ in\ L = 0.0551L$

There are 0.0551L in 55.1mL.

Temperature scales

Kelvin temperature scale

$$Temperature\ in\ Kelvin = (Temperature\ in\ °C + 273.15°C) \times \frac{1K}{1°C}$$

$$Temperature\ in\ °C = (Temperature\ in\ K - 273.15K) \times \frac{1°C}{1K}$$

Absolute Zero- temperature at which molecules have no kinetic energy (velocity of molecules= 0 μm/s); occurs at 0K (-273.15°C)

Example 1
The boiling point of water is 100°C. What is this temperature in Kelvin?
Temperature in °C= 100°C
Temperature in K= ?K

$$Temperature\ in\ Kelvin = (Temperature\ in\ °C + 273.15°C) \times \frac{1K}{1°C}$$

$$Temperature\ in\ Kelvin = (100°C + 273.15°C) \times \frac{1K}{1°C}$$

$$Temperature\ in\ Kelvin = 373.15\cancel{°C} \times \frac{1K}{1\cancel{°C}}$$

$Temperature\ in\ Kelvin = 373.15K$

The boiling point of water is 373.15K.

Precision and accuracy

$$Error = experimental\ value - accepted\ value$$

$$\%\ Error = \frac{|experimental\ value - accepted\ value|}{accepted\ value} \times 100\%$$

Note: | | means absolute value (all negative values become positive) (ex. |-6°C|= 6°C)
Note: experimental value comes from the lab, accepted value comes from calculations, and error measures the discrepancy between data obtained in the lab and data calculated

Example 1
The accepted mass of a penny is 2.35g. You measured the mass to be 2.41g. Find the % error.
 Experimental value= 2.41g
Accepted value= 2.35g
% error= ?%

$$\% \ Error = \frac{|experimental \ value - accepted \ value|}{accepted \ value} \times 100\%$$

$$\% \ Error = \frac{|2.41g - 2.35g|}{2.35g} \times 100\%$$

$$\% \ Error = 2.55\%$$

Percent error was 2.55%.

Significant figures

Rule	Examples
All numbers other than zero are significant. See the rules below to determine whether a zero is significant.	124 has 3 significant figures 13.416 has 5 significant figures
All zeros between 2 significant digits are significant	1.002 has 4 significant figures Significant 15.019 has 5 significant figures
All zeros that are to the right of the rest of significant digits are not significant	500 has 1 significant figure Not significant 14000 has 2 significant figures
If there is a decimal point, then the zeroes that are to the right of the rest of significant digits are significant	Decimal point 500. has 3 significant figures Significant 1400.00 has 6 significant figures Decimal point

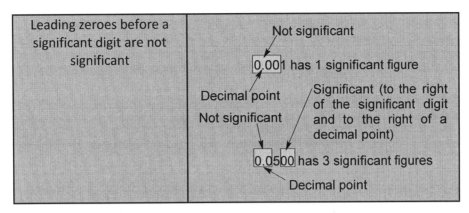

Addition and subtraction

- Determine which number (that is added/subtracted) has the lowest amount of decimal places→ the number of decimal places in the answer should be the same as this number

Example 1
Perform the following calculation: 6.01g+12.000g=?g

6.01 has 2 decimal places

12.000 has 3 decimal places

The answer should have 2 decimal places.

6.01g+ 12.000g= 18.01g

Multiplication/division

- Determine which number (that is multiplied/divided) has the lowest amount of significant figures→ the number of significant figures in the answer should be the same as this number

Example 2
Perform the following calculation: 6.00mLx2.1mL=?mL^2

6.00 has 3 significant figures

2.1 has 2 significant figures

The answer should have 2 significant figures.
6.00mLx 2.1mL= 13mL

Part 2

Atoms, Molecules, and Ions

Surviving University: First Year Chemistry

Atomic structure

Isotopes

Atomic weight

Periodic table

Fundamental laws

Ions

Naming ions and compounds

Coulomb's law

Moles and molar mass

Percent composition

Empirical formula

Molecular formula

Atoms, Molecules, and Ions

Element- cannot be broken down by chemical means into 2 or more pure substances (ex. Na)

Atom- the smallest particle that has all of the chemical properties of an element

Molecule- a combination of elements; is the smallest unit that has all of the properties of a substance (ex. a water molecule (1 H_2O) has all of the properties of water)

Atomic structure

- An atom is mostly made up of empty space
    - The nucleus is very small comparing to the size of the atom

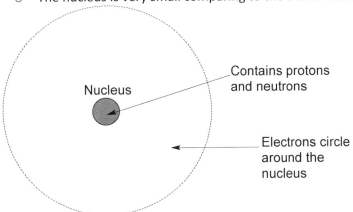

Electron (e⁻)- a negatively charged particle, circles around the nucleus, is much lighter than a proton or a neutron

Proton (p)- a positively charged particle, is inside of the nucleus

Neutron (n)- a particle that has no charge, is inside of the nucleus

	Mass
Electron (e⁻)	9.109×10^{-28}g
Proton (p)	1.673×10^{-24}g
Neutron (n)	1.675×10^{-24}g

Atomic number- # of protons= # of electrons (in a neutral atom)

Mass number- # of protons + # of neutrons

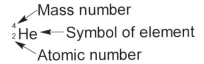

Isotopes

Isotopes- atoms of the same element that have the same # of protons (same atomic number), but different # of neutrons

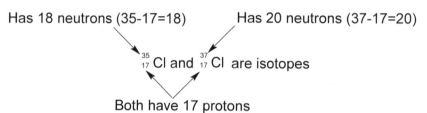

Has 18 neutrons (35-17=18)   Has 20 neutrons (37-17=20)

$^{35}_{17}$Cl and $^{37}_{17}$Cl are isotopes

Both have 17 protons

- In nature, an element exists as a mixture of its isotopes

Isotopic abundance- relative amount of a certain isotope that is present among a mixture of isotopes

$$\% \ abundance = \frac{\# \ atoms \ of \ a \ specific \ isotope}{\# \ of \ atoms \ of \ all \ of \ the \ isotopes} \times 100\%$$
$$100\% = \% \ abundance \ of \ isotope \ 1 + \% \ abundance \ of \ isotope \ 2 + \cdots$$

Note: % abundance is measured experimentally using a mass spectrometer (the value will most likely be given to you→ do not need to calculate)

Atomic weight

Atomic weight- average mass of all isotopes of an element

- Atomic weight is the mass seen on the periodic table

Chlorine

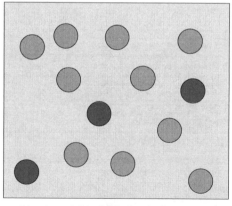

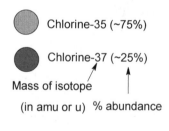

Chlorine-35 (~75%)

Chlorine-37 (~25%)

Mass of isotope

(in amu or u)   % abundance

Atomic weight of chlorine is the average mass of all of its naturally occuring isotopes (35.45amu). This mass appears on the periodic table.

- Atomic weight is measured in atomic mass units (u or amu)

Surviving University: First Year Chemistry

o   1 atomic mass unit (u or amu) is equal to 1/12 of mass of carbon 12 (has 6 protons and 6 neutrons)

$$1amu = 1u = 1.66054 \times 10^{-24}g$$

$$Atomic\ weight = \frac{\%\ A_1}{100\%} \times m_1 + \frac{\%\ A_2}{100\%} \times m_2 + \frac{\%\ A_3}{100\%} \times m_3 + \cdots$$

Note: $\%A_1$ is percentage abundance of isotope 1 and m_1 is the mass of isotope 1 (u)

Example 1
Find mass of atom of ^{13}C in grams with atomic mass of 13.00355u.

$$Mass\ in\ grams = 13.00355u \times \frac{1.66054 \times 10^{-24}g}{1u}$$

$$Mass\ in\ grams = 2.15926 \times 10^{-23}g$$

The mass of carbon-13 atom with atomic mass of 13.00355u is 2.15926×10^{-23}g.

Example 2
Boron has 2 isotopes: m_1= 10.01294u, m_2= 11.00931u
Atomic weight of boron is 10.81u. Find percentage abundance of each isotope.

$100\% = \%\ abundance\ of\ isotope\ 1 + \%\ abundance\ of\ isotope\ 2$
Which is the same as
$100\% = \%A_1 + \%A_2$
Let x be the percentage abundance of isotope 2 ($\%A_2$).
$100\% = \%A_1 + x$ Rearranging for $\%A_1$
$100\% - x = \%A_1$
Know:
m_1= 10.01294u
m_2= 11.00931u
$\%A_1$= 100-x
$\%A_2$= x
Atomic weight= 10.81u

$$Atomic\ weight = \frac{\%\ A_1}{100\%} \times m_1 + \frac{\%\ A_2}{100\%} \times m_2$$

$$10.81 = \frac{(100-x)(10.01294)}{100} + \frac{(x)(11.00931)}{100}$$

This is the same as (common denominator)

$$10.81 = \frac{(100-x)(10.01294) + (x)(11.00931)}{100}$$

Multiply both sides by 100 to remove the fraction

$$\mathbf{100} \times 10.81 = \left(\frac{(100-x)(10.01294) + (x)(11.00931)}{\cancel{100}} \right) \times \mathbf{\cancel{100}}$$

$1081 = (100 - x)(10.01294) + (x)(11.00931)$ Expand
$1081 = 1001.294 - 10.01294x + 11.00931x$
$1081 = 1001.294 + 0.99637x$
$79.706 = 0.99637x$
$x = 80$

% abundance of isotope 2= 80%
% abundance of isotope 1= 100%-80%=20%
Percentage abundance of isotopes 1 and 2 were 80% and 20% respectively.

Example 3
Antimony has 2 isotopes: antimony-121 (120.904amu, % abundance of 57.20%), and antimony-123 (122.904amu, % abundance of 42.80%). Find atomic weight of antimony.

m_1= 120.904amu
m_2= 122.904amu
$\%A_1$= 57.20%
$\%A_2$= 42.80%
Atomic weight= ?amu

$$Atomic\ weight = \frac{\%\ A_1}{100\%} \times m_1 + \frac{\%\ A_2}{100\%} \times m_2$$

$$Atomic\ weight = \frac{57.20\%}{100\%} \times 120.904amu + \frac{42.80\%}{100\%} \times 122.904amu$$

$Atomic\ weight = 69.16amu + 52.60amu$
$Atomic\ weight = 121.76amu$

The atomic weight of antimony is 121.76amu.

Periodic table- history

- Mendeleyev (1869) arranged elements by mass, left space for unknown elements, predicted unknown elements' properties
- Moseley organized elements by their atomic numbers (# of protons)

Periodic table

Row= period
Column= group
Metals- solids, conduct electricity
Nonmetals- solids, liquids, gases, do not conduct electricity (except for carbon)
Transition metals- metals in groups 3-12
Main group metals- all metals that are not transition metals
Alkali metals- group 1, most reactive metals (most reactive is francium)

Surviving University: First Year Chemistry

Alkaline earth metals- group 2
Halogens- group 17, most reactive nonmetals (most reactive is fluorine)
Noble gases- not reactive
- Heaviest abundant element is uranium (heaviest element in nature)
- Br and Hg are liquids at room temperature

Periodic table- electron arrangement

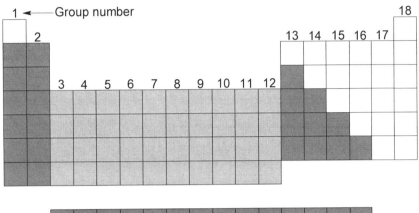

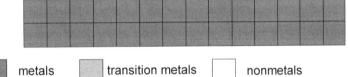

metals   transition metals   nonmetals

Valence electrons- electrons in the outer shell of an atom

Group #	# valence electrons
1	1
2	2
13	3
14	4
15	5
16	6
17	7
18	8

- Metals lose electrons

Group #	# of electrons that an atom can lose
1	1
2	2
13	3
14	Can either gain or lose 4 electrons

- Transition metals can lose different amount of electrons (depending on the situation)

Element	# of electrons that an atom can lose	Charges	Element	# of electrons that an atom can lose	Charges
Cr	2, 3, or 6	+2, +3, +6	Mn	2, 3, 4, or 7	+2, +3, +4, +7
Co	2 or 3	+2, +3	Hg	1 or 2	+1, +2
Cu	1 or 2	+1, +2	Ni	2 or 3	+2, +3
Au	1 or 3	+1, +3	Sn	2 or 4	+2, +4
Fe	2 or 3	+2, +3	Pb	2 or 4	+2, +4

- Nonmetals gain electrons

Group #	# of electrons that an atom can gain
15	3
16	2
17	1
18	Do not gain or lose any electrons

Fundamental laws

Law of conservation of matter
- Matter cannot be created or destroyed during a chemical reaction

Law of conservation of mass
- Mass cannot be created or destroyed during a chemical reaction

Law of conservation of energy
- Energy cannot be created of destroyed during a chemical reaction

Law of definite proportions

- All compounds have the same proportion of elements by mass (ex. NaCl- 1 sodium will combine with 1 chlorine to form NaCl)

Law of multiple proportions
- Atoms combine in whole number ratios (ex. H_2O- 2 hydrogen atoms combine with 1 oxygen atom→ cannot have 1.5 hydrogen atoms combining with 0.6 oxygen atoms)

Ions

Neutral atom- an atom which has no charge (ex. Cl)
- A neutral atom has the same number of protons as the number of electrons

Ion- an electrically charged atom (ex. Cl^-)
- An ion does not have the same number of protons as the number of electrons→ the atom has lost or gained electron(s)

Monatomic ion- a single atom that has gained/lost electron(s) (ex. Na^+)
- **Cation**- a +ively charged atom(ex. Li^+)- has lost electron(s)
- **Anion**- a -ively charged atom (ex. Cl^-)- has gained electron(s) (has gained negative charge, became more negative)

Polyatomic ion- 2 or more atoms with an overall electric charge (ex. CO_3^{2-})
- Adding a hydrogen to a polyatomic ion increases the charge by 1

$$PO_4^{3-} + H^+ \longrightarrow PO_4^{2-}$$
ex.

Oxyanion- polyatomic ion that contains oxygen (ex. MnO_4^-)
It is important to memorize this chart

Polyatomic ion	Name	Polyatomic ion	Name
NH_4^+	ammonium	HPO_4^{2-}	hydrogen phosphate
CN^-	cyanide	OH^-	hydroxide
$CH_3CO_2^-$	acetate	SO_4^{2-}	sulfate
CO_3^{2-}	carbonate	ClO_3^-	chlorate
HCO_3^-	hydrogen carbonate	CrO_4^{2-}	chromate
NO_3^-	nitrate	$Cr_2O_7^{2-}$	dichromate
PO_4^{3-}	phosphate	MnO_4^-	permanganate

Naming ions

Naming monatomic ions

> *Name of cation = Element name + ion*
> For transition metals, put the charge as a Roman numeral in brackets after the element's name
> *Name of anion = Element name (remove − ine, add − ide) + ion*

Examples

Ion	Name	Ion	Name
Li^+	lithium ion	F^-	fluoride ion
Na^+	sodium ion	Br^-	bromide ion
Ca^{2+}	calcium ion	Cl^-	chloride ion
Fe^{3+}	iron (III) ion	I^-	iodide ion
Sn^{2+}	tin (II) ion	O^{2-}	oxide ion
Cu^+	copper (I) ion	S^{2-}	sulfide ion
Al^{3+}	aluminum ion	N^{3-}	nitride ion

Naming oxyanions

Polyatomic ion	Name	
ClO_4^-	**Perchlorate** ion	has 1 more oxygen atom than chlorate ion
ClO_3^-	Chlor**ate** ion	
ClO_2^-	Chlor**ite** ion	has 1 less oxygen atom than chlorate ion
ClO^-	**hypo**chlor**ite** ion	has 2 less oxygen atoms than chlorate ion

Examples

Polyatomic ion	Name	Polyatomic ion	Name
NO_3^-	nitrate ion	SO_4^{2-}	sulfate ion
NO_2^-	nitrite ion	SO_3^{2-}	sulfite ion

Overview of compounds

Compound- made up of 2 or more elements, can be broken down by chemical means (ex. LiBr)

Types of compounds
- Ionic compounds (ex. NaCl)

- o Functional groups can contain C, H, S, O, Cl, Br, I, N
- o Metal+ nonmetal
- o Metals lose electrons (become +ively charged (become cations)), nonmetals gain electrons (become -ively charged (become anions))
- o Cations and anions combine to form a neutral ionic compound (no charge) (ex. $Li^+ + Cl^- \rightarrow LiCl$)
- **Molecular compounds** (ex. H_2O)
  - o Nonmetal + nonmetal
  - o Electrons are shared between atoms
- **Polyatomic compounds**
  - o Polyatomic ions + cation/anion (ex. $LiHSO_4$)
- **Anhydrous compounds**
  - o Do not contain H_2O (ex. $CaCl_2$)
- **Hydrated compounds**
  - o Contain H_2O (ex. $CuCl_2 \cdot 2H_2O$)
  - o Need to include mass of water when calculating the molar mass of a compound

Naming compounds

Naming ionic compounds

$Name = First\ element\ name + second\ element\ name\ (remove - ine, add - ide)$

For transition metals, put the charge as a Roman numeral in brackets after the first element's name

Examples

Compound	Name	Compound	Name
LiCl	lithium chloride	CaS	calcium sulfide
MgO	magnesium oxide	$AlCl_3$	aluminum chloride
PbO	lead (II) oxide	$FeCl_3$	iron (III) chloride

Naming molecular compounds

$Name = Prefix\ of\ first\ element + first\ element\ name$
$+ prefix\ of\ second\ element$
$+ second\ element\ name\ (remove - ine, add - ide)$

- Prefix refers to the number of atoms of that element
- If there is 1 atom of the first element, mono is <u>not</u> used
- If there is 1 atom of the second element, mono is used

# of elements	Prefix	# of elements	Prefix
1	Mono	6	Hexa
2	Di	7	Hepta
3	Tri	8	Octa
4	Tetra	9	Nona
5	Penta	10	Deca

Examples

Compound	Name	Compound	Name
CO	carbon monoxide (not monocarbon monoxide)	CO_2	carbon dioxide
H_2O	dihydrogen monoxide	N_2O_3	dinitrogen trioxide

Naming polyatomic compounds

> *Name = Element name (that is before the polyatomic ion)*
> *+ polyatomic ion name*
> For transition metals, put the charge as a Roman numeral in brackets after the first element's name

Examples

Compound	Name	Compound	Name
$K_2Cr_2O_7$	potassium dichromate	$NaOH$	sodium hydroxide
$Ba(NO_2)_2$	barium nitrite	$NaHSO_4$	sodium hydrogen sulfate
$Cu(CN)_2$	copper (II) cyanide	$KMnO_4$	potassium permanganate

Coulomb's law

- Opposite charges attract, similar charges repel
- Attraction/repulsion force is proportional to the distance between the charges and the magnitude of the charges

$$Force = \frac{q_1 \times q_2}{r^2}$$

Note: q_1= magnitude of charge of the first charge (ex. 6 Coulombs), q_2= magnitude of charge of the second charge (ex. 6 Coulombs), r= distance between charges (m)

Moles and molar mass

- 1 **mole** of any element consists of 6.0221415×10^{23} particles of that element
    - 1 mole of atoms= 6.0221415×10^{23} atoms
    - 1 mole of molecules= 6.0221415×10^{23} molecules

$$1 \, mol = 6.0221415 \times 10^{23} particles$$
$$Avogadro's \, number = 6.0221415 \times 10^{23} particles/mol$$
$$\# \, particles = n \times 6.0221415 \times 10^{23} particles/mol$$

Note: n= number of moles (mol)

Molar mass (M)- atomic mass of an element (from periodic table) per 1 mole (g/mol)

Examples

Molar mass	Calculation	Explanation
M_{Na}	$22.99g/mol$	From periodic table
M_{O_2}	$2(16.00g/mol) = 32.00g/mol$	There are 2 O atoms→ multiply molar mass of O by 2
M_{H_2O}	$2(1.01g/mol) + 16.00g/mol = 18.02g/mol$	There are 2 H atoms→ multiply molar mass of H by 2, then add molar masses of H and O together
M_{NaCl}	$22.99g/mol + 35.45g/mol = 58.44g/mol$	Add molar masses of Na and Cl together

$$n = \frac{m}{M}$$

Note: n= number of moles (mol), m= mass (g), M= molar mass (g/mol)

Example 1
a) *Find number of moles in 16.5g of $H_2C_2O_4$.*
b) *How many molecules are in 16.5g of $H_2C_2O_4$?*
c) *How many atoms of carbon are there in 16.5g of $H_2C_2O_4$?*

a) *Find number of moles in 16.5g of $H_2C_2O_4$.*
m= 16.5g
n= ? mol
$$M = 2(1.01g/mol) + 2(12.01g/mol) + 4(16.00g/mol)$$
$$= 90.04g/mol$$

$$n = \frac{m}{M}$$

$$n = \frac{16.5g}{90.04g/mol}$$

$$n = 0.183mol$$

In 16.5g of $H_2C_2O_4$ there are 0.183mol.

b) *How many molecules are in 16.5g of $H_2C_2O_4$?*
$\#molecules = n \times (6.0221415 \times 10^{23} molecules/mol)$
$\#molecules = 0.183mol \times (6.0221415 \times 10^{23} molecules/mol)$
$\#molecules = 1.10 \times 10^{23} molecules$
In 16.5g of $H_2C_2O_4$ there are 1.10×10^{23} molecules.

c) *How many atoms of carbon are there in 16.5g of $H_2C_2O_4$?*

$$\# C\ atoms = 1.10 \times 10^{23} molecules \times \frac{2\ C\ atoms}{1\ molecule}$$

$$\# C\ atoms = 2.20 \times 10^{23} C\ atoms$$

In 16.5g of $H_2C_2O_4$ there are 2.20×10^{23} carbon atoms.

Example 2
Find the number of atoms which are present in 12u of carbon 12.
Molecular weight= 12amu
atoms= ?atoms
Steps
1. Find mass of carbon using $1amu = 1u = 1.66054 \times 10^{-24} g$
2. Find number of moles using $n = \frac{m}{M}$
Find # of atoms using $\# particles = \# moles \times 6.0221415 \times 10^{23} particles/mol$

$$m_C = 12u \times \frac{1.66054 \times 10^{-24} g}{1u}$$

$$m_C = 1.99 \times 10^{-23} g$$

From the periodic table, $M_C = 12.01g/mol$

$$n_C = \frac{m}{M}$$

$$n_C = \frac{1.99 \times 10^{-23} g}{12.01g/mol}$$

$$n_C = 1.66 \times 10^{-24} mol$$

$\# C\ atoms = \# moles \times 6.0221415 \times 10^{23} atoms/mol$
$\# C\ atoms = 1.66 \times 10^{-24} mol \times 6.0221415 \times 10^{23} atoms/mol$
$\# C\ atoms = 0.999atoms \approx 1atom$
Thus, there is 1 atom in 12u of carbon 12.

Percent composition

$$\% \ composition = \frac{mass \ of \ an \ element}{mass \ of \ a \ molecule} \times 100\%$$

$$\% \ composition = \frac{\# \ atoms \ of \ element \ in \ a \ molecule \ \times \ molar \ mass \ of \ an \ element}{molar \ mass \ of \ a \ molecule} \times 100\%$$

Example 1

Find the % composition by mass of C atom in aspirin ($C_9H_8O_4$).

Steps

1. Find molar mass of the entire molecule
2. Find molar mass of C atom (from periodic table)
3. Find % composition using

$$\% \ composition = \frac{\# \ atoms \ of \ element \ in \ a \ molecule \ \times \ molar \ mass \ of \ an \ element}{molar \ mass \ of \ a \ molecule} \times 100\%$$

$M_{C_9H_8O_4} = 9(12.01 \ g/mol) + 8(1.01 \ g/mol) + 4(16.00 \ g/mol)$

$M_{C_9H_8O_4} = 180.17g/mol$

$M_C = 12.01g/mol$

There are 9 C atoms in $C_9H_8O_4$

$$\% \ composition = \frac{9 \times 12.01g/mol}{180.17g/mol} \times 100\%$$

$\% \ composition = 59.99\%$

The percent composition by mass of C atom in aspirin was 59.99%.

Example 2

Find % composition of carbon in C_8H_{18}. What is the mass of carbon in 454g of C_8H_{18}?

Let's assume that there is only 1mol of C_8H_{18} (not 454g).

Steps

1. Find mass of C_8H_{18} in 1mol of C_8H_{18} by finding the molar mass of C_8H_{18}
2. Find molar mass of C atom (from periodic table)
3. Find mass of C in 1mol of C_8H_{18} using $m = n \times M$
4. Find % composition of C atoms in 1 mol of C_8H_{18} using

$$\% \ composition = \frac{mass \ of \ an \ element}{mass \ of \ a \ molecule} \times 100\%$$

5. Find mass of C in 454g of C_8H_{18} using $mass \ of \ C \ (in \ 454g) = \frac{\% \ carbon}{100\%} \times 454g$

$M_{C_8H_{18}} = 8(12.01g/mol) + 18(1.01g/mol) = 114.26g/mol$

The molar mass indicates that the mass of 1 mol of C_8H_{18} is 114.26g.

In 1mol of C_8H_{18}, there are 8mol of C atoms

$n_c = 8mol$
$M_c = 12.01g/mol$
$m_c = ? g$
$m = n \times M$
$m_c = 8mol \times 12.01g/mol$
$m_c = 96.08g$

This means that there are 96.08g of C in 1 mol of C_8H_{18}.

$$\% \ carbon \ (in \ 1 \ mol) = \frac{96.08g}{114.26g} \times 100\%$$

$\% \ carbon \ (in \ 1 \ mol) = 84.09\%$

This means that 84.09% of mass of C_8H_{18} is due to C atoms.

$$mass \ of \ carbon \ (in \ 454g) = \frac{84.09\%}{100\%} \times 454g$$

$mass \ of \ carbon \ (in \ 454g) = 382g$

The percent composition of carbon in C_8H_{18} was 84.12%. In 454g of C_8H_{18}, there were 382g of carbon.

Empirical and molecular formulas

Molecular formula- identifies the names and the actual number of atoms present in a molecule (ex. C_2H_8)
- Is a multiple of the empirical formula

Empirical formula- lowest ratio of atoms in a molecule (ex. CH_4)
- To find the empirical formula, divide the subscripts of the molecular formula by the greatest common factor

Example 1
Find the empirical formula for the following compounds.

$$C_2H_6O_2 \qquad\qquad H_2O_2 \qquad\qquad CH_2O$$

$$A \qquad\qquad\qquad B \qquad\qquad\qquad C$$

Molecule	Molecular formula	Empirical formula
A	$C_2H_6O_2$	$C_{\frac{2}{2}}H_{\frac{6}{2}}O_{\frac{2}{2}} = CH_3O$
B	H_2O_2	$H_{\frac{2}{2}}O_{\frac{2}{2}} = HO$
C	CH_2O	The molecular formula is already in the lowest ratio CH_2O

Example 2
What is the molecular formula of the following compound? What is its empirical formula?

H$_3$C⁀
⎺⎺CH$_3$

Count the number of C and H atoms present in this molecule.

1 C, 3 H atoms
↓
     1 C, 2 H atoms
     ↓
H$_3$C⎯
     ⎺CH$_3$
   ↑ ↑
1 C, 2 H atoms ↑
    1 C, 3 H atoms

In total, there are 4 C atoms and 10 H atoms. This means that the molecular formula is C$_4$H$_{10}$.
However, C$_4$H$_{10}$ is not the lowest ratio of atoms in the molecule. Both 4 and 10 can be divided by 2.

$$\frac{C_4 H_{10}}{2 \quad 2} = C_2 H_5$$

This means that the empirical formula is C$_2$H$_5$.
Thus, the molecular formula is C$_4$H$_{10}$ and the empirical formula is C$_2$H$_5$.

Example 3
Find empirical formula for a compound ($N_x H_y$) consisting of 87.42% N and 12.58% H.

Steps
1. Convert percentages to masses (assume that you are using 100g)
2. Find # of moles of N and H in 100g sample using $n = \frac{m}{M}$
3. Find the molar ratio

Assuming that 100g sample is used

$$m_N \ (in \ 100g) = \frac{87.42\%}{100\%} \times 100g = 87.42g$$

$$m_H \ (in \ 100g) = \frac{12.58\%}{100\%} \times 100g = 12.58g$$

$$M_N = 14.01g/mol$$
$$M_H = 1.008g/mol$$
$$n_N = ? \, mol$$
$$n_H = ? \, mol$$
$$n = \frac{m}{M}$$

$$n_N = \frac{87.42g}{14.01g/mol}$$

$$n_N = 6.241mol$$

$$n_H = \frac{12.58g}{1.008g/mol}$$

$$n_H = 12.48mol$$

$$Ratio = \frac{n_H}{n_N} = \frac{12.48mol\ H}{6.241mol\ N} = \frac{2mol\ H}{1mol\ N}$$

The empirical formula is NH_2.

Example 4

1.25g of Ga combines with O to form 1.68g of Ga_xO_y. Find empirical formula of the compound.

Steps

1. Find mass of oxygen in the sample using $m_o = m_{total} - m_{Ga}$
2. Find # of moles of Ga and O using $n = \frac{m}{M}$
3. Find the molar ratio

$m_{Ga} = 1.25g$

$m_o = m_{total} - m_{Ga} = 1.68g - 1.25g = 0.43g$

$M_{Ga} = 69.72g/mol$

$M_O = 16.0g/mol$

$n_{Ga} = ?mol$

$n_o = ?mol$

$$n = \frac{m}{M}$$

$$n_{Ga} = \frac{1.25g}{69.72g/mol}$$

$$n_{Ga} = 0.0179mol$$

$$n_O = \frac{0.43g}{16.0g/mol}$$

$$n_O = 0.027mol$$

$$Ratio = \frac{n_O}{n_{Ga}} = \frac{0.027mol\ O}{0.0179mol\ Ga} = \frac{1.5mol\ O}{1mol\ Ga} = \frac{3mol\ O}{2mol\ Ga}$$

The empirical formula is Ga_2O_3.

Example 5

When heated, 0.235g of $NiCl_2 \cdot xH_2O$ yields 0.128g of $NiCl_2$. Find x.

Steps

1. Find mass of water in the sample using $m_{xH_2O} = m_{total} - m_{NiCl_2}$
2. Find # of moles of $NiCl_2$ and H_2O using $n = \frac{m}{M}$
3. Find the molar ratio

$$m_{NiCl_2 \cdot xH_2O} = 0.235g$$

$$m_{NiCl_2} = 0.128g$$

$$m_{xH_2O} = m_{total} - m_{NiCl_2} = 0.235g - 0.128g = 0.107g$$

$$M_{NiCl_2} = 129.59g/mol$$

$$M_{xH_2O} = 18.00g/mol$$

$$n_{NiCl_2} = ? \, mol$$

$$n_{xH_2O} = ? \, mol$$

$$n = \frac{m}{M}$$

$$n_{NiCl_2} = \frac{0.128g}{129.59g/mol}$$

$$n_{NiCl_2} = 9.88 \times 10^{-4} mol$$

$$n_{H_2O} = \frac{0.107g}{18.00g/mol}$$

$$n_{H_2O} = 0.00594mol$$

$$Ratio = \frac{n_{H_2O}}{n_{NiCl_2}} = \frac{0.00594 \, mol \, H_2O}{9.88x10^{-4} \, mol \, NiCl_2} = \frac{6 \, mol \, H_2O}{1 \, mol \, NiCl_2}$$

x= 6, the compound is $NiCl_2 \cdot 6H_2O$.

Part 3

Chemical Reactions

Chemical equations

Balancing equations

Complete combustion

Chemical equilibrium

Ionic compounds in an aqueous

solution

Solubility

Precipitation reaction

Acid-base reaction

Oxides of metals and nonmetals

Gas-forming reactions

Oxidation-reduction reaction

Oxidation states

Balancing redox equations

Surviving University: First Year Chemistry

Chemical Reactions

Chemical equations

- The states of matter in a chemical reaction are (s)= solid, (l)=liquid, (g)=gas, and (aq)=aqueous (substance has been dissolved in water)
- On the left side of arrow are **reactants**, on the right side of arrow are **products**
- Direction of the reaction is given by an arrow
- The number before each reactant/product is a **stoichiometric coefficient**
  - Stoichiometric coefficients indicate the proportion of reactants that are required for the reaction and the proportion of products formed

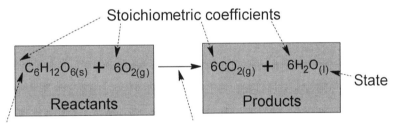

Stoichiometric coefficients

$$C_6H_{12}O_{6(s)} + 6O_{2(g)} \longrightarrow 6CO_{2(g)} + 6H_2O_{(l)}$$

Reactants — Products — State

Stoichiometric coefficient is 1 Direction of reaction

6 molecules of O_2 are needed to react with 1 molecule of $C_6H_{12}O_6$ to produce 6 molecules of CO_2 and 6 molecules of H_2O

Balancing chemical equations

- The same number of atoms of every element must be present on both sides of the equation
- Subscripts cannot be changed to balance equation (H_2 is always $H_2 \rightarrow$ cannot change H_2 to H_4)
- Stoichiometric coefficients are used to balance equation (ex. having $2H_2$ instead of H_2)

Steps
1. Balance all atoms but C, H, and O
2. Balance C
3. Balance H
4. Balance O
5. Check that there is the same number of atoms of each element on both sides

Example 1
Balance the following equation.
$Fe_{(s)} + H_2O_{(g)} \rightarrow Fe_3O_{4(s)} + H_{2(g)}$
There are 3 iron atoms on the right→ put 3 in front of Fe on the left.
$3Fe_{(s)} + H_2O_{(g)} \rightarrow Fe_3O_{4(s)} + H_{2(g)}$
There are 2 hydrogen atoms on each side→ hydrogen is balanced.
There are 4 oxygen atoms on the right→ put 4 in front of H_2O on the left.
$3Fe_{(s)} + 4H_2O_{(g)} \rightarrow Fe_3O_{4(s)} + H_{2(g)}$
Now there are 8 hydrogen atoms on the left and 2 hydrogen atoms on the right→ put 4 in front of H_2 on the right.
$3Fe_{(s)} + 4H_2O_{(g)} \rightarrow Fe_3O_{4(s)} + 4H_{2(g)}$
Check # atoms of each element: 3 iron atoms on each side, 8 hydrogen atoms on each side, and 4 oxygen atoms on each side→ the equation is balanced.

Complete combustion

- Occurs when there is an excess amount of oxygen

$$hydrocarbon + O_{2(g)} \rightarrow CO_{2(g)} + H_2O_{(l)}$$

Note: hydrocarbon is a compound that is made up of hydrogen and carbon atoms (ex. CH_4)
Note: make sure that the equation is balanced!

Example 1
Write an equation for complete combustion of methane.
Methane is a hydrocarbon and has a formula of $CH_{4(g)}$.
$CH_{4(g)} + O_{2(g)} \rightarrow CO_{2(g)} + H_2O_{(l)}$
Need to check whether the equation is balanced.
Check # atoms of each element: 1 C atom on each side, 4 H atoms on the left and 2 H atoms on the right (not balanced!), 2 O atoms on the left and 3 O atoms on the right (not balanced!).
Need to balance the equation.
$CH_{4(g)} + 2O_{2(g)} \rightarrow CO_{2(g)} + 2H_2O_{(l)}$
Check # atoms of each element: 1 C atom on each side, 4 H atoms on each side, 4 O atoms on each side→ the equation is balanced.

Chemical equilibrium

- In most reactions, reactants produce products
- However, some chemical reactions are reversible
  - Reactants form products (**forward reaction**) and products form reactants (**reverse reaction**)

- ⇌ arrow is used to show that the reaction occurs in both directions
$2NOCl_{(g)} \rightleftharpoons 2NO_{(g)} + Cl_{2(g)}$
- Beginning of reaction: NOCl forms NO and Cl_2 at a fast rate (forward)→ the rate of production of NOCl is very slow (reverse)
- Then: the rate of forward reaction decreases and the rate of the reverse reaction increases until rate of forward reaction is the same as the rate of reverse reaction

Equilibrium- the forward and reverse reactions are occurring in the flask at the same rate

Product favoured reaction- the concentration of products is greater than the concentration of reactants at equilibrium

Reactant favoured reaction- the concentration of reactants is greater than the concentration of products at equilibrium

Aqueous solution

Solution- is a homogeneous mixture, consists of at least 2 substances
Solute- the substance that is being dissolved
Solvent- the substance in which the solute is being dissolved
(ex. NaCl is being dissolved in H_2O→ NaCl is solute, H_2O is solvent)
Aqueous solution- water is the solvent

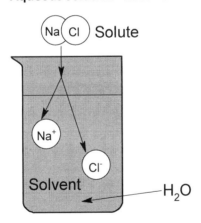

Exchange reaction- $AB + CD \rightarrow AD + BC$ (note: metal changes with metal, nonmetal changes with nonmetal)
ex. $HCl_{(aq)} + NaOH_{(aq)} \rightarrow H_2O_{(l)} + NaCl_{(aq)}$

Ionic compounds in an aqueous solution

- When an ionic compound is placed into an aqueous solution, it **dissociates** (breaks down) into its ions
  - ex. $NaCl_{(s)} \rightarrow Na^+_{(aq)} + Cl^-_{(aq)}$

- o Ionic compound that has a polyatomic ion breaks down into a metal ion and a polyatomic ion
  - ■ ex. $NaNO_{3(s)} \rightarrow Na^+_{(aq)} + NO_3^-_{(aq)}$
- o Ions move randomly in the solution
- ■ When 2 **electrodes** (metals that conduct electricity) are put into the solution, opposite charges attract
  - o Cations (+ive) move to the negative electrode, anions (-ive) move to the positive electrode

Electrolytes- compounds that conduct electricity when placed into an aqueous solution
- ■ All ionic compounds are electrolytes

Strong electrolytes- good conductors of electricity
- ■ Ionic compounds are strong electrolytes

Weak electrolytes- weak conductors of electricity
- ■ Strong and weak acids and weak bases are weak electrolytes
  - o Some atoms in the solution will form ions, some atoms in the same solution will remain as compounds

Nonelectrolytes- compounds that do not conduct electricity when placed into aqueous solution
- ■ All molecular compounds are nonelectrolytes

Solubility

Solubility- the amount of a solute that can dissolve in a specific amount of solvent at a specific temperature

Soluble- an ionic compound which breaks down (dissociates) into its ions when placed into a solvent

Insoluble- an ionic compound which does not break down into its ions when placed into a solvent → it remains as a solid

All compounds with this ion are <u>soluble</u> in water	Exceptions These compounds are <u>insoluble</u> in water
Cl^-	$AgCl$, Hg_2Cl_2, $PbCl_2$
Br^-	$AgBr$, Hg_2Br_2, $HgBr_2$, $PbBr_2$
I^-	AgI, Hg_2I_2, HgI_2, PbI_2
ClO_3^-, NO_3^-, CH_3COO^-	
SO_4^{2-}	$CaSO_4$, $SrSO_4$, $BaSO_4$, Hg_2SO_4, $HgSO_4$, $PbSO_4$, Ag_2SO_4

All compounds with this ion are insoluble in water	Exceptions These compounds are soluble in water
PO_4^{3-}, CO_3^{2-}, O^{2-}	with NH_4^+ with group I metals
OH^-	with NH_4^+ with group I metals with group II metals from Ca down
S^{2-}	with NH_4^+ with group I metals with group II metals

Example 1
Which of the following compounds are soluble in water? Which ions are produced when these compounds are dissolved in water?

$BaSO_4$ $Ba(NO_3)_2$ $BaCO_3$

A   B   C

Barium is a second group element.

	Soluble?
A	Sulphates are insoluble with barium→ insoluble
B	Nitrates are soluble with all elements→ soluble $Ba(NO_3)_{2(s)} \rightarrow Ba^{2+}_{(aq)} + 2NO_3^-{}_{(aq)}$
C	Carbonates are insoluble with barium→ insoluble

Reactions in aqueous solutions

Types of reactions in aqueous solutions

1. Precipitation
2. Acid-base
3. Gas-forming
4. Oxidation-reduction

Precipitation reaction

- Precipitation reaction is a reaction in which a **precipitate** (a solid) is formed
  - The precipitate does not dissociate into its ions

Complete ionic equation- shows all ions present in an aqueous solution→ the precipitate is shown as a solid

Spectator ions- ions which appear on both sides of the complete ionic equation

- Spectator ions do not participate in the reaction

Net ionic equation- shows only molecules which are involved in the reaction (does not show spectator ions)

- Make sure that both masses and charges in the net ionic equation are balanced!

Example 1
Write the balanced chemical equation, the complete ionic equation, and the net ionic equation for the following reaction. Indicate the spectator ions and the states of each of the species.

$CdCl_{2(aq)}+NaOH_{(aq)}\rightarrow$?

This is an exchange reaction ($AB + CD \rightarrow AD + BC$). A metal changes with a metal and a nonmetal changes with a nonmetal. Use solubility rules to determine states.

$CdCl_{2(aq)}+NaOH_{(aq)}\rightarrow Cd(OH)_{2(s)}+NaCl_{(aq)}$

Balanced chemical equation:	$CdCl_{2(aq)}+2NaOH_{(aq)}\rightarrow Cd(OH)_{2(s)}+2NaCl_{(aq)}$
Complete ionic equation:	Break all of the compounds in (aq) state into their ions. The solid remains unbroken. $Cd^{2+}_{(aq)}+2Cl^-_{(aq)}+2Na^+_{(aq)}+2OH^-_{(aq)}\rightarrow Cd(OH)_{2(s)}+ 2Na^+_{(aq)}+2Cl^-_{(aq)}$

Surviving University: First Year Chemistry

Cancel ions that appear on both sides of the equation→ they are spectator ions (Cl⁻, Na⁺).

$$Cd^{2+}_{(aq)} + \cancel{2Cl^-_{(aq)}} + \cancel{2Na^+_{(aq)}} + 2OH^-_{(aq)} \rightarrow Cd(OH)_{2(s)} + \cancel{2Na^+_{(aq)}} + \cancel{2Cl^-_{(aq)}}$$

Net ionic equation:	$Cd^{2+}_{(aq)} + 2OH^-_{(aq)} \rightarrow Cd(OH)_{2(s)}$ Both the masses and the charges are balanced (the overall charge on both sides is 0).

Example 2
$FeCl_3$ and $AgNO_3$ are mixed together. Will a precipitate form? I
Both compounds are ionic and are soluble in water. When these compounds are placed into water, they will dissociate into their ions.

$FeCl_{3(s)} \rightarrow Fe^{3+}_{(aq)} + 3Cl^-_{(aq)}$

$AgNO_{3(s)} \rightarrow Ag^+_{(aq)} + NO_3^-_{(aq)}$

Ions will then combine with each other (use solubility rules to determine states),

$Fe^{3+}_{(aq)} + NO_3^-_{(aq)} \rightarrow Fe(NO_3)_{3(aq)}$

$Ag^+_{(aq)} + Cl^-_{(aq)} \rightarrow AgCl_{(s)}$

Silver chloride is the precipitate and precipitates out of the solution.

Definition of acids and bases *(see part 24 for more information)*

- Acids change litmus paper's colour from blue to red

Arrhenius definition
- When an acid dissolves in H_2O, the concentration of H^+ increases
- When a base dissolves in H_2O, the concentration of OH^- increases

Brønsted-Lowry definition
Acid- a proton (H^+) donor
Base- a proton (H^+) acceptor
Conjugate acid- a specie that is formed when a base gains a proton
Conjugate base- a specie that is formed when an acid loses a proton
Conjugate acid-base pair- a base and its conjugate acid or an acid and its conjugate base
Acid-base reaction- a proton (H^+) is transferred from an acid to a base
- The equilibrium in an acid-base reaction lies towards the side with the weaker acid/base pair

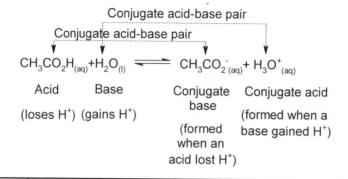

Conjugate acid-base pair

Conjugate acid-base pair

$$CH_3CO_2H_{(aq)} + H_2O_{(l)} \rightleftharpoons CH_3CO_2^-{}_{(aq)} + H_3O^+{}_{(aq)}$$

Acid   Base   Conjugate   Conjugate acid

(loses H$^+$) (gains H$^+$)   base   (formed when a

                  (formed   base gained H$^+$)

                  when an

                  acid lost H$^+$)

		Examples
Strong acid	<ul><li>Ionizes 100% in water to produce H_3O^+ (hydronium ion)→ equilibrium lies towards products</li><li>Is a strong electrolyte</li></ul>ex. $HBr_{(aq)} + H_2O_{(l)} \rightarrow H_3O^+{}_{(aq)} + Br^-{}_{(aq)}$	HCl, HBr, HI, HNO_3, $HClO_4$, H_2SO_4
Weak acid	<ul><li>Ionizes <<100% in water to produce H_3O^+ (hydronium ion)→ equilibrium lies towards reactants</li><li>Is a weak electrolyte</li></ul>ex. $HC_9H_8O_{4(aq)} + H_2O_{(l)} \rightleftharpoons H_3O^+{}_{(aq)} + C_9H_8O_4^-{}_{(aq)}$	HF, H_3PO_4, H_2CO_3, CH_3CO_2H, $H_2C_2O_4$, $H_2C_2H_4O_6$, $H_3C_6H_5O_7$, $HC_9H_8O_4$
Diprotic acid	<ul><li>Can donate 2 protons (has 2H$^+$)</li><li>Equilibrium lies towards products in 1st step and towards reactants in 2nd step</li></ul>Step 1: $H_2CO_{3(aq)} + H_2O_{(l)} \rightleftharpoons H_3O^+{}_{(aq)} + HCO_3^-{}_{(aq)}$ Step 2: $HCO_3^-{}_{(aq)} + H_2O_{(l)} \rightleftharpoons H_3O^+{}_{(aq)} + CO_3^{2-}{}_{(aq)}$	H_2CO_3, H_2SO_3, $H_2C_2O_4$
Strong base	<ul><li>Ionizes <100% in water to produce OH$^-$ (hydroxide ion)→ equilibrium lies towards products</li><li>Is a strong electrolyte</li></ul>$NaOH_{(s)} \rightarrow Na^+{}_{(aq)} + OH^-{}_{(aq)}$	LiOH, NaOH, KOH, $Ba(OH)_2$, $Ca(OH)_2$, $Sr(OH)_2$
Weak base	<ul><li>Ionizes <100% in water to produce OH$^-$ (hydroxide ion)→ equilibrium lies towards reactants</li><li>Is a weak electrolyte</li></ul>$NH_{3(aq)} + H_2O_{(l)} \rightleftharpoons NH_4^+{}_{(aq)} + OH^-{}_{(aq)}$	NH_3, F^-, B^-

Amphiprotic	▪ A substance that can act as an acid or a base (depending on the situation) $$CH_3CO_2H_{(aq)} + H_2O_{(l)} \rightleftharpoons CH_3CO_2^-{}_{(aq)} + H_3O^+{}_{(aq)}$$ Acid Base (loses H⁺) (gains H⁺) $$F^-{}_{(aq)} + H_2O_{(l)} \rightleftharpoons HF_{(aq)} + HO^-{}_{(aq)}$$ Base Acid (gains H⁺)(loses H⁺)	H_2O

Example 1
Write a balanced chemical equation of ionization of hydrochloric acid in water.
$HCl_{(aq)} + H_2O_{(l)} \rightarrow H_3O^+{}_{(aq)} + Cl^-{}_{(aq)}$
Both the masses and the charges are balanced.

Acid-base reactions

Neutralization reaction- occurs between a strong acid and a strong base

$$Acid + base \rightarrow salt + H_2O_{(l)}$$

Example 1
Write a balanced chemical equation and a balanced net ionic equation for reaction of sodium hydroxide with hydrochloric acid.
This is an exchange reaction $(AB + CD \rightarrow AD + BC)$

Chemical equation:	$HCl_{(aq)} + NaOH_{(aq)} \rightarrow H_2O_{(l)} + NaCl_{(aq)}$ This chemical equation is balanced.
Complete ionic equation:	All species in (aq) state are broken apart into their ions→ species in (l) state are not broken apart into their ions $H^+{}_{(aq)} + Cl^-{}_{(aq)} + Na^+{}_{(aq)} + OH^-{}_{(aq)} \rightarrow H_2O_{(l)} + Na^+{}_{(aq)} + Cl^-{}_{(aq)}$
Note: cancel ions that appear on both sides of the equation→ they are spectator ions (Cl⁻, Na⁺) $H^+{}_{(aq)} + \cancel{Cl^-{}_{(aq)}} + \cancel{Na^+{}_{(aq)}} + OH^-{}_{(aq)} \rightarrow H_2O_{(l)} + \cancel{Na^+{}_{(aq)}} + \cancel{Cl^-{}_{(aq)}}$	
Net ionic equation:	$H^+{}_{(aq)} + OH^-{}_{(aq)} \rightarrow H_2O_{(l)}$ Both the masses and the charges are balanced (the overall charge on both sides is 0).

Example 2

Potassium hydroxide is mixed with hydrogen bromide. State the spectator ions in this reaction.

This is an exchange reaction $(AB + CD \rightarrow AD + BC)$

Chemical equation:	$HBr_{(aq)} + KOH_{(aq)} \rightarrow H_2O_{(l)} + KBr_{(aq)}$ This chemical equation is balanced.
Complete ionic equation:	All species in (aq) state are broken apart into their ions → species in (l) state are not broken apart into their ions $H^+_{(aq)} + Br^-_{(aq)} + K^+_{(aq)} + OH^-_{(aq)} \rightarrow H_2O_{(l)} + K^+_{(aq)} + Br^-_{(aq)}$
Note: cancel ions that appear on both sides of the equation → they are spectator ions (Br^-, K^+) $H^+_{(aq)} + \cancel{Br^-_{(aq)}} + \cancel{K^+_{(aq)}} + OH^-_{(aq)} \rightarrow H_2O_{(l)} + \cancel{K^+_{(aq)}} + \cancel{Br^-_{(aq)}}$	
Net ionic equation:	$H^+_{(aq)} + OH^-_{(aq)} \rightarrow H_2O_{(l)}$

The spectator ions are K^+ and Br^-.

Oxides of metals and nonmetals

- Oxides of metals (aka **basic oxides**) react with water to form a base
- Oxides of nonmetals (aka **acidic oxides**) react with water to form a weak acid
  - Weak acid reacts with water to produce $H_3O^+_{(aq)}$

Example 1

Write a balanced chemical equation for the reaction of barium oxide with water.

$BaO_{(s)} + H_2O_{(l)} \rightarrow Ba(OH)_{2(s)}$ (this is a base)

Example 2

Write a balanced chemical equation for the reaction of nitrogen dioxide with water.

$NO_{2(g)} + H_2O_{(l)} \rightarrow H_2NO_{3(aq)}$ (this is a weak acid)

Then: $H_2NO_{3(aq)} + H_2O_{(l)} \rightleftharpoons HNO_3^-_{(aq)} + H_3O^+_{(aq)}$

Gas forming reactions

$$Metal\ carbonate\ (ex.\ Na_2CO_3) + acid \rightarrow metal\ salt + CO_{2(g)} + H_2O_{(l)}$$
$$Metal\ bicarbonate\ (ex.\ NaHCO_3) + acid \rightarrow metal\ salt + CO_{2(g)} + H_2O_{(l)}$$
$$Metal\ sulfide\ (ex.\ K_2S) + acid \rightarrow metal\ salt + H_2S_{(g)}$$
$$Metal\ sulfide + acid \rightarrow metal\ salt + SO_{2(g)} + H_2O_{(l)}$$
$$Ammonium\ salt\ (ex.\ NH_4Cl) + strong\ base$$
$$\rightarrow metal\ salt + NH_{3(g)} + H_2O_{(l)}$$

S u r v i v i n g   U n i v e r s i t y :   F i r s t   Y e a r   C h e m i s t r y

Example 1
Write balanced chemical equation for reaction of hydrobromic acid with
$(NH_4)_2S$.
$(NH_4)_2S_{(aq)}$+ $HBr_{(aq)}$→ ?
HBr is an acid and $(NH_4)_2S$ is a metal sulfide.
$Metal\ sulfide\ (ex. K_2S) + acid \rightarrow metal\ salt + H_2S_{(g)}$
$(NH_4)_2S_{(aq)}$+ $HBr_{(aq)}$→ $H_2S_{(aq)}$+ $NH_4Br_{(aq)}$
Now balance
$(NH_4)_2S_{(aq)}$+ $2HBr_{(aq)}$→ $H_2S_{(aq)}$+ $2NH_4Br_{(aq)}$

Example 2
Write balanced chemical equation for reaction of hydrochloric acid with
K_2CO_3.
$K_2CO_{3(aq)}$+ $HCl_{(aq)}$→ ?
HCl is an acid and K_2CO_3 is a metal carbonate.
$Metal\ carbonate\ (ex. Na_2CO_3) + acid \rightarrow metal\ salt + CO_{2(g)} + H_2O_{(l)}$
$K_2CO_{3(aq)}$+ $HCl_{(aq)}$→ $KCl_{(aq)}$+ $CO_{2(g)}$+ $H_2O_{(g)}$
Now balance
$K_2CO_{3(aq)}$+ $2HCl_{(aq)}$→ $2KCl_{(aq)}$+ $CO_{2(g)}$+ $H_2O_{(g)}$

Oxidation-reduction reactions (redox reactions)

Oxidation	Reduction
Loss of electrons Loss of H atom(s) Gain of O atom(s)	Gain of electrons Gain of H atom(s) Loss of O atom(s)
Oxidation state ↑	Oxidation state ↓

- In an oxidation-reduction reaction, electrons are transferred
    - 1 species loses electron(s)→ becomes **oxidized**
    - 1 species gains electron(s)→ becomes **reduced**
    - **Reducing agent**- a species that donates electron(s)
    - **Oxidizing agent**- a species that accepts electron(s)

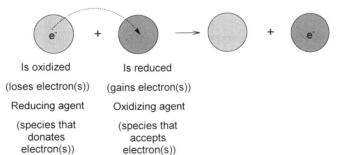

Is oxidized

(loses electron(s))

Reducing agent

(species that donates electron(s))

Is reduced

(gains electron(s))

Oxidizing agent

(species that accepts electron(s))

- There are 2 **half-reactions**→ 1 half reaction shows oxidation, 1 half-reaction shows reduction

Oxidation state

- Oxidation state indicates the degree of oxidation that an atom has within a molecule
    - The oxidation state is simply an arbitrary number that is used to keep track of electrons
- Oxidation state of an atom changes when it undergoes oxidation or reduction
    - Oxidation: oxidation state ↑
    - Reduction: oxidation state ↓

Rules for assigning atom's oxidation state

Oxidation state	With	Exceptions
0	free element (ex. O_2)	
ion's charge	monatomic ions (ex. -1 in Cl^-)	
-2	oxygen	is -1 in peroxides (H_2O_2) is +ive when with F is -1/2 in superoxides (KO_2)
+1	hydrogen	is −1 with metal (ex. NaH)
-1	fluorine	
-1	Cl, Br, I	is positive with O or F

Sum of oxidation states in a species is equal to the charge of the species

Example 1
Determine oxidation states of each element in N_2O_5 and $H_2AsO_4^-$
N_2O_5→ oxygen has oxidation state of -2, overall charge of compound is 0.
So the sum of oxidation states is 0.
Let x represent nitrogen's oxidation state.
Since there are 2 nitrogen atoms, the sum of nitrogen's oxidation number is 2x.
$$2x + 5\,(-2) = 0$$
$$2x - 10 = 0$$
$$2x = 10$$
$$x = 5$$

Surviving University: First Year Chemistry

The oxidation state of nitrogen is +5 and of oxygen is -2.

$H_2AsO_4^-$ → oxygen has oxidation state of -2, hydrogen has oxidation state of +1, and the overall charge of species is -1.
So the sum of oxidation states is -1.
Let x represent arsenic's oxidation state.
$2(+1) + x + 4(-2) = -1$
$2 + x - 8 = -1$
$x - 6 = -1$
$x = 5$
The oxidation state of of arsenic is +5.

Example 2
Is this a redox reaction? If yes, which species is being oxidized, which one is being reduced, which is the oxidizing agent, which is the reducing agent?
Steps
1. Assign oxidation states to all elements
2. Look at change in oxidation states between elements in reactants and elements in products→ if oxidation state ↑ then the species has been oxidized; if oxidation state ↓ then the species has been reduced

$C_2H_{4(g)} + 3O_{2(g)} \rightarrow 2CO_{2(g)} + 2H_2O_{(l)}$

Specie	Oxidation state in reactants	Oxidation state in products	Oxidized/reduced
C	-2	+4	# ↑, has been oxidized
H	+1	+1	no change
O	0	-2	#↓, has been reduced

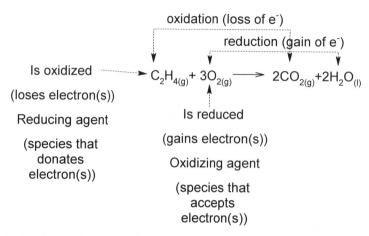

Is oxidized

(loses electron(s))

Reducing agent

(species that donates electron(s))

Is reduced

(gains electron(s))

Oxidizing agent

(species that accepts electron(s))

Balancing redox equations→ using half-reaction method

Steps

1. Split reaction into half-reactions (1 for oxidation, 1 for reduction)
2. Balance each half-reaction separately for mass balance
3. If in acidic solution, add H_2O to balance oxygen atoms and H^+ to balance hydrogen atoms
4. If in basic solution, add H_2O to balance oxygen atoms and OH^- to balance hydrogen atoms
5. Multiply each half-reaction by a factor to balance the total # of e^-
6. Add 2 half-reactions
7. Cancel species that occur on both sides of the net reaction
8. Add states of each reactant and product (s, l, aq, or g)

Example 1
Balance the following redox reaction in an acidic solution.
$VO_2^+ + Zn \rightarrow VO^{2+} + Zn^{2+}$

Specie	Oxidation state in reactants	Oxidation state in products	Oxidized/reduced
V	+5	+4	#↓, has been reduced
O	-2	-2	no change
Zn	0	+2	# ↑, has been oxidized

Step 1: Divide reaction into half-reactions (1 for oxidation, 1 for reduction)

Surviving University: First Year Chemistry

Oxidation half-reaction	$Zn \rightarrow Zn^{2+} + 2e^-$
Reduction half-reaction	$VO_2^+ + e^- \rightarrow VO^{2+}$

Step 2: Balance each half-reaction for mass; add H_2O to balance oxygen atoms and H^+ to balance hydrogen atoms

Oxidation half-reaction	$Zn \rightarrow Zn^{2+} + 2e^-$
Reduction half-reaction	**$2H^+ + VO_2^+ + e^- \rightarrow VO^{2+} + H_2O$**

Step 3: Multiply each half-reaction by a factor to balance the total # of e⁻
Your goal is to have the same # of electrons in the reactants of 1 half-reaction and products of 2nd half-reaction.
Right now you have 1e⁻ in reactants of reduction half-reaction and 2e⁻ in products of oxidation half-reaction. Multiply reduction half-reduction by 2 to have the same # of electrons.

Oxidation half-reaction	$Zn \rightarrow Zn^{2+} + 2e^-$
Reduction half-reaction	$(2H^+ + VO_2^+ + e^- \rightarrow VO^{2+} + H_2O)$ **x2** $= 4H^+ + 2VO_2^+ + 2e^- \rightarrow 2VO^{2+} + 2H_2O$

Step 4: Add 2 half-reactions
Add all of the reactants together and all of the products together.
$Zn + 4H^+ + 2VO_2^+ + 2e^- \rightarrow Zn^{2+} + 2e^- + 2VO^{2+} + 2H_2O$

Step 5: Cancel species that occur on both sides
$Zn + 4H^+ + 2VO_2^+ + \cancel{2e^-} \rightarrow Zn^{2+} + \cancel{2e^-} + 2VO^{2+} + 2H_2O$
$Zn + 4H^+ + 2VO_2^+ \rightarrow Zn^{2+} + 2VO^{2+} + 2H_2O$
Now add states
$Zn_{(s)} + 4H^+_{(aq)} + 2VO_2^+_{(aq)} \rightarrow Zn^{2+}_{(aq)} + 2VO^{2+}_{(aq)} + 2H_2O_{(l)}$

Example 2
Balance the following redox reaction in a basic solution.
$Zn_{(s)} + Cu(OH)_{2(s)} \rightarrow [Zn(OH)_4]^{2-}_{(aq)} + Cu_{(s)}$

Specie	Oxidation # in reactants	Oxidation # in products	Oxidized/reduced
H	+1	+1	no change
O	-2	-2	no change

| Zn | 0 | +2 | # ↑, has been oxidized |
| Cu | +2 | 0 | #↓, has been reduced |

Oxidation half-reaction	$Zn \rightarrow [Zn(OH)_4]^{2-} + 2e^-$
Reduction half-reaction	$Cu(OH)_2 + 2e^- \rightarrow Cu$

Mass balance

Oxidation half-reaction	$Zn + 4OH^- \rightarrow [Zn(OH)_4]^{2-} + 2e^-$
Reduction half-reaction	$Cu(OH)_2 + 2e^- \rightarrow Cu + 2OH^-$

Charge balance→ already same # e⁻ on both sides!

Sum up

$Cu(OH)_2 + 2e^- + Zn + 4OH^- \rightarrow [Zn(OH)_4]^{2-} + 2e^- + Cu + 2OH^-$

$Cu(OH)_2 + Zn + 2OH^- \rightarrow [Zn(OH)_4]^{2-} + Cu$

Add states

$Cu(OH)_{2(s)} + Zn_{(s)} + 2OH^-_{(aq)} \rightarrow [Zn(OH)_4]^{2-}_{(aq)} + Cu_{(s)}$

Surviving University: First Year Chemistry

Part 4

Stoichiometry

Basic stoichiometry problems

Limiting reagent

Percent yield

Atom economy, atom efficiency

Purity

Determining molecular and empirical formulas from combustion

Molarity

Dilution

Stoichiometry in an aqueous solution

Titrations

Stoichiometry

Stoichiometry- quantitative relationship between reactants and products

Basic stoichiometry problems

Example 1
If 2mol of NaOH fully reacts in the following reaction, how many moles of water are produced?
$NaOH_{(s)} + CO_{2(g)} \rightarrow Na_2CO_{3(s)} + H_2O_{(l)}$
*Always check whether the equation is balanced! *
This equation is not balanced→ there is 1 Na atom on the left side and 2 Na atoms on the right side; there is 1 H atom on the left side and 2 H atoms on the right side.
Balanced equation is: $\mathbf{2}NaOH_{(s)} + CO_{2(g)} \rightarrow Na_2CO_{3(s)} + H_2O_{(l)}$
Steps
1. Make a chart
2. Ratio to find # moles of O_2
NaOH fully reacts with CO_2 means that all moles of NaOH are converted to products.

	$2NaOH_{(s)}$	$CO_{2(g)}$	$\rightarrow Na_2CO_{3(s)}$	$+ H_2O_{(l)}$
n	2mol			?mol
Ratio	2	1	1	1

Note: n= # moles, ratio= stoichiometric coefficient

$$n_{H_2O} = 2mol\ NaOH \times \frac{1mol\ H_2O}{2mol\ NaOH}$$

$$n_{H_2O} = 1mol$$

1 mol of water was produced.

Example 2
Combustion of glucose occurs according to the following equation:
$C_6H_{12}O_{6(s)} + 6O_{2(g)} \rightarrow 6CO_{2(g)} + 6H_2O_{(l)}$
How much oxygen (in grams) is needed to fully react with 25.0g of glucose? Find the mass of water that is produced.
Steps
3. Make a chart
4. Convert mass of $C_6H_{12}O_6$ to moles using $n = \frac{m}{M}$
5. Ratio to find # moles of O_2
6. Convert # moles of O_2 to grams using $n = \frac{m}{M}$
7. Ratio to find # moles of H_2O produced

Surviving University: First Year Chemistry

8. Convert # moles of H_2O to grams using $n = \frac{m}{M}$

Glucose fully reacts with oxygen means that all moles of glucose are converted to products.

	$C_6H_{12}O_{6(s)}$	$+ 6O_{2(g)}$	$\rightarrow 6CO_{2(g)}$	$+ 6H_2O_{(l)}$
m	25.0g	?g		?g
M	180.18g/mol	32.00g/mol		
n	?mol	?mol		?mol
Ratio	1	6	6	6

Note: m= mass, M=molar mass, n= # moles, ratio= # that goes before each compound (ex. $6CO_{2(g)} \rightarrow$ ratio is 6)

$M_{C_6H_{12}O_6} = 6(12.01 \ g/mol) + 12 \ (1.01 \ g/mol) + (16.00 \ g/mol)$

$M_{C_6H_{12}O_6} = 180.18g/mol$

$M_{O_2} = 2(16.00 \ g/mol) = 32.00g/mol$

$M_{H_2O} = 2(1.01g/mol) + 16.00g/mol = 18.02g/mol$

$n_{O_2} = ? \ mol$

$n_{C_6H_{12}O_6} = ? \ mol$

$n_{H_2O} = ? \ mol$

$n = \frac{m}{M}$

$n_{C_6H_{12}O_6} = \frac{25.0g}{180.18g/mol}$

$n_{C_6H_{12}O_6} = 0.139mol$

$n_{O_2} = 0.139mol \ C_6H_{12}O_6 \ \times \frac{6mol \ O_2}{1mol \ C_6H_{12}O_6}$

$n_{O_2} = 0.832mol$

$m_{O_2} = n \times M$

$m_{O_2} = 0.832mol \ \times 32.00g/mol$

$m_{O_2} = 26.6g$

Now to find the mass of water produced,

$n_{H_2O} = 0.139mol \ C_6H_{12}O_6 \ \times \frac{6mol \ H_2O}{1mol \ C_6H_{12}O_6}$

$n_{H_2O} = 0.832mol$

$m_{H_2O} = n \times M$

$m_{H_2O} = 0.832mol \ \times 18.02g/mol$

$m_{H_2O} = 15.0g$

26.6g fully reacted with 25.0g of glucose. 15.0g of water was produced.

Limiting Reagent

Note: in a limiting reagent type of a problem, you are usually given masses of both of the reactants
Limiting reagent- a reactant that is completely used up in the chemical reaction

- Limiting reagent is the reactant that has the least amount of moles
    - The reaction runs out of the limiting reagent
- Limiting reagent limits the amount of products that can be formed

Example 1
356g of carbon monoxide and 65.0g of hydrogen were put into a flask.
$CO_{(g)} + 2H_{2(g)} \rightarrow CH_3OH_{(l)}$
a) What is the limiting reagent?
b) Find the mass of the product.
c) What is the mass of the excess reactant?

a) What is the limiting reagent?
Steps
1. Make a chart
2. Convert mass of all reactants to moles using $n = \frac{m}{M}$
3. Ratio to find the limiting reagent (divide # moles of 1 reactant by # moles of second reactant)

	$CO_{(g)}$	$+ 2H_{2(g)}$	$\rightarrow CH_3OH_{(l)}$
m	356g	65.0g	?g
M	28.01g/mol	2.02g/mol	32.05g/mol
n	?mol	?mol	
Ratio	1	2	1

$M_{CO} = 12.01 \, g/mol + 16.00 g/mol$
$M_{CO} = 28.01 g/mol$
$M_{H_2} = 2(1.01 \, g/mol) = 2.02 g/mol$
$M_{CH_3COH} = 12.01 \, g/mol + 3(1.01 \, g/mol) + 16.00 \, g/mol$
$\qquad\qquad + 1.01 \, g/mol$
$M_{CH_3COH} = 32.05 g/mol$
$n_{CO} = \dfrac{356g}{28.01g/mol}$
$n_{CO} = 12.7 mol$
$n_{H_2} = \dfrac{65.0g}{2.02g/mol}$
$n_{H_2} = 32.2 mol$

Surviving University: First Year Chemistry

$$Ratio = \frac{n_{H_2}}{n_{CO}} = \frac{32.2 mol\ H_2}{12.7 mol\ CO} = \frac{2.54 mol\ H_2}{1 mol\ CO}$$

Since there is less carbon monoxide than hydrogen, CO is the limiting reagent. This means that all CO is used up in the reaction to produce products. Some of hydrogen gas is left in the beaker once the reaction is complete.

b) Find the mass of the product.

Steps

1. Do a ratio- use the limiting reagent to find # moles of products

Use # moles of limiting reagent to find # moles of reactant produced (do not use # moles of hydrogen gas since it is not the limiting reagent!)

$$n_{CH_3OH} = 12.7 mol\ CO \times \frac{1 mol\ CH_3OH}{1 mol\ CO}$$

$$n_{CH_3OH} = 12.7 mol$$

$$m_{CH_3OH} = n \times M$$

$$m_{CH_3OH} = 12.7 mol\ \times 32.05 g/mol$$

$$m_{CH_3OH} = 407.0 g$$

407.0g of CH_3OH was produced.

c) What is the mass of the excess reactant?

Steps

1. Subtract the # moles of limiting reagent (which is the # of moles of each reactant that was used) from # moles of each of the reactants

You know that 12.7mol of CO reacted with $H_2 \rightarrow$ 0mol of CO remained in the beaker. You need to find out how many moles of H_2 reacted with CO. Use ratios from the table.

$$n_{H_2} = 12.7 mol\ CO\ \times \frac{2 mol\ H_2}{1 mol\ CO}$$

$$n_{H_2} = 25.4\ mol$$

You know that 32.2mol of H_2 was placed into the beaker. 25.4mol of H_2 reacted with CO to produce products. The amount of H_2 that remained was

$$n_{H_2\ left} = 32.2 mol - 25.4 mol$$

$$n_{H_2\ left} = 6.8 mol$$

Now you need to find the mass of H_2 left.

$$m_{H_2} = n \times M$$

$$m_{H_2} = 6.8 mol\ \times 2.02 g/mol$$

$$m_{H_2} = 14 g$$

14g of H_2 was left in the beaker.

Percent Yield

Theoretical yield- the mass of reactant/product that was calculated using stoichiometry
Actual yield- the mass of reactant/product that was obtained in the lab
Percent yield- discrepancy (in %) between the results expected through calculations and the results obtained in the lab

$$\% \; yield = \frac{actual \; yield}{theoretical \; yield} \times 100\%$$

Example 1
You found in example 1 of limiting reagent question that 14g of $H_{2(g)}$ should be left in the beaker once the chemical reaction is complete. Then you went to the lab and performed the experiment. You measured that 13.9g of $H_{2(g)}$ was left in the beaker once the reaction was complete. Find the percent yield.
Actual yield= 13.9 g
Theoretical yield= 14g

$$\% \; yield = \frac{13.9g}{14g} \times 100\%$$
$$\% \; yield = 99.3\% \approx 99\%$$
The percent yield was 99%.

Atom economy, atom efficiency

- The goal of chemical industry is to maximize the yield of products
  - Although the yield of product can be 100%, other waste materials may be produced

Principle of atom economy- synthetic methods need to be designed such that all of the starting materials (reactants) are converted into the desired product

- The goal is to minimize amount of waste produced

Atom efficiency- % of reactant atoms of a specific element (ex. S atom) that are converted into the desired product

- Atom efficiency is calculated separately for each element
- The goal is to have atom efficiency= 100%
  - All reactant atoms are converted into the desired product

$$Atom \; efficiency = \frac{\# \; of \; atoms \; of \; an \; element \; in \; a \; desired \; product}{\# of \; atoms \; of \; an \; element \; in \; reactants} \times 100\%$$

Desired product
90%

10%

Not all of the reactant atoms were converted into the
desired product.

The goal is to have the most amount of reactant atoms
which are converted into the desired product.

Overall atom efficiency (OAE)- % of product atoms that are the desired
product
- Not all products are always desired→ some undesired products can be
  produced
- The goal is to have OAE= 100%
  o All products are desired products

$$OAE = \frac{mass\ of\ a\ desired\ product}{total\ mass\ of\ all\ products} \times 100\%$$

Note: OAE= overall atom efficiency

E factor- ratio of mass of wastes to mass of desired product
- The goal is to have E factor= 0
  o No waste→ only desired product is produced

$$E\ factor = \frac{mass\ of\ waste}{mass\ of\ a\ desired\ product}$$

Example 1
*The goal of the following is to produce ethyl acetate. Find atom efficiency
for C, H, and O; OAE; and the E factor.*

Acetic acid   Ethanol   Ethyl acetate

Desired product

Note: catalyst is used to speed up the reaction without being consumed in
the reaction.

Steps
1. Make sure that the equation is balanced
2. Find number of C, H, and O atoms in <u>all</u> of the reactants
3. Find number of C, H, and O atoms in the desired product (ethyl acetate)
4. Find atom efficiency for C, H, and O atoms using

$$Atom\ efficiency = \frac{\#\ of\ atoms\ of\ an\ element\ in\ a\ desired\ product}{\#of\ atoms\ of\ an\ element\ in\ reactants} \times 100\%$$

5. Find mass of each product using $n = \frac{m}{M}$
6. Find overall atom efficiency using $OAE = \frac{mass\ of\ desired\ product}{total\ mass\ of\ all\ products} \times 100\%$
7. Find E factor using $E\ factor = \frac{mass\ of\ waste}{mass\ of\ desired\ product}$

	# of atoms in all of the reactants	# of atoms in ethyl acetate
C	4	4
H	10	8
O	3	2

	Atom efficiency
C	100%
H	80%
O	66.7%

$$Atom\ efficiency\ for\ C = \frac{\#\ C\ atoms\ in\ a\ desired\ product}{\#\ C\ atoms\ in\ reactants} \times 100\%$$

$$Atom\ efficiency\ for\ C = \frac{4\ mol}{4\ mol} \times 100\% = 100\%$$

$$Atom\ efficiency\ for\ H = \frac{8\ mol}{10\ mol} \times 100\% = 80\%$$

$$Atom\ efficiency\ for\ O = \frac{2\ mol}{3\ mol} \times 100\% = 66.7\%$$

	Ethyl acetate	H$_2$O
n	1 mol	1 mol
M	88.12 g/mol	18.02 g/mol
m	88.12g	18.02g

Note: # mol of ethyl acetate and water comes from the equation (coefficient before ethyl acetate is 1→ 1 mol; coefficient before H$_2$O is 1→ 1 mol)

Surviving University: First Year Chemistry

$$M_{ethyl\ acetate} = 2(16.00\ g/mol) + 8(1.01\ g/mol) + 4(12.01\ g/mol)$$
$$M_{ethyl\ acetate} = 88.12\ g/mol$$
$$m_{ethyl\ acetate} = n \times M$$

$$m_{ethyl\ acetate} = 1\ mol\ \times 88.12\ g/mol$$
$$m_{ethyl\ acetate} = 88.12\ g$$
$$M_{H_2O} = 2(1.01\ g/mol) + 16.00\ g/mol$$
$$M_{H_2O} = 18.02\ g/mol$$
$$m_{H_2O} = n \times M$$
$$m_{H_2O} = 1\ mol \times 18.02\ g/mol$$
$$m_{H_2O} = 18.02\ g$$
$$OAE = \frac{mass\ of\ ethyl\ acetate}{total\ mass\ of\ all\ products} \times 100\%$$
$$OAE = \frac{88.12g}{(88.12g + 18.02g)} \times 100\%$$
$$OAE = 83.02\%$$
$$E\ factor = \frac{mass\ of\ waste}{mass\ of\ desired\ product}$$
Since water is waste (not the desired product),
$$E\ factor = \frac{mass\ of\ water}{mass\ of\ ethyl\ acetate}$$
$$E\ factor = \frac{18.02g}{88.12g}$$
$$E\ factor = 0.2045$$
Atom efficiencies for C, H, and O were 100%, 80%, and 66.7% respectively. OAE was 83.02%. E factor was 0.2045.

Purity

Pure metal- contains 1 type of a metallic element
Impure metal- contains 2 or more metallic elements
Purity- how much of a sample (in %) contains 1 type of an element

$$Purity = \frac{mass\ obtained\ in\ a\ lab}{mass\ calculated} \times 100\%$$

Example 1
A sample of Na$_2$SO$_4$ contains 1.85g of impure metal. The sample was dissolved in water and BaCl$_2$ was added. 2.75g of BaSO$_4$ precipitated in the lab. Find the purity of the metal.
First, you need to understand the setup of this problem.
First, Na$_2$SO$_4$ is dissolved in water.

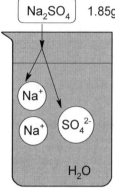 1.85g of impure metal

According to solubility rules,
Na_2SO_4 is soluble in water
(so it dissociates into its ions)

Then, $BaCl_2$ is added to the solution.

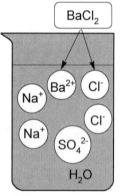

According to solubility rules,
$BaCl_2$ is soluble in water (so
it dissociates into its ions)

Na^+ combined with Cl^- to produce NaCl. Ba^{2+} combined with SO_4^{2-} to produce $BaSO_4$.

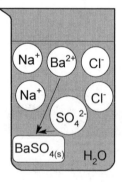

According to solubility rules,
$BaSO_4$ is insoluble in water
(so was a solid)

According to solubility rules,
NaCl is soluble in water
(dissociated into its ions)

The mass of $BaSO_4$ was then measured. The mass obtained in lab was 2.75g.
The overall reaction was: $Na_2SO_{4(aq)} + BaCl_{2(aq)} \rightarrow BaSO_{4(s)} + 2NaCl_{(aq)}$

Surviving University: First Year Chemistry

Your goal is to find the theoretical mass of $BaSO_4$ (mass of $BaSO_4$ that should have precipitated). You will use this to find purity.

Steps

1. Make a chart
2. Convert mass of Na_2SO_4 into moles using $n = \frac{m}{M}$
3. Ratio to find # moles of $BaSO_4$
4. Convert to # moles of $BaSO_4$ to mass using $n = \frac{m}{M}$
5. Find purity using $Purity = \frac{mass\ obtained\ in\ lab}{mass\ calculated} \times 100\%$

	$Na_2SO_{4(aq)}$	+ $BaCl_{2(aq)}$	→ $BaSO_{4(s)}$	+ $2NaCl_{(aq)}$
m	1.85g		?g	
M	142g/mol		233.4g/mol	
n	?mol		?mol	
Ratio	1	1	1	2

$M_{Na_2SO_4} = 2(22.99\ g/mol) + 32.07\ g/mol + 4(16.00\ g/mol)$
$M_{Na_2SO_4} = 142g/mol$
$M_{BaSO_4} = 137.3\ g/mol + 32.07\ g/mol + 4(16.00\ g/mol)$
$M_{BaSO_4} = 233.4g/mol$
$n_{Na_2SO_4} = ?\ mol$
$n = \frac{m}{M}$

$n_{Na_2SO_4} = \frac{1.85g}{142g/mol}$
$n_{Na_2SO_4} = 0.0130mol$

$n_{BaSO_4} = 0.0130mol\ Na_2SO_4 \times \frac{1mol\ BaSO_4}{1mol\ Na_2SO_4}$

$n_{BaSO_4} = 0.0130mol$

$m_{BaSO_4} = n \times M$

$m_{BaSO_4} = 0.0130mol \times 233.4g/mol$
$m_{BaSO_4} = 3.04g$

3.04g of $BaSO_4$ should theoretically be produced.

$Purity = \frac{mass\ obtained\ in\ lab}{mass\ calculated} \times 100\%$

$Purity = \frac{2.75g}{3.04g} \times 100\%$

$Purity = 90.5\%$

The purity of the metal was 90.5%.

Determining molecular and empirical formulas from combustion

*Example 1 *This is a good exam problem**
0.450g of caprotic acid (116.2g/mol) was burned to produce 1.023g of carbon dioxide gas and 0.418g of water. Find empirical and molecular formula of $C_xH_yO_z$.

Steps
1. Make a chart
2. Find # moles of each of the products produced using $n = \frac{m}{M}$
3. Ratio to find # moles of C and H→ all carbon atoms will come from CO_2 and all hydrogen atoms will come from H_2O
4. Make a chart with just C, H, O
5. Find masses of C and H using $n = \frac{m}{M}$
6. Find mass of oxygen using $m_O = m_{Total} - m_C - m_H$
7. Find # moles of O using $n = \frac{m}{M}$
8. Write $C_xH_yO_z$, but instead of writing x, y, and z, write the # of moles of each element
9. Divide each # by the smallest # of moles→ this will give the empirical formula
10. Find molar mass of empirical formula
11. Divide molar mass of compound by molar mass of the empirical formula
12. Multiply empirical formula by factor found in step 11→ this will give the molecular formula

	$C_xH_yO_z$	+ $O_{2(g)}$	→ $CO_{2(g)}$	+ $H_2O_{(l)}$
m	0.450g		1.023g	0.418g
M	116.2g/mol		44.01g/mol	18.02g/mol
n	?mol		?mol	?mol
Ratio	1	1	1	1

$$M_{CO_2} = 12.01\,g/mol + 2(16.00\,g/mol) = 44.01g/mol$$
$$M_{H_2O} = 2(1.01\,g/mol) + 16.00\,g/mol = 18.02g/mol$$
$$n_{CO_2} = ?\,mol$$
$$n_{H_2O} = ?\,mol$$
$$n = \frac{m}{M}$$
$$n_{CO_2} = \frac{1.023g}{44.01g/mol}$$
$$n_{CO_2} = 0.02324mol$$

Surviving University: First Year Chemistry

$$n_{H_2O} = \frac{0.418g}{18.02g/mol}$$

$n_{H_2O} = 0.0232mol$

In $C_xH_yO_z$ all carbons will come from CO_2 and all hydrogen atoms will come from H_2O.

$$n_C = 0.02324mol\ CO_2\ \times \frac{1mol\ C}{1mol\ CO_2}$$

Note: since there is 1 carbon in CO_2, that means there is 1 mole of C in CO_2. Since there are 2 oxygen atoms in CO_2, that means there are 2 moles of O in CO_2.

$n_C = 0.02324mol\ C$

$$n_H = 0.0232mol\ H_2O\ \times \frac{2mol\ H}{1mol\ H_2O}$$

Note: since there are 2 hydrogen atoms in H_2O, that means that there are 2 moles of H in H_2O.

$n_H = 0.0464mol\ H$

Now make a second chart with just C, H, and O.

	C	H	O	$C_xH_yO_z$
m	?g	?g	?g	0.450g ← total mass of molecule
M	12.01g/mol	1.01g/mol	16.00g/mol	116.2g/mol
n	0.02324mol	0.0464mol	? mol	

You know the total mass of the molecule. Total mass consists of masses of C, H, and O.

$m_T = m_H + m_C + m_O$

If you know masses of H, C, and total mass, you can find mass of O.

$m_O = m_T - m_C - m_H$

$m_C = n \times M$

$m_C = 0.02324mol\ \times 12.01g/mol$

$m_C = 0.2791g$

$m_H = 0.0464mol\ \times 1.01g/mol$

$m_H = 0.0469g$

$m_O = m_T - m_C - m_H$

$m_O = 0.450g - 0.2791g - 0.0469g$

$m_O = 0.124g$

So the mass of oxygen in the molecule was 0.124g.

$$n = \frac{m}{M}$$

$$n_O = \frac{0.124g}{16.00g/mol}$$

$n_O = 0.00775 mol$

Now write $C_xH_yO_z$, but instead of writing x, y, and z, write the # of moles of each element.

$C_{0.02324mol}H_{0.0464mol}O_{0.00775mol}$

The smallest # of moles is 0.00775mol. Divide each # by 0.00775mol.

$C_{\frac{0.02324mol}{0.00775mol}}H_{\frac{0.0464mol}{0.00775mol}}O_{\frac{0.00775mol}{0.00775mol}}$

$= C_3H_6O_1$

$= C_3H_6O$

C_3H_6O is the empirical formula of the compound. You also need to find the molecular formula.

You were given in the problem that molar mass of $C_xH_yO_z$ was 116.2g/mol. Find molar mass of C_3H_6O and see if it is 116.2g/mol or a multiple of 116.2g/mol.

$M_{C_3H_6O} = 3(12.01\,g/mol) + 6(1.01\,g/mol) + 16.00\,g/mol$

$M_{C_3H_6O} = 58.09g/mol$

$Ratio = \dfrac{M_{actual}}{M_{C_3H_6O}}$

$Ratio = \dfrac{116.2g/mol}{58.09g/mol}$

$Ratio = 2$

Multiply empirical formula by ratio.

$C_3H_6O \times 2 = C_6H_{12}O_6$

The molecular formula of the compound is $C_6H_{12}O_6$.

Molarity

- In order to make a solution, a solute must be dissolved in a solvent

Molarity- how much solute (mol) is dissolved per 1L of a solution

$$C = \frac{n}{V}$$

Note: C= concentration of solution (mol/L or M), n= # moles (mol), V= volume (L)

Example 1

13.2g of $FeCl_3$ are dissolved in water to make a 500mL solution. Find the concentration of $FeCl_3$.

Steps

1. Find # moles of $FeCl_3$ using $n = \dfrac{m}{M}$
2. Find concentration of $FeCl_3$ using $C = \dfrac{n}{V}$

$M_{FeCl_3} = 55.85g/mol + 3(35.45g/mol) = 162.20g/mol$

Surviving University: First Year Chemistry

$$m_{FeCl_3} = 13.2g$$
$$n = \frac{m}{M}$$
$$n_{FeCl_3} = \frac{13.2g}{162.20g/mol}$$
$$n_{FeCl_3} = 0.0814mol$$
$$C = \frac{n}{V}$$
$$C_{FeCl_3} = \frac{0.0814mol}{0.500L}$$
$$C_{FeCl_3} = 0.163M$$

The concentration of $FeCl_3$ in a 500mL solution was 0.163M.

Example 2
Find concentration of each ion in a 0.164M solution of Na_2SO_4.
According to solubility rules, Na_2SO_4 is soluble in water. This means that it will dissociate into its ions.
$$Na_2SO_{4(s)} \rightarrow 2Na^+_{(aq)} + SO_4^{2-}_{(aq)}$$
Steps
1. Ratio to find concentrations of Na^+ and SO_4^{2-}

	$Na_2SO_{4(s)} \rightarrow$	$2Na^+_{(aq)} +$	$SO_4^{2-}_{(aq)}$
C	0.164M	?M	?M
Ratio	1	2	1

$$C_{Na^+} = 0.164M\ Na_2SO_4 \times \frac{2mol\ Na^+}{1mol\ Na_2SO_4}$$
$$C_{Na^+} = 0.328M$$
$$C_{SO_4^{2-}} = 0.164M\ Na_2SO_4 \times \frac{1mol\ SO_4^{2-}}{1mol\ Na_2SO_4}$$
$$C_{SO_4^{2-}} = 0.164M$$

The concentration of Na^+ is 0.328M, and concentration of SO_4^{2-} is 0.164M.

Example 3
25.3g of Na_2CO_3 are dissolved in water to make a 250mL solution. Find the concentrations of Na_2CO_3, Na^+, CO_3^{2-}.
Steps
2. Find # moles of Na_2CO_3 using $n = \frac{m}{M}$
3. Find concentration of Na_2CO_3 using $C = \frac{n}{V}$
4. Ratio to find concentrations of Na^+ and CO_3^{2-}

	Na_2CO_3
m	25.3g
M	105.99g/mol
n	?mol
V	0.250L
C	?M

$$M_{Na_2CO_3} = 2(22.99 \, g/mol) + 12.01g/mol + 3(16.00 \, g/mol)$$
$$M_{Na_2CO_3} = 105.99g/mol$$
$$n = \frac{m}{M}$$
$$n_{Na_2CO_3} = \frac{25.3g}{105.99g/mol}$$
$$n_{Na_2CO_3} = 0.239mol$$
$$C = \frac{n}{V}$$
$$C_{Na_2CO_3} = \frac{0.239mol}{0.250L}$$
$$C_{Na_2CO_3} = 0.955M$$

In 1 mole Na_2CO_3 there are 2 moles of Na^+ and 1 mole of CO_3^{2-}.

$$C_{Na^+} = 0.955M \, Na_2CO_3 \times \frac{2mol \, Na^+}{1mol \, Na_2CO_3}$$
$$C_{Na^+} = 1.91M$$
$$C_{CO_3^{2-}} = 0.955M \, Na_2CO_3 \times \frac{1mol \, CO_3^{2-}}{1mol \, Na_2CO_3}$$
$$C_{CO_3^{2-}} = 0.955M$$

The concentration of Na_2CO_3 in the solution is 0.955M, concentration of Na^+ is 1.91M, and concentration of CO_3^{2-} is 0.955M.

Dilution

Note: these types of problems have 2 scenarios→ 1st before addition of water and 2nd after addition of water

- Water is added to a concentrated solution in order to decrease its concentration (by increasing the volume)

If the number of moles in the solution remain the same, then

$$C_1V_1 = C_2V_2$$

Note: C_1 is the original concentration of the solution (M), V_1 is the original volume of the solution (L), C_2 is the final concentration of the solution (M), and V_2 is the final volume of the solution (L).

Example 1
1.00mL of 0.236M iron (III) nitrate is added to 100.0mL of water. What is the new concentration of iron (III) nitrate?

This problem has 2 scenarios. 1st scenario is when iron(III) nitrate is in the 1.00mL solution. 2nd scenario is when iron(III) nitrate is in the 101.0mL solution.

Since 1.00mL of iron (III) nitrate is added to 100.0mL of water, then the total final volume becomes 101.0mL.

$C_1V_1 = C_2V_2$

C_1= 0.236M

V_1=0.00100L

C_2=?M

V_2=0.1010L

$$C_2 = \frac{C_1V_1}{V_2}$$

$$C_2 = \frac{(0.236\,M)(0.00100\,L)}{0.1010\,L}$$

$$C_2 = 0.00234\,M$$

The final concentration of the solution was 0.00234M.

Example 2
1.00mL of 0.104M sodium nitrate is added to water to make 100.0mL solution. What is the new concentration of sodium nitrate?

Note the difference between example 1 and 2. In example 1, 1.00mL of iron(III) nitrate was added to 100.0mL of water to make a total volume of 101.0mL. In example 2, 1.00mL of sodium nitrate is added to water to make the total volume of 100.0mL.

$C_1V_1 = C_2V_2$

C_1= 0.104M

V_1=0.00100L

C_2=?M

V_2=0.1000L

$$C_2 = \frac{C_1V_1}{V_2}$$

$$C_2 = \frac{(0.104\,M)(0.00100\,L)}{0.1000\,L}$$

$$C_2 = 0.00104\,M$$

The final concentration of the solution was 0.00104M.

Stoichiometry in an aqueous solution

Example 1

$Zn_{(s)} + 2HCl_{(aq)} \rightarrow ZnCl_{2(aq)} + H_{2(g)}$

What volume of 2.50M of HCl is needed to convert 11.8g of Zn into products?

Steps

1. Make a chart
2. Find # of moles of Zn using $n = \frac{m}{M}$
3. Ratio to find # moles of HCl
4. Use $C = \frac{n}{V}$ to find volume of HCl

	$Zn_{(s)}$	$+ 2HCl_{(aq)}$	$\rightarrow ZnCl_{2(aq)}$	$+ H_{2(g)}$
m	11.8g			
M	65.39g/mol			
n	?mol	?mol		
C		2.50M		
V		?L		
Ratio	1	2	1	1

$n = \frac{m}{M}$

$n_{Zn} = \frac{11.8g}{65.39g/mol}$

$n_{Zn} = 0.180mol$

$n_{HCl} = 0.180mol\ Zn \times \frac{2mol\ HCl}{1mol\ Zn}$

$n_{HCl} = 0.360mol$

$C = \frac{n}{V}$ rearranging

$v = \frac{n}{C}$

$v_{HCl} = \frac{0.360mol}{2.50mol/L}$

$v_{HCl} = 0.144L$

The volume of hydrochloric acid needed to convert 11.8g of Zn into products is 0.144L or 144mL.

Example 2

1.00L solution is made by dissolving 25.0g of $CuSO_4 \cdot 5H_2O$ (M=249.7g/mol) in water. Find concentration of Cu^{2+} ions in M and g/L. Note: the molar mass of $5H_2O$ is included into the total molar mass of the compound

Steps
1. Make a chart
2. Convert to mass of $CuSO_4 \cdot 5H_2O$ into moles using $n = \frac{m}{M}$
3. Ratio to find # moles of Cu^{2+}
4. Use $C = \frac{n}{V}$ to find concentration of Cu^{2+}
5. Convert moles to grams using $n = \frac{m}{M}$ to find concentration in g/L

	$CuSO_4 \cdot 5H_2O$	Cu^{2+}
m	25.0g	?g
M	249.7g/mol	63.55g/mol
n	?mol	?mol
C		?M
v		1.00L
Ratio	1	1

There is 1 mole of copper ions in $CuSO_4 \cdot 5H_2O$, so the ratio is 1 to 1.

$$n = \frac{m}{M}$$

$$n_{CuSO_4 \cdot 5H_2O} = \frac{25.0g}{249.7g/mol}$$

$$n_{CuSO_4 \cdot 5H_2O} = 0.100mol$$

$$n_{Cu^{2+}} = 0.100mol \; CuSO_4 \cdot 5H_2O \; \times \frac{1mol \; Cu^{2+}}{1mol \; CuSO_4 \cdot 5H_2O}$$

$$n_{Cu^{2+}} = 0.100mol$$

$$C = \frac{n}{V}$$

$$C_{Cu^{2+}} = \frac{0.100mol}{1.00L}$$

$$C_{Cu^{2+}} = 0.100mol/L$$

Now you need the concentration in g/L. You need to find # grams in 1.00L. Convert moles of Cu^{2+} into grams.

$$m_{Cu^{2+}} = n \times M$$

$$m_{Cu^{2+}} = 0.100mol \; \times 63.55g/mol$$

$$m_{Cu^{2+}} = 6.35g$$

So there are 6.35g of Cu^{2+} ions in 1.00L of the solution.
The concentration of copper ions was 0.100mol/L or 6.35g/L.

Example 3

What mass of $AgNO_3$ will be needed to make 0.0200M of Ag^+ in a 250mL flask?

Steps

1. Make a chart
2. Find # moles of Ag^+ using $C = \frac{n}{V}$
3. Ratio to find # moles of $AgNO_3$
4. Use $n = \frac{m}{M}$ to find mass of $AgNO_3$

	$AgNO_3$	Ag^+
m	?g	
M	169.9g/mol	
n	?mol	?mol
C		0.0200M
v		0.250L
Ratio	1	1

There is 1 mole of silver ions in $AgNO_3$, so the ratio is 1 to 1.

$C = \frac{n}{V}$ rearranging

$n = C \times v$

$n_{Ag^+} = 0.0200\,mol/L \times 0.250L$

$n_{Ag^+} = 0.00500mol$

$n_{AgNO_3} = 0.00500mol\,Ag^+ \times \dfrac{1mol\,AgNO_3}{1mol\,Ag^+}$

$n_{AgNO_3} = 0.00500mol$

$m_{AgNO_3} = n \times M$

$m_{AgNO_3} = 0.00500mol \times 169.9g/mol$

$m_{AgNO_3} = 0.850g$

The mass of silver nitrate required was 0.850g.

Titrations

Titration- a laboratory technique which is used to determine a concentration and/or identity of a solute in a solution

- *See part 26 of this book for more details*
- Types of titrations
  - Acid-base titration
  - Redox titration

Acid-base titration

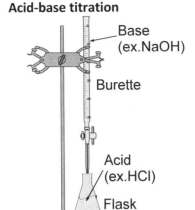

Base
(ex.NaOH)

Burette

Acid
(ex.HCl)

Flask

- An acid is placed into a flask, a base is placed into a burette
- Phenolphthalein is added to the flask
  - It is an indicator that changes from clear to pink colour when pH=7
- A base is added to an acid through the burette until the solution permanently changes its colour to pink
  - At this point the solution is at the **equivalence point** (the concentration of acid is equal to the concentration of base)

Standardization of an acid or a base- finding concentration of a base or an acid using an acid-base titration

Example 1
1.034g of impure $H_2C_2O_4$ (90.04g/mol) is added to water.
Phenolphthalein is added to the flask. In order to reach equivalence point (where pH=7), 0.03447L of 0.485M of NaOH is added. What is the mass of $H_2C_2O_4$ in the solution? What is the mass percent of $H_2C_2O_4$?

An impure mixture means that the mixture contains $H_2C_2O_4$ and other elements/compounds. You need to find % of the mixture which consists of $H_2C_2O_4$. To do this, you need to find the mass of $H_2C_2O_4$ (acid) that reacted with NaOH (base) to produce water.

At the equivalence point (after the addition of 0.03447L of NaOH), all of $H_2C_2O_4$ molecules reacted with NaOH.

Steps
1. Make a chart
2. Find # moles of NaOH using $C = \frac{n}{V}$
3. Ratio to find # moles of $H_2C_2O_4$
4. Use $n = \frac{m}{M}$ to find mass of $H_2C_2O_4$

5. Find mass % of $H_2C_2O_4$ using

$$Mass\ \% = \frac{mass\ of\ compound/element\ in\ the\ sample}{total\ mass\ of\ sample} \times 100\%$$

	$H_2C_2O_{4(aq)}$	+ 2NaOH$_{(aq)}$	→ 2H$_2$O$_{(l)}$	+ NaC$_2$O$_{4(aq)}$
m	?g			
M	90.04g/mol			
n	?mol	?mol		
C		0.485M		
v		0.03447L		
Ratio	1	2	2	1

$n = C \times v$

$n_{NaOH} = 0.485\ mol/L \times 0.03447L$

$n_{NaOH} = 0.0167mol$

$n_{H_2C_2O_4} = 0.0167mol\ NaOH\ \times \dfrac{1mol\ H_2C_2O_4}{2mol\ NaOH}$

$n_{H_2C_2O_4} = 0.00836mol$

$m_{H_2C_2O_4} = n \times M$

$m_{H_2C_2O_4} = 0.00836mol\ \times 90.04g/mol$

$m_{H_2C_2O_4} = 0.753g$

The total mass of impure mixture is 1.034g. 0.753g of this mixture is $H_2C_2O_4$.

$$Mass\ \% = \frac{mass\ of\ compound/element\ in\ the\ sample}{total\ mass\ of\ sample} \times 100\%$$

$$Mass\ \% = \frac{0.753g}{1.034g} \times 100\%$$

$$Mass\ \% = 72.8\%$$

72.8% of mixture consists of $H_2C_2O_4$.

Example 2

0.02835L of HCl is needed for 0.263g of Na$_2$CO$_3$ (a base, M=106.0g/mol) to reach the equivalence point. Find the concentration of hydrochloric acid.

Steps

1. Make a chart
2. Find # moles of Na$_2$CO$_3$ using $n = \dfrac{m}{M}$
3. Ratio to find # moles of HCl
4. Use $C = \dfrac{n}{V}$ to find concentration of HCl

	$Na_2CO_{3(aq)}$	+ $2HCl_{(aq)}$	→ $2NaCl_{(aq)}$	+ $H_2O_{(l)}$	+ $CO_{2(g)}$
m	0.263g				
M	106.0g/mol				
n	? mol	? mol			
C		? M			
v		0.02835L			
Ratio	1	2	2	1	1

$$n = \frac{m}{M}$$

$$n_{Na_2CO_3} = \frac{0.263g}{106.0g/mol}$$

$$n_{Na_2CO_3} = 0.00248mol$$

$$n_{HCl} = 0.00248mol\ Na_2CO_3 \times \frac{2mol\ HCl}{1mol\ Na_2CO_3}$$

$$n_{HCl} = 0.00496mol$$

$$C = \frac{n}{V}$$

$$C_{HCl} = \frac{0.00496mol}{0.02835L}$$

$$C_{HCl} = 0.175M$$

The concentration of hydrochloric acid was 0.175M.

Redox titration

Example 1
1.026g of iron ore is needed to titrate 0.02435L of 0.0195M MnO_4^- solution. Find the iron content in the sample.

Iron ore means there is iron in the sample and there are other elements/compounds present in the sample. This is a mass % problem. So the goal is to find the % of iron present in the sample. You need to find the mass of iron present in the sample.

Steps
1. Make a chart
2. Find # moles of MnO_4^- using $C = \frac{n}{V}$
3. Ratio to find # moles of Fe^{2+}
4. Use $n = \frac{m}{M}$ to find mass of Fe^{2+}
5. Find mass % of Fe^{2+} using
$$Mass\ \% = \frac{mass\ of\ compound/element\ in\ the\ sample}{total\ mass\ of\ sample} \times 100\%$$

	$MnO_4^-{}_{(aq)}$	+ $5Fe^{2+}{}_{(aq)}$	+$8H_3O^+{}_{(aq)}$	→ $Mn^{2+}{}_{(aq)}$	+ $5Fe^{2+}{}_{(aq)}$	+ $12H_2O_{(g)}$
m		?g				
M		55.9g/mol				
n	?mol	?mol				
C	0.0195M					
v	0.02435L					
Ratio	1	5	8	1	5	12

$$n = C \times v$$
$$n_{MnO_4^-} = 0.0195 \, mol/L \times 0.02435L$$
$$n_{MnO_4^-} = 4.75 \times 10^{-4} mol$$

$$n_{Fe^{2+}} = 4.75 \times 10^{-4} mol \, MnO_4^- \times \frac{5mol \, Fe^{2+}}{1mol \, MnO_4^-}$$

$$n_{Fe^{2+}} = 0.00237mol$$
$$m_{Fe^{2+}} = n \times M$$

$$m_{Fe^{2+}} = 0.00237mol \times 55.9g/mol$$
$$m_{Fe^{2+}} = 0.133g$$

The total mass of impure mixture is 1.026g. 0.133g of this mixture is Fe^{2+}.

$$Mass \, \% = \frac{mass \, of \, compound/element \, in \, the \, sample}{total \, mass \, of \, sample} \times 100\%$$

$$Mass \, \% = \frac{0.133g}{1.026g} \times 100\%$$

$$Mass \, \% = 12.9\%$$

12.9% of ore consists of Fe^{2+}.

Part 5

Chemical Reactivity

Energy

Laws of thermodynamics

Exothermic/endothermic reactions

Specific heat capacity

Isolated system

Physical changes

Changes of phase/state

Phase diagrams

Enthalpy calculations

Standard enthalpy values

Calorimetry

Hess's law

Bond dissociation enthalpy

Chemical Reactivity

Energy

Energy- capacity to do work, measured in Joules (J) and calories (cal)

$$1 \, cal = 4.184 \, J$$
$$1 \, dietary \, calorie = 1000 cal$$

Calorie- the amount of heat needed to raise 1g of H_2O by 1 °C
Potential energy- energy stored in bonds between atoms
Kinetic energy- energy used for motion of atoms
Conservation of energy- energy cannot be created or destroyed

Heat

Heat- energy that flows between 2 objects due to difference in their temperature
- Energy flows from higher temperature to lower temperature

Thermodynamic equilibrium- 2 objects have the same temperature
- Energy is transferred between objects until the thermodynamic equilibrium is established

Temperature- measures the amount of internal kinetic energy that molecules in a substance have

Zeroth law of thermodynamics

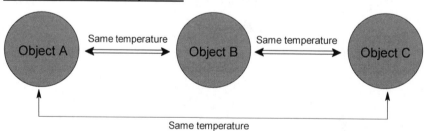

- If A and B are in equilibrium (have the same temperature) and B and C are in equilibrium (have the same temperature), then C and A are in equilibrium (have the same temperature)

First law of thermodynamics

- Energy cannot be created or destroyed, can only be converted (Law of Conservation of Energy)

Surviving University: First Year Chemistry

- The change in energy of the system is the sum of heat transferred to/from the system and work done by/on the system

$$\Delta U = q + W$$

Note: ΔU= change of energy in the system (J), q= energy absorbed/released by system (J), W= work done by or on the system (J)

A chemical reaction

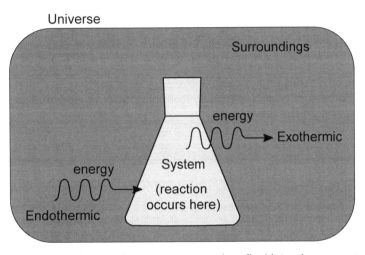

System- where a chemical reaction occurs (ex. flask)→ where reactants are transferred into products

Surroundings- is outside of the system, interacts with the system (ex. air around the flask)

Universe- system + surroundings

Endothermic reaction- heat is absorbed during a chemical reaction

- In an endothermic reaction, energy flows from the surroundings to the system
    - The temperature of the system increases, the temperature of the surroundings decreases

Exothermic reaction- heat is released during a chemical reaction

- In an exothermic reaction, energy flows from the system to the surroundings
    - The temperature of the system decreases, the temperature of the surroundings increases

q		
+ive	Endothermic	Energy is transferred into the system
-ive	Exothermic	Energy is transferred out of the system

Specific heat capacity

Specific heat capacity- the energy needed to raise the temperature of 1g of a substance by 1°C

- Specific heat capacity is different for each substance and depends on state of a substance (s, l, or g)

$$Specific\ heat\ capacity\ of\ H_2O = 4.18\ J/g \cdot K$$

$$q = m \times C_p \times \Delta T \text{ where } \Delta T = T_f - T_i$$

Note: the temperature must be in Kelvin

Note: q= energy gained/lost in the chemical reaction (J), m= mass of substance (g), C_p= specific heat capacity (J/g•K), Δ T= change in temperature (K), T_f= final temperature of the system (K), T_i= initial temperature of the system (K)

See part 1 of this book for conversion of °C to K.

Example 1

The specific heat capacity of copper is 0.385J/g •K. Find its molar heat capacity (in J/mol •K).

$$C_p = 0.385 J/g \cdot K$$

$$C_{molar} = ? J/mol \cdot K$$

The difference between specific heat capacity and molar heat capacity is the units. You need to get replace g with mol→ use the molar mass of copper.

$$M_{Cu} = 63.546 g/mol$$

$$C_{molar} = \frac{0.385J}{g \cdot K} \times \frac{63.546g}{mol}$$

$$C_{molar} = 24.5 J/mol \cdot K$$

The molar heat capacity of copper is 24.5J/mol•K.

Example 2

The temperature of 25.0g of Al decreases from 583.15K to 310.15K. How much energy has been transferred by Al? (Specific heat capacity of Al is 0.897 J/g •K)

	Al
m	25.0g
c	0.89J/g•K
q	?J
T_i	583.15K
T_f	310.15K

$q = m \times C_p \times \Delta T$ where $\Delta T = T_f - T_i$

$q = (25.0g)(0.897J/g \cdot K)(310.15K - 583.15K)$

$q = -6120J$

6120J of energy has been transferred from Al. Since q is negative, the reaction was exothermic.

Example 3

A 10.2g piece of gold (at 65.3°C) is placed into an ice bath. 45.0J of energy is lost. Find the final temperature of gold. Specific heat capacity of gold is 0.128J/g ·K.

Since energy was lost, the reaction is exothermic (q is negative).

The temperature needs to be in K (not °C).

$Temperature\ in\ Kelvin = (Temperature\ in\ °C + 273.15°C) \times \dfrac{1K}{1°C}$

$Temperature\ in\ Kelvin = (65.3°C + 273.15°C) \times \dfrac{1K}{1°C}$

$Temperature\ in\ Kelvin = 338.5K$

	Au
m	10.2g
c	0.128J/g·K
q	-45.0J
T_i	338.5K
T_f	?K

$q = m \times C_p \times \Delta T$ where $\Delta T = T_f - T_i$

$\Delta T = \dfrac{q}{mC_p}$

$\Delta T = \dfrac{-45.0J}{10.2g \times 0.128J/g \cdot K}$

$\Delta T = -34.5K$

$\Delta T = T_f - T_i$

$T_f = \Delta T + T_i$

$T_f = -34.5K + 338.5K$

$T_f = -34.5K + 338.5K$

$T_f = 304.0K$

You can leave this in K or convert to °C.

$Temperature\ in\ °C = (Temperature\ in\ K - 273.15K) \times \dfrac{1°C}{1K}$

$Temperature\ in\ °C = (304.0 - 273.15K) \times \dfrac{1°C}{1K}$

Temperature in °C = 30.9°C
The final temperature of gold was 304.0K or 30.9°C.

Isolated system

Isolated system- there is no flow of energy between the system and the surroundings

- Energy changes inside of the system add up to 0

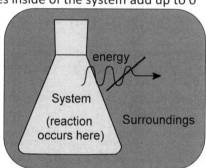

$$q_1 + q_2 + q_3 \ldots = 0$$
where $q = m \times C_p \times \Delta T$ where $\Delta T = T_f - T_i$

Note: the temperature must be in Kelvin

Note: q_1= energy gained/lost in the 1st chemical reaction (J), q_2= energy gained/lost in the 2nd chemical reaction (J), q_3= energy gained/lost in the 3rd chemical reaction (J), m= mass of substance (g), C_p= specific heat capacity (J/g•K), Δ T= change in temperature (K), T_f= final temperature of the system (K), T_i= initial temperature of the system (K)

Example 1
88.5g of iron (c= 0.499J/g •K) with temperature of 78.8˚C was placed into a beaker with 244g of water with temperature of 18.8˚C. What was the temperature of both substances at equilibrium?
At equilibrium, both iron and water have the same temperature.
Need to convert temperatures from °C to K.

$$T_i = (78.8°C + 273.2°C) \times \frac{1K}{1°C}$$
$$T_i = 352.0K$$
$$T_f = (18.8°C + 273.2°C) \times \frac{1K}{1°C}$$
$$T_f = 292.0K$$

	Fe	H₂O
m	88.5g	244g

c	0.499J/g•K	4.18J/g•K
q	?J	?J
T_i	352.0K	292.0K
T_f	?K	

$q_{water} + q_{metal} = 0$ ①

Also $q = m \times C_p \times \Delta T$ where $\Delta T = T_f - T_i$

So $q = m \times C_p \times (T_f - T_i)$ ②

Substituting ② into ①

$m_{Fe} \times C_{Fe} \times (T_f - T_{iFe}) + m_{H_2O} \times C_{H_2O} \times (T_f - T_{i\,H_2O}) = 0$

$m_{Fe} \times C_{Fe} \times T_f - m_{Fe} \times C_{Fe} \times T_{iFe} + m_{H_2O} \times C_{H_2O} \times T_f - m_{H_2O} \times C_{H_2O} \times T_{iH_2O} = 0$

$m_{Fe} \times C_{Fe} \times T_f + m_{H_2O} \times C_{H_2O} \times T_f - m_{Fe} \times C_{Fe} \times T_{iFe} - m_{H_2O} \times C_{H_2O} \times T_{iH_2O} = 0$

Common factoring T_f

$T_f(m_{Fe} \times C_{Fe} + m_{H_2O} \times C_{H_2O}) - m_{Fe} \times C_{Fe} \times T_{iFe} - m_{H_2O} \times C_{H_2O} \times T_{iH_2O} = 0$

$T_f(m_{Fe} \times C_{Fe} + m_{H_2O} \times C_{H_2O}) = m_{Fe} \times C_{Fe} \times T_{iFe} + m_{H_2O} \times C_{H_2O} \times T_{iH_2O}$

$T_f = \dfrac{(m_{Fe} \times C_{Fe} \times T_{iFe} + m_{H_2O} \times C_{H_2O} \times T_{iH_2O})}{(m_{Fe} \times C_{Fe} + m_{H_2O} \times C_{H_2O})}$

$T_f = \dfrac{(88.5g) \times (0.499J/g \cdot K) \times (352.0K) + (244g) \times (4.18J/g \cdot K) \times (292.0K)}{(88.5g) \times (0.499J/g \cdot K) + (244g) \times (4.18J/g \cdot K)}$

$T_f = 294K$

$T_f = (294K - 273.2K) \times \dfrac{1°C}{1K}$

$T_f = 20.8°C$

The final temperature of the system was 22°C.

Physical changes

Physical change- does not result in production of a new chemical substance (ex. water turns into ice)

- During a physical change, no intramolecular forces are broken/created→ only intermolecular forces are broken/created
    - *See part 11 of this book for intermolecular/intramolecular forces*
- During a physical change,

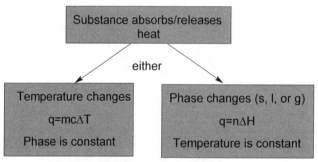

Both cannot occur at the same time!

Note: q= energy gained/lost in the chemical reaction (J), m= mass of substance (g), C_p= specific heat capacity (J/g•K), Δ T= change in temperature (K), n= # of moles of a substance, ΔH= heat of transition (J/mol). Note: see below for information about ΔH.

<u>Changes of phase/state</u>

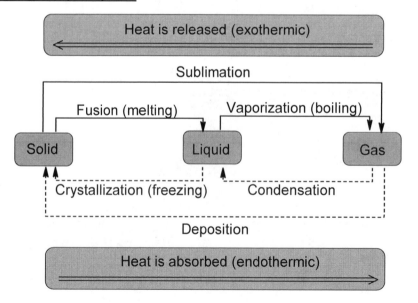

Surviving University: First Year Chemistry

State of H_2O	Temperature
Ice (solid)	50°C-0°C
Liquid	0°C- 100°C
Steam (gas)	100°C- 200°C

Heat of transition (ΔH)- the amount of energy required to change phase

- **Heat of fusion** (ΔH_{fus})- the amount of energy required to bring a substance from a solid to a liquid state
- **Heat of vaporization** (ΔH_{vap})- the amount of energy required to bring a substance from a liquid to a gas state
- **Heat of sublimation** (ΔH_{sub})- the amount of energy required to bring a substance from a solid to a gas state
- **Heat of condensation** (ΔH_{cond})- the amount of energy required to bring a substance from a gas to a liquid state
- **Heat of crystallization** (ΔH_{cryst})- the amount of energy required to bring a substance from a liquid to a solid state
- **Heat of deposition** (ΔH_{dep})- the amount of energy required to bring a substance from a gas to a solid state

$$q = n \times \Delta H$$

Note: q= energy gained/lost during a phase change (J), n= # of moles of a substance, ΔH= heat of transition (J/mol)

q	ΔH		
+ive	**+ive**	Endothermic	Energy is transferred into the system
-ive	**-ive**	Exothermic	Energy is transferred out of the system

Phase transition diagram

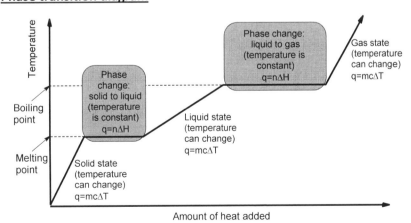

Example 1
How much energy is needed to convert 200.0g of water from 5°C to 90°C?
You know that water's melting point is 0°C and boiling point is 100°C.
Water is in its liquid state when it is brought from 5°C to 90°C.
Note: the following diagram is not to scale.

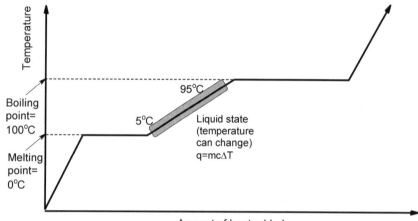

The temperature needs to be in K (not °C).

$$Temperature\ in\ Kelvin = (Temperature\ in\ °C + 273.15°C) \times \frac{1K}{1°C}$$

$$Initial\ temperature\ in\ Kelvin = (5°C + 273.15°C) \times \frac{1K}{1°C}$$

$$Initial\ temperature\ in\ Kelvin = 278.15K$$

$$Final\ temperature\ in\ Kelvin = (95°C + 273.15°C) \times \frac{1K}{1°C}$$

$$Final\ temperature\ in\ Kelvin = 368.15K$$

	H$_2$O
m	200.0g
c	4.18J/g•K
q	?J
T$_i$	278.15K
T$_f$	368.15K

$q = m \times C_p \times \Delta T$ where $\Delta T = T_f - T_i$
$q = (200.0g)(4.18J/g•K)(368.15K - 278.15K)$
$q = 75240J$
75240J of energy is needed to convert 200.0g of water from 5°C to 90°C.

Example 2
How much energy is needed to convert 115.0g of water from -10°C to 140°C? ΔH_{fus}= -6.00kJ/mol. ΔH_{vap}= 40.65kJ/mol.
You know that water's melting point is 0°C and boiling point is 100°C.
Note: the following diagram is not to scale.

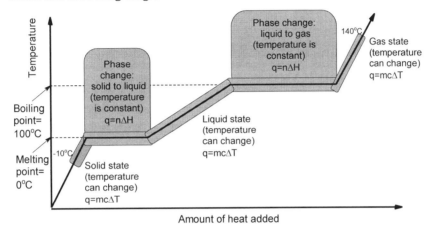

	H_2O
m	115.0g
M	?g/mol
n	?mol
c	4.18J/g•K
q	?J

This problem needs to be solved in several steps.
The temperature needs to be in K (not °C). See part 1 of this book for how to convert °C into K.

	Temperature	
Step 1	-10°C to 0°C or 263.15K to 273.15K	Solid state→ q=mcΔT
Step 2	0°C or 273.15K	Phase change: solid to liquid→ q=nΔH
Step 3	0°C to 100°C or 273.15K to 373.15K	Liquid state→ q=mcΔT
Step 4	100°C	Phase change: liquid to gas→ q=nΔH

	or 373.15K	
Step 5	100°C to 140°C or 373.15K to 413.15K	Gas state→ q=mcΔT

$q_{Total} = q_1 + q_2 + q_3 + q_4 + q_5$ (each subscript represents a step)

Step 1: 263.15K to 273.15K

$q_1 = m \times C_p \times \Delta T$ where $\Delta T = T_f - T_i$

$q_1 = (115.0g)(4.18J/g \cdot K)(273.15K - 263.15K)$

$q_1 = 4807J = 4.807kJ$

Step 2: at 273.15K

$q = n \times \Delta H$ where $n = \frac{m}{M}$

First, need to find n.

$M_{H_2O} = 16.00g/mol + 2(1.01g/mol) = 18.02g/mol$

$m_{H_2O} = 115.0g$

$n_{H_2O} = \dfrac{115.0g}{18.02g/mol}$

$n_{H_2O} = 6.382mol$

Know that ΔH$_{fus}$= -6.00kJ/mol (fusion since going from a solid to a liquid).

$q_2 = n \times \Delta H$

$q_2 = 6.382mol \times (-6.00kJ/mol)$

$q_2 = -38.3kJ$

Step 3: 273.15K to 373.15K

$q_3 = m \times C_p \times \Delta T$ where $\Delta T = T_f - T_i$

$q_3 = (115.0g)(4.18J/g \cdot K)(373.15K - 273.15K)$

$q_3 = 48070J = 48.070kJ$

Step 4: at 373.15K

$q = n \times \Delta H$ where $n = \frac{m}{M}$

$n_{H_2O} = 6.382mol$

Know that *ΔH$_{vap}$= 40.65kJ/mol* (vaporization since going from a liquid to a gas).

$q_4 = n \times \Delta H$

$q_4 = 6.382mol \times (40.65kJ/mol)$

$q_4 = 259.5kJ$

Step 5: 373.15K to 413.15K

$q_5 = m \times C_p \times \Delta T$ where $\Delta T = T_f - T_i$

$q_5 = (115.0g)(4.18J/g \cdot K)(413.15K - 373.15K)$

$q_5 = 19228J = 19.228kJ$

$q_{Total} = q_1 + q_2 + q_3 + q_4 + q_5$

$q_{Total} = 4.807kJ + (-38.3kJ) + 48.070kJ + 259.5kJ + 19.228kJ$

$q_{Total} = 293.3kJ$

It takes 293.3kJ to raise water from -10°C to 140°C.

Phase diagrams

- A phase diagram shows how a substance's phase is dependent upon temperature and pressure
    - At low temperatures and high pressures, solids are favoured
    - At high temperatures and low pressures, gases are favoured
- Understanding phase diagrams
    - Solid lines represent phase boundaries
        - At these conditions, a phase changes
    - Crossing the phase boundary results in a phase transition (ex. from solid to liquid)

Normal melting point- the temperature of the solid-liquid boundary when the pressure is 1atm

Normal boiling point- the temperature of the liquid-gas boundary when the pressure is 1atm

Triple point- the temperature and pressure when all 3 phases (solid, liquid, and gas) occur simultaneously at equilibrium

Critical point- the temperature and pressure of the end of a liquid-gas boundary

- Beyond the critical point, a substance is a **supercritical fluid**
    - A substance has both properties of a liquid and a gas
    - If pressure is applied to a supercritical fluid, it does not go back into a liquid phase

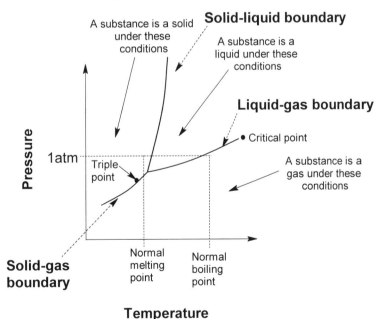

Enthalpy calculations

Enthalpy (ΔH)- energy is transferred as heat at a constant pressure

$$\Delta H = \Delta U + P\Delta V$$

$$\Delta H = H_f - H_i$$

Note: ΔH= enthalpy (J), ΔU= change in energy of the system (J), P= pressure of the system (kPa), ΔV= change in volume (L)

ΔH, q		
+ive	Endothermic	Reactant favoured reaction (concentration of reactants ↑)
-ive	Exothermic	Product favoured reaction (concentration of products ↑)

Standard enthalpy values

- ΔH°→ ° means that this is a **state function** (ΔH° was measured under standard conditions→ pressure of 1 bar, concentration of 1M, temperature of 25°C)

Ways to calculate ΔH

1. Calorimetry (experimentally) ($\Delta_r H$)
2. Standard molar enthalpy change of formation ($\Delta_f H°$)
3. Finding standard enthalpy change ($\Delta_r H°$) from $\Delta_f H°$
4. Hess's law ($\Delta_r H$)
5. From bond energies ($\Delta_r H$)

1) Calculating Δ_rH from calorimetry

- Calorimetry is a technique used to experimentally measure heat absorbed/released during a chemical reaction and to calculate ΔH
- A **calorimeter** (an apparatus) contains water and another material whose specific heat capacity (C_p) is known
- A calorimeter forms an isolated system
    - No heat can enter and escape the calorimeter
    - Heat can only flow between the reaction and the calorimeter
        - All of the heat absorbed/released by a reaction is released/absorbed by the calorimeter

Surviving University: First Year Chemistry

- The initial and final temperatures of solution inside of the calorimeter is used to determine the amount of energy absorbed/released during a chemical reaction

$$q_{reaction} = -q_{calorimeter}$$

$$q_{calorimeter} = c_{calorimeter}\Delta T \text{ where } \Delta T = T_f - T_i$$

$$\text{where } c_{calorimeter} \cong m_{solution}c_{solution}$$

Note: the temperature must be in Kelvin

Note: $q_{reaction}$= energy gained/lost during a chemical reaction (J), $q_{calorimeter}$= energy gained/lost by the calorimeter during a chemical reaction (J), $c_{calorimeter}$= specific heat capacity of the calorimeter (J/g•K), ΔT= change in temperature (K), T_f= final temperature of the system (K), T_i= initial temperature of the system (K), $m_{solution}$= mass of solution inside of the calorimeter (g), $c_{solution}$= specific heat capacity of solution inside of the calorimeter (J/g•K)

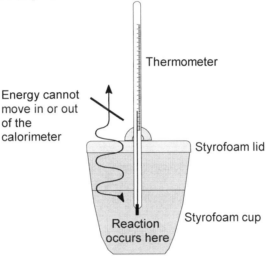

Example 1
14.4g of NH$_4$NO$_3$ is placed into a calorimeter containing 110.0g of water. The temperature decreases from 23.1°C to 13.8°C.
a) Find the amount of heat (q) which was absorbed/released by the solution.
b) Was the reaction exothermic or endothermic?
c) Find the enthalpy change for the reaction per 1 mol of NH$_4$NO$_3$.

a) Find the amount of heat (q) which was absorbed/released by the solution.

Steps

1. Find $c_{calorimeter}$ using $c_{calorimeter} \cong m_{solution}c_{solution}$
2. Find $q_{calorimeter}$ using $q_{calorimeter} = c_{calorimeter}\Delta T$
3. Find $q_{reaction}$ using $q_{reaction} = -q_{calorimeter}$

	H₂O
m	110.0g
c	4.18J/g•K

$c_{calorimeter} \cong m_{solution}c_{solution}$
$c_{calorimeter} \cong 110.0g \times 4.18J/g \cdot K$
$c_{calorimeter} \cong 459.8J/g \cdot K$
$q_{calorimeter} = c_{calorimeter}\Delta T$ where $\Delta T = T_f - T_i$
Need to convert temperatures from °C to K.

$$Temperature\ in\ Kelvin = (Temperature\ in\ °C + 273.15°C) \times \frac{1K}{1°C}$$

$$Initial\ temperature\ in\ Kelvin = (23.1°C + 273.15°C) \times \frac{1K}{1°C}$$

$$Initial\ temperature\ in\ Kelvin = 296.25K$$

$$Final\ temperature\ in\ Kelvin = (13.8°C + 273.15°C) \times \frac{1K}{1°C}$$

$$Final\ temperature\ in\ Kelvin = 286.95K$$

$q_{calorimeter} = 459.8J/g \cdot K \times (286.95K - 296.25K)$
$q_{calorimeter} = -4276J = -4.276kJ$
$q_{reaction} = -q_{calorimeter}$
$q_{reaction} = -(-4.276kJ)$
$q_{reaction} = 4.276kJ$
4.276kJ of energy was absorbed when 14.4g of NH_4NO_3 dissolved in the calorimeter.

b) Was the reaction exothermic or endothermic?
Since $q_{reaction}$ is a positive value, the reaction was endothermic (heat was transferred from the calorimeter to the reaction).

c) Find the enthalpy change for the reaction per 1 mol of NH₄NO₃.
Steps

1. Find # moles of NH_4NO_3 using $n = \frac{m}{M}$
2. Find ΔH using $q = n \times \Delta H$

	NH₄NO₃
m	14.4g
M	?g/mol

Surviving University: First Year Chemistry

n	?mol
q	4.276kJ
ΔH	?kJ/mol

$$M_{NH_4NO_3} = 2(14.01g/mol) + 4(1.01g/mol) + 3(16.00g/mol)$$
$$M_{NH_4NO_3} = 80.06g/mol$$
$$n_{NH_4NO_3} = \frac{m}{M}$$
$$n_{NH_4NO_3} = \frac{14.4g}{80.06g/mol}$$
$$n_{NH_4NO_3} = 0.180mol$$
$$\Delta H = \frac{q_{reaction}}{n_{NH_4NO_3}}$$
$$\Delta H = \frac{4.276kJ}{0.180mol}$$
$$\Delta H = 23.76kJ/mol$$
The enthalpy change for the reaction is 23.76kJ/mol.

2) Standard molar enthalpy change of formation ($\Delta_f H°$)

- Forming **1 mol** of a compound from its elements at the standard conditions (pressure of 1 bar, concentration of 1M, temperature of 25°C)
- $\Delta_f H°$ for elements= 0kJ/mol

Example 1
a) Write a balanced chemical equation for formation of CH_3OH from its elements ($\Sigma \Delta_f H° = -201.0kJ/mol$).
b) Find change in enthalpy if 2.4g of carbon is used.

a) Write a balanced chemical equation for formation of CH_3OH from its elements ($\Sigma \Delta_f H° = -201.0 kJ/mol$).
Formation of CH_3OH means that CH_3OH was formed (it is a product). The reactants are all of the elements that make up CH_3OH (C, H, O).
Remember that H and O are diatomic molecules (they come in pairs→ H_2, O_2)
$C_{(s)} + H_{2(g)} + O_{2(g)} →$ ‖$CH_3OH_{(l)}$← make sure that only 1 mol of the compound is formed (the coefficient before the compound is 1)!
So the balanced chemical equation for formation of CH_3OH from its elements is
$C_{(s)} + 2H_{2(g)} + ½O_{2(g)} → CH_3OH_{(l)}$

b) Find change in enthalpy if 2.4g of carbon is used.

Surviving University: First Year Chemistry

You know that $\Sigma\Delta_f H°$= -201.0kJ/mol. This change in enthalpy is for 1mol of the reaction. You need to find the change in enthalpy for 2.4g of carbon. You need to find the # mole moles of C.

$$n = \frac{m}{M}$$

$$n_C = \frac{2.4g}{12.01g/mol}$$

$$n_C = 0.1998mol$$

$\Sigma\Delta_f H°$= -201.0kJ/mol is for 1mol of the reaction. You need to find how much $\Sigma\Delta_f H°$ is for 0.1998mol.

$$\Delta_r H°_C = -\frac{201.0KJ}{1mol\ reaction} \times \frac{1mol\ reaction}{0.1998mol\ C}$$

$$\Delta_r H°_C = -1006.0\ KJ/mol\ C$$

The change in enthalpy for carbon was 1006.0kJ/mol. Since ΔH was negative, the reaction was exothermic.

3) Finding standard enthalpy change (Δ$_r$H°) from Δ$_f$H°

- Use this methods when you are given only the overall reaction and need to calculate the <u>standard</u> enthalpy change
  - Standard refers to the standard conditions (pressure of 1 bar, concentration of 1M, temperature of 25°C)

$$\Delta_r H° = \Sigma\Delta_f H°_{products} - \Sigma\Delta_f H°_{reactants}$$

The enthalpy value for elements (ex. O_2) is 0kJ/mol

Multiply $\Delta_f H°_{product}$ and $\Delta_f H°_{reactant}$ of each compound by its stoichiometric coefficient

Note: $\Sigma\Delta_f H°_{products}$= enthalpy of products (kJ/mol), $\Sigma\Delta_f H°_{reactants}$= enthalpy of reactants (kJ/mol), $\Delta_r H°$= enthalpy of the reaction (kJ/mol)
Note: $\Delta_f H°$ values for each reactant/product can be found in a table at the back of your chemistry textbook.

Example 1
Calculate the standard enthalpy change for the following reaction.
$2Al_{(s)}$+ $Fe_2O_{3(s)}$→ $2Fe_{(s)}$+ $Al_2O_{3(s)}$ $\qquad\qquad$ $\Delta_r H° =? kJ/mol$

	$\Delta_f H°$	Stoichiometric coefficient
Al	0kJ/mol	2
Fe$_2$O$_3$	-824.2kJ/mol	1
Fe	0kJ/mol	2

Surviving University: First Year Chemistry

Al_2O_3	-1675.7kJ/mol	1

$$\Delta_r H° = \Sigma \Delta_f H°_{products} - \Sigma \Delta_f H°_{reactants}$$

$$\Delta_r H° = \left(\frac{2mol\ Fe}{1mol\ reaction} \times \Delta_f H°_{Fe} + \frac{1mol\ Al_2O_3}{1mol\ reaction} \times \Delta_f H°_{Al_2O_3}\right)$$
$$- \left(\frac{2mol\ Al}{1mol\ reaction} \times \Delta_f H°_{Al} + \frac{1mol\ Fe_2O_3}{1mol\ reaction}\right.$$
$$\left. \times \Delta_f H°_{Fe_2O_3}\right)$$

$$\Delta_r H° = \left(\frac{2mol\ Fe}{1mol\ reaction} \times 0kJ/mol + \frac{1mol\ Al_2O_3}{1mol\ reaction}\right.$$
$$\left. \times (-1675.7kJ/mol)\right)$$
$$- \left(\frac{2mol\ Al}{1mol\ reaction} \times 0kJ/mol + \frac{1mol\ Fe_2O_3}{1mol\ reaction}\right.$$
$$\left. \times (-824.2kJ/mol)\right)$$

$$\Delta_r H° = -851.5kJ/mol$$

The standard enthalpy change for the following reaction was -851.5kJ/mol. Since $\Delta_r H°$ was a negative value, the reaction was exothermic.

Example 2
Find the change in enthalpy when 10.0g of nitroglycerin (M= 227.1g/mol) is used.
$$2C_3H_5(NO_3)_{3(l)} \rightarrow 3N_{2(g)} + \tfrac{1}{2}O_{2(g)} + 6CO_{2(g)} + 5H_2O_{(g)}$$
$\Delta_f H°_{products}$ and $\Delta_f H°_{reactants}$ values can be found at the back of your chemistry textbook.

	$2C_3H_5(NO_3)_{3(l)} \rightarrow$	$3N_{2(g)}+$	$\tfrac{1}{2}O_{2(g)}+$	$6CO_{2\,(g)}+$	$5H_2O_{(g)}$
$\Delta_r H°$	-364kJ/mol	0	0	-393.5kJ/mol	-241.8kJ/mol

$$\Sigma \Delta_f H°_{products} = \frac{6mol\ CO_2}{1mol\ reaction}\left(-\frac{393.5kJ}{1mol\ CO_2}\right) + \frac{5mol\ H_2O}{1mol\ reaction}\left(-\frac{241.8kJ}{1mol\ H_2O}\right)$$

$$\Sigma \Delta_f H°_{products} = -3570\ kJ/mol\ reaction$$

$$\Sigma \Delta_f H°_{reactants} = \frac{2mol\ C_3H_5(NO_3)_3}{1mol\ reaction}\left(-\frac{364kJ}{1mol\ C_6H_5(NO_3)_3}\right)$$

$$\Sigma \Delta_f H°_{reactants} = -728\ kJ/mol\ reaction$$

$$\Delta_r H° = \Sigma \Delta_f H°_{products} - \Sigma \Delta_f H°_{reactants}$$

$$\Delta_r H° = -3570kJ/mol - (-728kJ/mol)$$

$$\Delta_r H° = -2842\ kJ/mol$$

This change in enthalpy is for 1 mol of the reaction. You need to find the change in enthalpy for 10.0g of nitroglycerin. You need to convert 10.0g into moles.

$$n = \frac{m}{M}$$

$$n_{nitroglycerin} = \frac{10.0g}{227.1g/mol}$$

$$n_{nitroglycerin} = 0.0440mol$$

$$\Delta_r H^\circ{}_{nitroglycerin} = -\frac{2842kJ}{1mol\ reaction} \times \frac{1mol\ reaction}{0.0440mol\ nitroglycerin}$$

$$\Delta_r H^\circ{}_{nitroglycerin} = -64591kJ/mol$$

The change in enthalpy for nitroglycerin was 64591kJ/mol. Since ΔH was negative, the reaction was exothermic.

4) Calculating Δ$_r$H from Hess's law

- This method is used when a chemical reaction occurs in multiple steps

> Change in enthalpy the overall reaction is equal to the sum of change in enthalpies of each of the steps of the reaction.
>
> $$\Delta_r H^\circ = \Delta H^\circ{}_1 + \Delta H^\circ{}_2 + \cdots$$

Note: $\Delta_r H^\circ$= enthalpy of the reaction (kJ/mol), $\Delta H^\circ{}_1$= enthalpy of step 1 of the reaction (kJ/mol), $\Delta H^\circ{}_1$= enthalpy of step 2 of the reaction (kJ/mol)

- In this type of a problem, you will need to rearrange each of the steps so that the species cancel out to give the overall reaction
  - In the following example, D appears on both sides (in step 1 as a product and in step 2 as a reactant)→ D can be cancelled out to give the overall reaction

	Overall reaction: A+B→ C	$\Delta_r H^\circ$=? kJ/mol $\Delta_r H^\circ = \Delta H^\circ{}_1 + \Delta H^\circ{}_2$
Step 1	A+B→D	$\Delta_r H_1^\circ$=#
Step 2	D→C	$\Delta_r H_2^\circ$=#

- Use the following rules when manipulating reactions

1. Multiplying a reaction by a number causes each of the coefficients in the reaction to be multiplied by that number

Surviving University: First Year Chemistry

2. Multiplying a reaction by a negative number reverses the direction of the reaction (reactants become products and products become reactants)
3. Multiplying a reaction by a number causes the enthalpy change of the reaction to be multiplied by that number
4. The reactions are added by putting all reactants from modified reactions on the reactants side and all products from modified reactions on the products side
5. The elements/compounds that appear on both sides are crossed out
6. The modified changes in enthalpies of each reaction are added to obtain the enthalpy change of overall reaction

Example 1
Find the enthalpy change of the reaction.

	Overall reaction: $C_{(s)}+ 2H_{2(g)} \rightarrow CH_{4(g)}$	$\Delta_rH°=?$ kJ/mol
	1. $C_{(s)}+ O_{2(g)} \rightarrow CO_{2(g)}$	$\Delta_rH_1°=-393.5$ kJ/mol
	2. $H_{2(g)}+ \frac{1}{2}O_{2(g)} \rightarrow H_2O_{(g)}$	$\Delta_rH_2°=-285.8$kJ/mol
	3. $CH_{4(g)}+ 2O_{2(g)} \rightarrow CO_{2(g)}+ 2H_2O_{(l)}$	$\Delta_rH_3°=-890.3$ kJ/mol

In order for the overall reaction to occur, the 3 steps (below the overall reaction) need to occur. Your goal is to add the 3 reactions and to cancel out the elements/compounds on both sides so that all that is left is
$C_{(s)}+ 2H_{2(g)} \rightarrow CH_{4(g)}$
If you were to add the 3 reactions as they are right now,
$C_{(s)}+ O_{2(g)}+H_{2(g)}+ \frac{1}{2}O_{2(g)}+CH_{4(g)}+ 2O_{2(g)} \rightarrow CO_{2(g)}+ H_2O_{(g)}+CO_{2(g)}+ 2H_2O_{(l)}$
There are no elements/compounds that are the same that are present on both sides, so nothing cancels out.
This means that you need to multiply each of the reactions by a number and then add the reactions together. Make sure to follow the rules.

	Overall reaction: $C_{(s)}+ 2H_{2(g)} \rightarrow CH_{4(g)}$	$\Delta_rH°=?$ kJ/mol
	1. $C_{(s)}+ O_{2(g)} \rightarrow CO_{2(g)}$	$\Delta_rH_1°=-393.5$ kJ/mol
x2	2. $H_{2(g)}+ \frac{1}{2}O_{2(g)} \rightarrow H_2O_{(g)}$	$\Delta_rH_2°=-285.8$kJ/mol **x2**
x (-1)	3. $CH_{4(g)}+ 2O_{2(g)} \rightarrow CO_{2(g)}+ 2H_2O_{(l)}$	$\Delta_rH_3°=-890.3$ kJ/mol **x(-1)**

The modified reactions become

	Overall reaction: $C_{(s)}+ 2H_{2(g)} \rightarrow CH_{4(g)}$	$\Delta_rH°=?$ kJ/mol
	1. $C_{(s)}+ O_{2(g)} \rightarrow CO_{2(g)}$	$\Delta_rH_1°=-393.5$ kJ/mol
	2. $2H_{2(g)}+ O_{2(g)} \rightarrow 2H_2O_{(g)}$	$\Delta_rH_2°=$**-571.6** kJ/mol

Surviving University: First Year Chemistry

3. $CO_{2(g)} + 2H_2O_{(l)} \rightarrow CH_{4(g)} + 2O_{2(g)}$	$\Delta_rH_3° = \textbf{890.3}$ kJ/mol

Now adding all modified reactions

$C_{(s)} + O_{2(g)} + 2H_{2(g)} + O_{2(g)} + CO_{2(g)} + 2H_2O_{(l)} \rightarrow CO_{2(g)} + 2H_2O_{(g)} + CH_{4(g)} + 2O_{2(g)}$

Cancel elements/compounds that are the same on both sides

$C_{(s)} + \cancel{O_{2(g)}} + 2H_{2(g)} + \cancel{O_{2(g)}} + \cancel{CO_{2(g)}} + \cancel{2H_2O_{(l)}} \rightarrow \cancel{CO_{2(g)}} + \cancel{2H_2O_{(g)}} + CH_{4(g)} + \cancel{2O_{2(g)}}$

This produces

$C_{(s)} + 2H_{2(g)} \rightarrow CH_{4(g)}$

Now, you need to find the change in enthalpy of the overall reaction.

$$\Delta_f H° = \Delta H°_1 + \Delta H°_2 + \cdots$$

$$\Delta_f H° = -393.5 KJ/mol + (-571.6 KJ/mol) + 890.3 KJ/mol$$

$$\Delta_f H° = -74.8 KJ/mol$$

The enthalpy change of the overall reaction was 74.8kJ/mol. Since ΔH was negative, the reaction was exothermic.

Example 2: the Born-Haber cycle for NaCl

Born- Haber cycle shows steps of formation of NaCl (steps are below). This process is exothermic (energy is released in the process). Find the enthalpy change for the overall reaction.

The enthalpy change for the overall reaction is the sum of energy changes for each step of the reaction.

	Step	Energy	Example	
1	Vaporization	ΔH_{vap}= +ive	$Na_{(s)} \rightarrow Na_{(g)}$	ΔH_{vap}= 108kJ/mol
2	Dissociation	ΔH_{diss}= +ive	$\frac{1}{2} Cl_{2(g)} \rightarrow Cl_{(g)}$	ΔH_{diss}=122kJ/mol
3	Ionization	E_i= +ive	$Na_{(g)} \rightarrow Na^+_{(g)} + e^-$	E_i=496kJ/mol
4	Electroaffinity	E_{ea}= -ive	$Cl_{(g)} + e^- \rightarrow Cl^-_{(g)}$	E_{ea}=-348kJ/mol
5	Lattice energy	ΔH_{lat}= -ive	$Na^+_{(g)} + Cl^-_{(g)} \rightarrow NaCl_{(s)}$	ΔH_{lat}= -787kJ/mol
	Net reaction	$Na_{(s)} + \frac{1}{2}Cl_{2(g)} \rightarrow NaCl_{(s)}$ ΔH_r= 108kJ/mol+122kJ/mol+496kJ/mol+ (-348kJ/mol)+(-787kJ/mol) ΔH_r= -409kJ/mol		

5) Calculating $\Delta_r H$ from bond energies

- Change in enthalpy when a bond is broken in a molecule→ both reactants and products are in a gas phase

Breaking bonds requires energy (endothermic (ΔH +ive))

Making bonds releases energy (exothermic (ΔH -ive))

$$\Delta_r H° = \Sigma energy\ to\ break\ bonds - \Sigma energy\ to\ make\ bonds$$

Multiply $\Sigma energy\ to\ break\ bonds$ and $\Sigma energy\ to\ make\ bonds$ of each bond by the number that particular bond broken/formed

Note: energy to break and to make bonds can be found at the back of your chemistry textbook. $\Delta_r H°$= enthalpy of the reaction (kJ/mol)

Example 1
Find enthalpy of a reaction for the production of hydrogen fluoride gas.
$H_{2(g)} + F_{2(g)} \rightleftharpoons 2HF_{(g)}$
Steps
1. Draw out each of the molecules
2. List all bonds that are broken and all bonds that are formed
3. Look up bond enthalpies (appendix section of your chemistry textbook) for each bond broken and each bond formed
4. Calculate enthalpy of the reaction using
   $\Delta_r H° = \Sigma energy\ to\ break\ bonds - \Sigma energy\ to\ make\ bonds$

H—H + F—F ⟶ H—F
                      H—F

Bonds broken

	# bonds	Bond enthalpy
H-H	1	435kJ/mol
F-F	1	155kJ/mol

Bonds formed

	# bonds	Bond enthalpy
H-F	2	565kJ/mol

$\Delta_r H° = \Sigma energy\ to\ break\ bonds - \Sigma energy\ to\ make\ bonds$
$\Delta_r H° = (435\ KJ/mol + 155KJ/mol) - (2(565KJ/mol))$
$\Delta_r H° = -540KJ/mol$
The enthalpy of the reaction is 540kJ/mol. The reaction is exothermic.

Part 6

Structure of Atoms

Electromagnetic radiation

Planck's equation

Electromagnetic spectrum

Photoelectric effect

Bohr's model of hydrogen atom

Atomic line spectra

Potential energy of an electron at an energy level

Bohr's theory of excited atoms

DeBroglie waves

Structure of Atoms

Electromagnetic radiation

- Light is an **electromagnetic wave**→ has 1 vertical component (electric) and 1 horizontal component (magnetic)
- Light travels at the speed of 3.00×10^8m/s, has a frequency, and a wavelength
- **Wavelength (λ)**- the distance between 2 crests (high points on a wave) or 2 troughs (low points on a wave)
    - As temperature ↑, wavelength ↓
    - Different colours of light have different wavelengths (ex. blue light λ=475nm, red light λ=650nm)

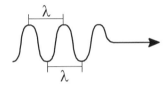

- **Frequency**- # of waves that pass through a specific point in space during a period of time

$$c = \lambda v$$

Note: c= speed of light (3.00×10^8m/s), λ= wavelength (m or nm), v= frequency (Hz= 1/s or s^{-1})

Example 1
Find the frequency of blue light whose wavelength is 475nm.

c	3.00×10^8m/s
λ	475nm
v	?Hz

Need to convert nm to m.

$$\lambda_{in\,m} = 475nm \times \frac{1m}{10^9 nm} = 4.75 \times 10^{-7}m$$

Rearranging $c = \lambda v$,

$$v = \frac{c}{\lambda}$$

$$v = \frac{3.00 \times 10^8 m/s}{4.75 \times 10^{-7}m}$$

$$v = 6.32 \times 10^{14}s^{-1} = 6.32 \times 10^{14}Hz$$

The frequency of blue light whose wavelength is 475nm is 6.32×10^{14}Hz.

Surviving University: First Year Chemistry

Planck's equation

- Energy is **quantized** (comes in bursts)→ it is not a continuous stream, but it comes in packets
    - A packet of energy is called a **photon**
    - Light is a stream of photons
    - As energy ↑, wavelength ↓

$$E = nh\nu = \frac{hc}{\lambda}$$
$$h = 6.626 \times 10^{-34} J \cdot s / \, photon$$
$$1nm = 1 \times 10^{-9}m$$

Note: E= energy (J or kJ), n= +ive integer, h= Planck's constant, ν = frequency (Hz), c= speed of light (3.00×10^8 m/s), λ= wavelength (m)

- Electromagnetic energy is caused by vibrating atoms in a heated object
    - Vibrating atoms are called **oscillators**
    - When oscillators vibrate from a higher energy level to a lower energy level, energy is released as electromagnetic radiation

$$\Delta E = E_{higher} - E_{lower} = \Delta nh\nu$$

Note: E= energy (J), E_{higher}= energy of the higher level (J), E_{lower}= energy of lower level (J), Δn= change in energy levels (ex. from level 3 to level 1→ Δn=n_{final}-$n_{initial}$= 3-1=2), h= Planck's constant ($6.626 \times 10^{-34} J \cdot s / \, photon$), ν = frequency (Hz= 1/s or s^{-1})

Example 1
An excited oxygen atom emits a red light whose wavelength is 630nm. Find the energy of a photon of this light.

c	3.00×10^8 m/s
λ	630nm
h	6.626×10^{-34} J·s/photon
E	?J

Need to convert nm to m.

$$\lambda_{in\,m} = 630nm \times \frac{1m}{10^9 nm} = 6.3 \times 10^{-7}m$$
$$E = \frac{hc}{\lambda}$$

$$E = \frac{(6.626x10^{-34}J \cdot s/photon)(3.00 \times 10^8 m/s)}{6.3 \times 10^{-7}m}$$

$$E = 3.16 \times 10^{-19}J$$

The energy of a photon was 3.16x10⁻¹⁹J.

Electromagnetic spectrum

Easy way to remember the order:

Rabbits **M**ate **I**n **V**ery **U**nusual e**X**pensive **G**ardens

Photoelectric effect

- When light strikes a metal, electrons can be liberated
    - The amount of electrons liberated does not depend on the brightness (or intensity) of the light
    - Electrons are liberated only when the light has a frequency that is higher than the threshold frequency of the metal

Threshold frequency- the minimum frequency required to liberate an electron from a metal

Ionization energy- energy required to liberate an electron

$$E = \frac{hcN}{\lambda}$$
$$N = 6.02 \times 10^{23} J/mol$$

Note: c= speed of light (3.00×10⁸m/s), h= Planck's constant ($h = 6.626x10^{-34}J \cdot s/photon$), E= energy (J), λ= wavelength (m)

Example 1
Find the energy of 3mol of a photon with frequency of 590nm.
Steps
1. Find energy per 1mol using $E = \frac{hcN}{\lambda}$
2. Find energy per 3mol of photon using $E_{3mol\ photon} = E \times n$

λ= 590×10⁻⁹m

$$E = \frac{hcN}{\lambda}$$

$$E = \frac{(6.626 \times 10^{-34} J \cdot s)(3.00 \times 10^8 m/s)(6.02 \times 10^{23} J/mol)}{590 \times 10^{-9} m}$$

$E = 202822 J/mol = 203 kJ/mol$

$E_{3mol\ photon} = 203 kJ/mol \times 3 mol$

$E_{3mol\ photon} = 609 kJ$

The energy of 3mol of photon is 609kJ.

Bohr model of hydrogen atom

- Electrons that orbit around the nucleus of an atom are in energy levels
    - Each energy level has a specific energy
    - Energy of an electron is –ive (ex. -2.18×10^{-18} J/atom)
- n is a quantum number and represents the # of energy levels in atom
    - The further away from the nucleus, the higher the energy level, the higher the n value
    - The lowest possible energy level is the **ground state** (n=1)
        - Ground state is closest to nucleus
    - Higher energy levels are called **excited states** (n>1)

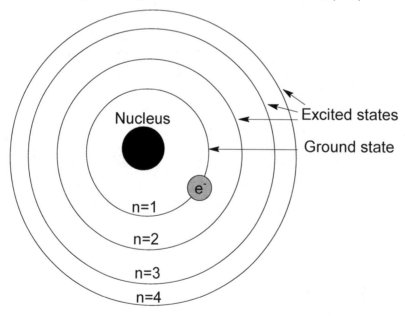

Atomic Line Spectra

- When an electrical current is applied to atoms in a gas state, atoms become excited→ excited atoms emit light
  - 1. Electric current is applied→ gives energy to an electron in an atom
  - 2. Electron jumps to a higher state (becomes excited)
  - 3. Electron falls back down to the lower state (ground state)→ electron loses energy→ energy is emitted as light

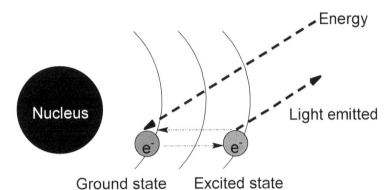

- Each element emits light at only specific frequencies
  - Each element emits specific colours of light
- Obtaining atomic line spectrum
  - An electrical current is sent through an element in its gas state
  - A prism is used to separate wavelengths of light (each wavelength has a different colour)
  - Lines of different colours can be seen on a screen→ this is the atomic line spectrum

Balmer series- 4 coloured lines that are present in the atomic line spectra of hydrogen gas

Balmer equation- used to calculate wavelengths of red, green, and blue lines seen in the atomic line spectra of hydrogen gas

$$\frac{1}{\lambda} = R\left(\frac{1}{2^2} - \frac{1}{n^2}\right) \text{ when n >2}$$

$$R = 1.097 \times 10^7 m^{-1}$$

Note: λ= wavelength (m), R= Rydberg constant (m^{-1}), n= integer

Surviving University: First Year Chemistry

Potential energy of an electron at an energy level

$$E_n = -\frac{hcR}{n^2}$$

Note: n= energy level, R= Rydberg constant ($1.097{\times}10^7\text{m}^{-1}$), c= speed of light ($3.00{\times}10^8$m/s), h= Planck's constant ($h = 6.626\text{x}10^{-34}J \cdot s/photon$)

Example 1
Find energies of n=1 and n=2 for a hydrogen atom (in J/atom and kJ/mol)
This question asks how much energy is present at the first level and how much energy is present at the second level.
At n=1
$$E_1 = -\frac{hcR}{1^2}$$
$$E_1 = -\frac{(1.097{\times}10^7 m^{-1})(6.626{\times}10^{-34}J\cdot s/\,photon)(3.00{\times}10^8 m/s)}{1^2}$$
$$E_1 = -2.179 \times 10^{-18}J/atom$$
To convert energies from J/atom to kJ/mol→ use the Avogadro's number ($6.022 \times 10^{23} atoms/mol$)
$$E_1 = -(2.179 \times 10^{-18}J/atom) \times (6.022 \times 10^{23} atoms/mol) \times 1kJ/1000\,J$$
$$E_1 = -1312kJ/mol$$
At n=2
$$E_2 = -\frac{hcR}{2^2}$$
$$E_2 = -\frac{(1.097{\times}10^7 m^{-1})(6.626{\times}10^{-34}J\cdot s/\,photon)(3.00{\times}10^8 m/s)}{2^2}$$
$$E_2 = -5.448 \times 10^{-19}J/atom$$
To convert energies from J/atom to kJ/mol→ use the Avogadro's number ($6.022 \times 10^{23} atoms/mol$)
$$E_2 = -(5.448 \times 10^{-19}J/atom) \times (6.022 \times 10^{23} atoms/mol) \times \frac{1KJ}{1000J}$$
$$E_2 = -328.1kJ/mol$$
The energy of n=1 is $-2.179 \times 10^{-18}J/atom$ or $-1312kJ/mol$. The energy of n=2 is $-5.448 \times 10^{-19}J/atom$ or $-328.1kJ/mol$.

Bohr's theory of excited atoms

- When an electron moves from 1 energy level to another, energy is absorbed or released

- The amount of energy absorbed/released can be calculated using the following equation

$$\Delta E = E_{final} - E_{initial} = -N_A Rhc \left(\frac{1}{n_{final}^2} - \frac{1}{n_{initial}^2} \right)$$
$$\text{Where } N_A Rhc = 1312 kJ/mol$$

Note: ΔE= change in energy (energy absorbed/released) (kJ/mol), E_{final}= energy of the final energy level (J), $E_{initial}$= energy of the initial energy level, n= energy level

Lyman series- the ground state is from n=1 to n>1
Balmer series- the ground state is from n=2 to n>2

Example 1
Find the wavelength of green light in visible spectrum of hydrogen atom if electrons jump from n=4 to n=2.
Steps
1. Find energy absorbed/released (change in energy→ ΔE)
2. Convert energy from kJ/mol to J/photon using the Avogadro's number
3. Find wavelength of light using $E = \frac{hc}{\lambda}$

$N_A Rhc$= 1312kJ/mol
$n_{initial}$= 4
n_{final}= 2

$$\Delta E = -N_A Rhc \left(\frac{1}{n_{final}^2} - \frac{1}{n_{initial}^2} \right)$$
$$\Delta E = -1312 kJ/mol \left(\frac{1}{2^2} - \frac{1}{4^2} \right)$$
$$\Delta E = -246.0 kJ/mol$$

Now you need to convert energy released into J/photon.

$$E = \frac{246.0 kJ}{mol} \times \frac{1 mol}{6.022 \times 10^{23} photon} \times \frac{1kJ}{1000J}$$
$$E = 4.085 \times 10^{-19} J/photon$$
$$E = \frac{hc}{\lambda}$$
$$\lambda = \frac{hc}{E}$$
$$\lambda = \frac{(6.626 \times 10^{-34} J \cdot s)(3.00 \times 10^8 m/s)(1\ photon)}{4.085 \times 10^{-19} J/photon}$$
$$\lambda = 4.085 \times 10^{-7} m$$

The wavelength of green light is 486.3nm.

DeBroglie waves

- **Wave-particle duality-** electron can behave as a wave or as a particle
    - An electron cannot be a wave or particle at the same time→ sometimes behaves as a wave, sometimes as a particle
- Matter can behave as a wave or a particle (cannot be both at the same time)
- When matter and electrons behave as waves, they have a wavelength

$$\lambda = \frac{h}{mv}$$

Note: λ= wavelength (m), h= h= Planck's constant ($h = 6.626 \times 10^{-34} J \cdot s/photon$), m= mass of an electron (9.1094×10^{-31}kg), v= velocity (m/s)

Example 1
What is the wavelength of an electron (m= 9.109x10^{-31}g) that moves at 38% of the speed of light (c= 3.00×10^{8}m/s)?

h	6.626×10^{-34}J·s/photon
m	9.109×10^{-28}g
v	?m/s
λ	?m
c	3.00×10^8m/s

First, you need to find the speed of the electron.

$$v_{electron} = \frac{38\%}{100\%} \times c$$

$$v_{electron} = \frac{38\%}{100\%}(3.00 \times 10^8 m/s)$$

$$v_{electron} = 1.14 \times 10^8 m/s$$

Now you can find the wavelength using $\lambda = \frac{h}{mv}$

$$\lambda = \frac{6.626 \times 10^{-34} J \cdot s/photon}{(9.109 \times 10^{-31} g)(1.14 \times 10^8 m/s)}$$

$$\lambda = 6.38 \times 10^{-12} m$$

The wavelength of an electron that moves at 38% of the speed of light is 6.38x10^{-12}m.

Part 7

Quantum Mechanics

Heisenberg's uncertainty principle

Quantum numbers

Shells

Orbitals

Quantum rules

Electron configurations

Orbital box notation

Magnetism

Quantum Mechanics

Heisenberg's uncertainty principle

- It is impossible to determine both the exact position and the energy of an electron in an atom
- There is only a probability of finding an electron with a certain energy in a certain region around the nucleus

Summary of quantum numbers

- 4 quantum numbers are used to describe the position of an electron in an atom

#	Name	Represents	Range
n	Principal quantum # (shell #)	Defines the size of orbital and energy of e⁻ ($\uparrow$ n, $\uparrow$ size of orbital, $\uparrow$ distance of e⁻ from nucleus, $\uparrow$ energy of e⁻)	n=1-7
	Maximum number of electrons in a shell = $2n^2$ *Number of orbitals (m_l) in a shell = n^2*		
l	Angular momentum quantum # (subshell #)	Shape of orbital	l= 0 to (n-1) $l= \dfrac{0 \quad 1 \quad 2 \quad 3}{s \quad p \quad d \quad f}$
	Maximum number of electrons in a subshell = $2(2l+1)$ *Number of orbitals (m_l) in a subshell = $2l+1$*		
m_l	Magnetic quantum # (orbital #)	Orientation in space of orbitals in a subshell There are 2 electrons per orbital (m_l)	m_l = -l to +l $m_l = \dfrac{-1 \quad 0 \quad +1}{x \quad y \quad Z}$
m_s	Spin #	Spin of electron (describes electron's magnetism)	+1/2 $\rightarrow$ clockwise -1/2 $\rightarrow$ counterclockwise

Example 1

How many electrons are permitted for n=3?

Look back at the quantum numbers chart.

#	Range	In this problem
n	n=1-7	n=3

| l | l= 0 to (n-1) l= $\frac{0 \quad 1 \quad 2 \quad 3}{s \quad p \quad d \quad f}$ | l= 0 to (3-1)=2 So l= 0, 1, 2 |

Since l= 0, 1, and 2→ s, p, and d orbitals are present

Since n=3→3s, 3p, 3d orbitals are present

An s orbital holds 2 electrons, a p orbital holds 6 electrons, and a d orbital holds 10 electrons.

$Total \; \# \, e^- = \# \, e^- \, 3s + \# \, e^- \, 3p + \# \, e^- \, 3d$

$Total \; \# \, e^- = 2e^- + 6e^- + 10e^-$

$Total \; \# \, e^- = 18e^-$

OR you can use the shortcut

$Maximum \; number \; of \; electrons \; in \; a \; shell = 2n^2$

$Maximum \; number \; of \; electrons \; in \; a \; shell = 2(3)^2$

$Maximum \; number \; of \; electrons \; in \; a \; shell = 18e^-$

18 electrons are permitted for n=3.

Example 2

How many electrons are permitted for n=3, l=2?

#	Range	In this problem
n	n=1-7	n=3
l	l= 0 to (n-1) l= $\frac{0 \quad 1 \quad 2 \quad 3}{s \quad p \quad d \quad f}$	l=2

Since l= 2→ d orbital is present

Since n=3→3d orbital is present

A d orbital holds 10 electrons.

$Total \; \# \, e^- = \# \, e^- \, 3d$

$Total \; \# \, e^- = 10e^-$

OR you can use the shortcut

$Maximum \; number \; of \; electrons \; in \; a \; subshell = 2(2l + 1)$

$Maximum \; number \; of \; electrons \; in \; a \; subshell = 2(2(2) + 1)$

$Maximum \; number \; of \; electrons \; in \; a \; subshell = 10e^-$

10 electrons are permitted for n=3, l=2.

Example 3

How many electrons can

a) An s sublevel hold?

b) A p sublevel hold?

c) A d sublevel hold?

d) An f sublevel hold?

You know that there are 2 electrons in each orbital (in each m_l).

a) An s sublevel hold?

An s sublevel has l=0. m_l = -l to +l→ so m_l = 0.
This means that there is 1 orbital.

$$Number\ of\ electrons = 1\ orbital \times \frac{2e^-}{1\ orbital}$$

$$Number\ of\ electrons = 2e^-$$

An s sublevel can hold 2 electrons.

b) A p sublevel hold?

A p sublevel has l=1. m_l = -l to +l→ so m_l = -1, 0, 1.
This means that there are 3 orbitals.

$$Number\ of\ electrons = 3\ orbitals \times \frac{2e^-}{1\ orbital}$$

$$Number\ of\ electrons = 6e^-$$

A p sublevel can hold 6 electrons.

c) A d sublevel hold?

A d sublevel has l=2. m_l = -l to +l→ so m_l = -2, -1, 0, 1, 2.
This means that there are 5 orbitals.

$$Number\ of\ electrons = 5\ orbitals \times \frac{2e^-}{1\ orbital}$$

$$Number\ of\ electrons = 10e^-$$

A d sublevel can hold 10 electrons.

d) An f sublevel hold?

An f sublevel has l=3. m_l = -l to +l→ so m_l = -3,-2, -1, 0, 1, 2, 3.
This means that there are 7 orbitals.

$$Number\ of\ electrons = 7\ orbitals \times \frac{2e^-}{1\ orbital}$$

$$Number\ of\ electrons = 14e^-$$

An f sublevel can hold 14 electrons.

Shells

Valence Shell- the outer shell (the shell from which electrons are gained or lost)

- o   Determines chemical properties of an atom
- o   **Valence Electrons**- electrons which are present in the valence shell
    - ▪ Elements in the same group (column) have the same number of valence electrons (ex. lithium has 1

valence electron, sodium also has 1 valence electron (same column))

Inner shell- the shell closer to the nucleus (electrons from this shell are not gained/lost during chemical reaction)

    ○ **Core electrons**- electrons which are present in the inner shell of an atom

Full (or filled) shell- the shell is completely filled with electrons

Half-filled shell- half of the shell is filled with electrons

- An atom which has a filled or a half-filled shell is stable

Orbitals

Orbital- a 3D area around the nucleus where electron(s) may be located

- The shapes of orbitals represent areas where there is probability of finding an electron→ these areas are called **electron clouds**

Nodal surface- area in which there is no probability of finding an electron

- # of nodal surfaces is equal to the value of angular momentum quantum # (l)

Orbital sizes

- As n increases, the size of an orbital increases

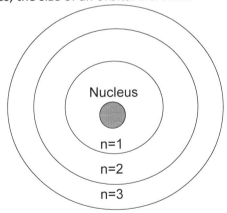

Orbital shapes

Name	Shape	# electrons	# nodal surfaces that run through the nucleus
s= sphere	○	2	0

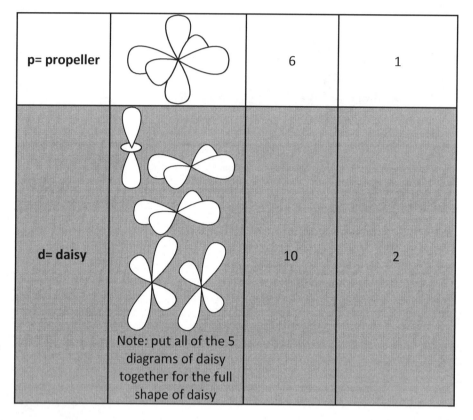

p= propeller		6	1
d= daisy	Note: put all of the 5 diagrams of daisy together for the full shape of daisy	10	2

Quantum rules

Pauli's Exclusion Principle- no 2 electrons can have the same set of 4 quantum numbers, no 2 electrons can have the same spin

Aufbau Principle- electrons are placed in the lowest energy level first; energy sublevel must be filled before moving to a higher sublevel

Hund's Rule- 1 electron must occupy each of several orbits of the same energy level before a second electron can occupy the same orbital

Electron configurations

Electron configuration- the way that electrons are arranged in an atom

- o **Expanded electron configuration-** shows all of the electrons in an atom
- o **Abridged electron configuration-** shows only valence electrons in an atom
- ▪ Electrons in an atom are filled in the following order

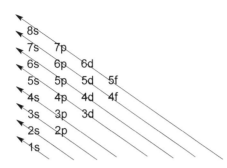

Orbital	# e⁻ an orbital can hold
s	2
p	6
d	10
f	14

where

- An easier way to think of the filling order would be to look at the periodic table

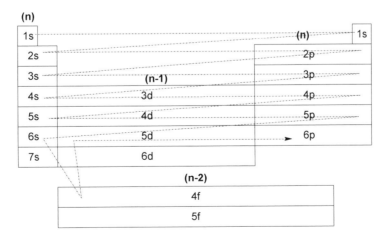

- Move across the periodic table
  - 1s, 2s, 2p, 3s, 3p, 4s, 3d, 4p, 5s, 4d, 5p, 6s, 4f, 5d, 6p, 7s, 5f, 6d

Surviving University: First Year Chemistry

Example 1

Write the expanded and abridged electron configurations for neon.

Looking at the periodic table, neon has atomic number 10 and is located in the 2p box. This means that the valence electrons are located in the 2p orbital. Looking at the filling order, 1s and 2s orbitals must be filled before 2p orbital is filled.

1s		1s
2s		2p	Neon
3s		3p
4s	3d	4p
5s	4d	5p
6s	5d	6p
7s	6d	

4f
5f

An s orbital can hold 2 electrons, and a p orbital can hold 6 electrons. Neon has atomic number 10. This means that it has 10 protons and 10 electrons.

Orbital	# e⁻ the orbital holds
1s	$2e^-$
2s	$2e^-$
2p	$6e^-$
	Total: $10e^-$

Electron configuration→ Ne: $1s^2 2s^2 2p^6$

Note: the numbers that are superscripted represent the number of electrons in that orbital.

For abridged electron configuration, find the noble gas that precedes Ne. This is helium. This means that neon has the electron configuration of helium plus a $2p^6$ orbital.

Abridged electron configuration→ Ne: $[He]2p^6$

Example 2

Write the expanded and abridged electron configurations for aluminum.

Looking at the periodic table, aluminum has atomic number 13 and is located in the 3p box. This means that the valence electrons are located in the 3p orbital. Looking at the filling order 1s, 2s, and 3s orbitals must be filled before a 3p orbital is filled.

Surviving University: First Year Chemistry

1s		1s
2s	Aluminum	2p
3s		3p
4s	3d	4p
5s	4d	5p
6s	5d	6p
7s	6d	

4f
5f

An s orbital can hold 2 electrons, and a p orbital can hold 6 electrons. Aluminum has atomic number 13. This means that it has 13 protons and 13 electrons.

Orbital	# e⁻ the orbital holds
1s	2e⁻
2s	2e⁻
2p	6e⁻
3s	2e⁻
3p	1e⁻
	Total: 13e⁻

Electron configuration→ Al: $1s^2 2s^2 2p^6 3s^2 3p^1$

The noble gas that precedes Al is neon. This means that aluminum has the electron configuration of neon plus $3s^2$ and $3p^1$ orbitals.

Abridged electron configuration→ Al: $[Ne] 3s^2 3p^1$

Electron configurations of transition elements

Transition elements- have electrons in the d subshell
- The d orbital can hold 10e⁻
- In the electron configuration, the d orbital is written before s and p orbitals
   - Ex. Ga: $[Ar] 3d^{10} 4s^2 4p^1$

Inner transition elements- have electrons in the f subshell→ are lactinides (have 4f orbital) and actinides (have 5f orbital)
- The f orbital can hold 14e⁻
- In the electron configuration, the f orbital is written before s, p, and d orbitals

Surviving University: First Year Chemistry

- Ex. Hf: [Xe] $4f^{14}5d^26s^2$

Example 1

Write the abridged electron configurations for uranium.

Looking at the periodic table, uranium has atomic number 92 and is located in the 5f box. This means that the valence electrons are located in the 5f orbital.

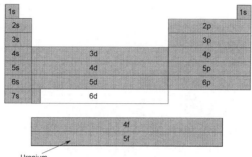

Uranium

The noble gas that precedes U is radon (Rn). This means that aluminum has the electron configuration of Rn plus $7s^2$, $6d^1$, and $5f^3$ orbitals.

Abridged electron configuration→ U: [Rn] $7s^26d^15f^3$

Exceptions to general rules

- There are some exceptions to general filling order rules
- An atom is stable when its d subshell is full or half-full
  - When it has d^5 or d^{10}
- An atom can take 1 electron from an s subshell and put it into a d subshell in order to have its d subshell is full or half-full
  - Cr: [Ar] $3d^54s^1$ (not Cr: [Ar] $3d^44s^2$)
  - Cu: [Ar] $3d^{10}4s^1$ (not Cu: [Ar] $3d^94s^2$)

Electron configurations of ions

- Metals lose electrons and form cations (+ive)
  - The electron electron configuration of a cation is the same as the electron configuration of the preceding noble gas
- Nonmetals gain electrons and form anions (-ive)
  - The electron electron configuration of an anion is the same as the electron configuration of the following noble gas
- Electrons are removed from the last subshell
  - ex. Na: $1s^22s^22p^6\mathbf{3s^1}$ Na^+: $1s^22s^22p^6$+ e^-
  - ex. Ge: [Ar] $3d^{10}4s^2\mathbf{4p^2}$ Ge^{2+}: [Ar] $3d^{10}4s^2$+ $2e^-$
- In transition metals→ electrons in s orbital are lost before electrons in d orbital
  - ex. Cu: [Ar] $3d^{10}\mathbf{4s^1}$ Cu^+: [Ar] $3d^{10}$+ e^-

Surviving University: First Year Chemistry

Orbital box notation

- The orbital box notation shows the number of electrons which are located in each orbital

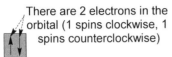

There are 2 electrons in the orbital (1 spins clockwise, 1 spins counterclockwise)

1s ◄-------Orbital

Example 1
Show the orbital box notation for
a) Neon
b) Aluminum
c) Phosphorus

a) Neon
From example 1 of electron configuration section, the electron configuration for neon is Ne: $1s^2 2s^2 2p^6$

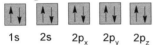

1s   2s   2p$_x$ 2p$_y$ 2p$_z$

b) Aluminum
From example 2 of electron configuration section, the electron configuration for aluminum is Al: $1s^2 2s^2 2p^6 3s^2 3p^1$

1s   2s   2p$_x$ 2p$_y$ 2p$_z$ 3s   3p$_x$ 3p$_y$ 3p$_z$

c) Phosphorus
The electron configuration for phosphorus is P: $1s^2 2s^2 2p^6 3s^2 3p^3$

1s   2s   2p$_x$ 2p$_y$ 2p$_z$ 3s   3p$_x$ 3p$_y$ 3p$_z$

Note: according to the Hund's Rule, 1 electron must occupy each of several orbits of the same energy level before a second electron can occupy the same orbital.

Magnetism

Paramagnetism- atom has 1 or more unpaired electrons→ element/compound is attracted to a magnet
Diamagnetism- all electrons are unpaired in an atom→ atom is not attracted to a magnet, but is repulsed by magnetic field

Part 8

Periodic Trends

Summary of the periodic trends

Effective nuclear charge (Z*)

Atomic radii

Ionization energy

Electron affinity

Ionic radii

Bond length

Lattice energy

Electronegativity

Surviving University: First Year Chemistry

Periodic Trends

Summary of the periodic trends

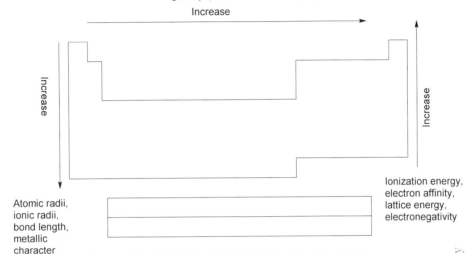

Ionic radii, ionization energy, electron affinity, Z*, electronegativity, power as an oxidizing agent

Increase

Increase

Increase

Ionization energy, electron affinity, lattice energy, electronegativity

Atomic radii, ionic radii, bond length, metallic character

Increase

Atomic radii, bond length, metallic character, power as a reducing agent

Effective nuclear charge (Z*)

- Attraction between a nucleus and electron(s) in an atom
- The higher the # of protons in an atom, the higher the attraction between a nucleus and electron(s), the higher the effective nuclear charge
    - More +ive charges (protons) are attracted to –ive charges (electrons)
- The order of increase in attraction of electrons is s > p > d > f
    - Z* is greater for s orbital than p orbital in the same shell

Atomic Radii

Internuclear distance- the distance from a nucleus of 1 atom to a nucleus of a another atom
- Ex. the distance between 2 chlorine atoms in Cl_2 is 198pm

Atomic radii- the distance from a nucleus of an atom to its outer shell (internuclear distance ÷ 2)
- Ex. atomic radii of chlorine is 198pm÷2= 99pm

Surviving University: First Year Chemistry

- Trend: atomic radii increases going down a group and increases from right to left going across a period
    - Going down a group
        - Since the principal quantum number increases, the # of shells increases
            - ↑ # of shells= bigger size of an atom
    - Right to left going across a period
        - The effective nuclear charge (Z*) decreases→ the attraction between nucleus and valence electrons decreases
            - Valence electrons can move further away from the nucleus→ bigger size of an atom

Ionization energy

Ionization energy- the energy required to remove an electron from an atom
- Removing a second/third electron from an atom requires more energy than removing the first electron
    - 2nd and 3rd electrons are more attracted to nucleus since they are closer to the nucleus
- As Z* increases (attraction between nucleus and electrons), the energy required to remove an electron increases
    - Removing electrons from an inner shell requires much energy
        - There is a strong attraction between the electrons and the nucleus

Electron affinity (EA)

Electron affinity- the change in energy when an electron is added to an atom
- Electron affinity is a negative value→ the process of adding electron(s) is exothermic (energy is released)
- Increase in affinity for an electron means that more energy is released during a reaction (EA value becomes more negative)
- As ionization energy ↑, the value of electron affinity becomes more negative
    - High ionization energy means that much energy is needed to remove an electron
    - When that electron is added to another atom, much energy is released

- Electron affinity value is large
- Since the process is exothermic, electron affinity value is negative

Ionic Radii

- Trend: atomic radii increases going down a group and increases from left to right going across a period
  - Going left to right across a period
    - Metals lose electrons, nonmetals gain electrons
    - When a metal loses electron(s), the atomic radii decreases
    - When a nonmetal gains electron(s), the atomic radii increases
  - Going down a group
    - Since the principal quantum number increases, the # of shells increases
      - ↑ # of shells= bigger size of an ion

Bond length

Bond length- the distance between nuclei of 2 atoms that share a bond
- Ex. HCl→ the distance between nuclei of H and Cl atoms is 127pm

Bond order- # of pairs of e⁻ that are shared between 2 atoms in a covalent bond

As bond order increases, bond length decreases

- A double bond (bond order=2) is shorter than a single bond (bond order= 1)
- A triple bond (bond order=3) is shorter than a double bond (bond order=2)

See part 9 of this book for more information about bond order

Lattice energy

Lattice energy- change in energy during formation of 1 mole of an ionic compound from its ions (ions are in a gas phase)
- Lattice energy determines the strength of ionic bond
  - Ionic compounds form of a crystal lattice structure
    - *For more information about ionic compounds, see part 11*
- Trend: lattice energy becomes more negative going up a row

o Going up a row means that the principal quantum number decreases→ # of shells decreases→ the attraction between ions increases→ more energy is required to break a bond

Electronegativity

- Electronegativity is the atom's ability to pull electrons towards itself
  o There is a difference in electron density between adjacent atoms
    - Electrons spend more time around δ^- atom
    - Shared electrons are pulled away from δ^+ atom towards δ^- atom
- Electronegativity indicates the type of bond that will be present in a molecule (ionic, covalent, or polar covalent)

Electronegativities of Elements

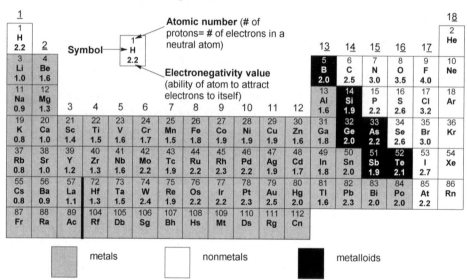

Metallic character

- Elements which are more metallic in character are more ionic in character
- The degree to which an element is metallic depends on the element's oxidation state
  o ↓ oxidation state= more metallic

Surviving University: First Year Chemistry

Part 9

Bonding and Molecular Structure

Valence electrons

Octet rule

Lewis dot symbols

Lewis structures

Isoelectronic molecules/ions

Formal charges

Resonance structures

Bond order

Bond length

VSEPR theory

Axial and equatorial positions

Molecular shapes

Surviving University: First Year, Chemistry

Bonding and Molecular Structure

Structure- the arrangement of atoms in a molecule in space
Bonding- forces that hold atoms in a molecule together
Ionic bond- occurs between a metal and a nonmetal; 1 or more valence electrons are transferred from a metal to a nonmetal

ex. $Na^{\bullet} + {}^{\bullet}\ddot{\underset{\ddot{}}{Cl}}: \longrightarrow [Na^{+} \; \ddot{\underset{\ddot{}}{Cl}}:^{-}]$

Covalent bond- occurs between a nonmetal and a nonmetal; valence electrons are shared between atoms

ex. $:\ddot{Cl}^{\bullet} + {}^{\bullet}\ddot{\underset{\ddot{}}{Cl}}: \longrightarrow :\ddot{Cl} \, \ddot{\underset{\ddot{}}{Cl}}:$

Bond pair electrons- electrons that are involved in bonding
Lone pair electrons- electrons that are not involved in bonding

Valence electrons

- *See part 2 of this book for more information about valence electrons*
- Electrons that are in the outer shell of an atom
- Valence electrons are involved in chemical reactions
  - Valence electrons are gained/lost during a chemical reaction

Octet rule

- A valence shell (the outermost shell) can accommodate a maximum of 8 electrons (4 e⁻ pairs)
  - When a valence shell has 8 electrons, an atom has a stable configuration
- Exceptions are H and He
  - A valence shell can accommodate a maximum of 2 electrons (1 e⁻ pair)
  - When a valence shell has 2 electrons, an atom has a stable configuration

Lewis dot symbols

- An atom is in the middle, valence electrons are positioned around the atom

Surviving University: First Year Chemistry

Element	# valence electrons	Lewis dot symbol
Li	1	Li •
Be	2	• Be •
B	3	• B •
C	4	• C •
N	5	• N •
O	6	: O •
F	7	: F •
Ne	8	: Ne :

Drawing Lewis structures

Central atom- an atom that is in the center of a Lewis dot structure
Terminal atoms- atoms that are around the central atom in a Lewis dot structure

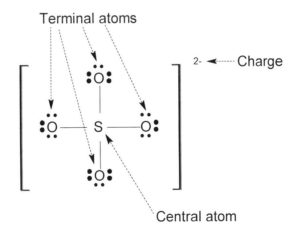

Steps to drawing Lewis structures
1. Arrange the atoms in a molecule
   - The central atom has the lowest electron affinity
     - It is usually C, N, P, S
   - Halogens (group 17) are central atoms in oxoacids
     - Oxoacids are acids that have oxygen atoms→ ex. $HClO_4$
   - Oxygen is the central atom in H_2O
2. Find the total number of valence electrons in a molecule
   - Add the # of valence electrons in each of the elements of a molecule
     - *See part 2 of this book of how to find how many valence electrons an atom has*
   - If a molecule has a +ive charge
     - <u>Subtract</u> the molecule's charge from the total # of valence electrons
   - If a molecule has a −ive charge
     - <u>Add</u> the molecule's charge from the total # of valence electrons
3. Put 1 pair of electrons between each of the atoms→ form a single bond between each pair of atoms
4. Put the remaining electrons on the terminal atoms to make each terminal atom have 8 electrons
5. Place left over electrons on the central atom
   - The central atom can have more than 8 electrons
6. If the central atom has less than 8 electrons, take 1 lone pair of e⁻ from any terminal atom and make a double or a triple bond with the central atom
7. If a molecule has a charge, place square brackets around the Lewis structure and indicate the charge

Example 1
Draw a Lewis dot structure for H_2O.

Element	# valence electrons
H	2(1e⁻)=2e⁻
O	6e⁻
Σ	8e⁻

You need to place 8 electrons. Oxygen is the central atom and hydrogens are the terminal atoms.

Surviving University: First Year Chemistry

Each hydrogen atom can have a maximum of 2 electrons. Put 2 electrons between each hydrogen and oxygen atoms. Put the rest of electrons on the central atom.

$$H : \overset{..}{\underset{..}{O}} : H$$

Form a single bond between each hydrogen and oxygen atoms.

$$H - \overset{..}{\underset{..}{O}} - H$$

The central atom has a full outer shell (8 electrons). Each hydrogen atom also has a full outer shell (2 electrons).

Example 2
Draw a Lewis dot structure for NH_3.

Element	# valence electrons
H	$3(1e^-)=3e^-$
N	$5e^-$
Σ	$8e^-$

You need to place 8 electrons. Nitrogen is the central atom and hydrogens are the terminal atoms.
Each hydrogen atom can have a maximum of 2 electrons. Put 2 electrons between each hydrogen and nitrogen atoms. Put the rest of electrons on the central atom.

$$H : \overset{..}{\underset{..}{N}} : H$$
$$H$$

Form a single bond between each hydrogen and nitrogen atoms.

$$H - \overset{..}{N} - H$$
$$|$$
$$H$$

The central atom has a full outer shell (8 electrons). Each hydrogen atom also has a full outer shell (2 electrons).

Example 3
Draw a Lewis dot structure for H₂O₂.

Element	# valence electrons
H	2(1e⁻)=2e⁻
O	2(6e⁻)=12e⁻
Σ	**14e⁻**

You need to place 14 electrons. Oxygens are the central atoms and hydrogens are the terminal atoms.

Each hydrogen atom can have a maximum of 2 electrons. Put 2 electrons between each hydrogen and oxygen atoms. Put the rest of electrons on oxygen atoms.

H $\overset{\displaystyle ..}{\underset{\displaystyle ..}{:O:}}$ $\overset{\displaystyle ..}{\underset{\displaystyle ..}{:O:}}$ H

Form single bond between each hydrogen and oxygen atoms.

H—$\overset{\displaystyle ..}{\underset{\displaystyle ..}{O}}$—$\overset{\displaystyle ..}{\underset{\displaystyle ..}{O}}$—H

The central atoms have a full outer shell (8 electrons). Each hydrogen atom also has a full outer shell (2 electrons).

Example 4
Draw a Lewis dot structure for NO₂⁺.

Element	# valence electrons
N	5e⁻
O	2(6e⁻)=12e⁻
Charge	-1e⁻ ← NO₂⁺ is a cation→ it lost 1 electron, so subtract 1 e⁻
Σ	**16e⁻**

You need to place 16 electrons. Nitrogen is the central atom and oxygens are the terminal atoms.

Each oxygen atom can have a maximum of 8 electrons. Put 2 electrons between each nitrogen and oxygen atoms.

$\overset{\displaystyle ..}{\underset{\displaystyle ..}{:O:}}$ N $\overset{\displaystyle ..}{\underset{\displaystyle ..}{:O:}}$

Form a single bond between each atom.

$\overset{\displaystyle ..}{\underset{\displaystyle ..}{:O}}$—N—$\overset{\displaystyle ..}{\underset{\displaystyle ..}{O:}}$

Surviving University: First Year Chemistry

Nitrogen does not have 8 electrons. Form a double bound between each oxygen and nitrogen atoms.

$$:\ddot{O}=N=\ddot{O}:$$

Now each atom has a full outer shell (8 electrons).
Since the molecule has a charge of +1, put brackets around the structure and indicate the charge.

$$\left[:\ddot{O}=N=\ddot{O}:\right]^{+}$$

Lewis structure predictions

- The general trend is that the elements on the periodic table that belong to each group will have the following Lewis structure

Group #	14	15	16	17
Structure	$-\overset{\vert}{\underset{\vert}{C}}-$	$-\overset{\bullet\bullet}{\underset{\vert}{N}}-$	$-\overset{\bullet\bullet}{\underset{\bullet\bullet}{O}}-$	$:\overset{\bullet\bullet}{\underset{\bullet\bullet}{F}}-$

Lewis structures of oxoacids

- Oxoacids are acids that have oxygen atoms
  - Examples: $HClO_4$, HNO_3, H_3PO_4, H_2SO_4, $HOCl$
- In an oxoacid, each hydrogen atom is attached to an oxygen atom
  - Each oxygen atom is attached to the central atom

Example 1
Draw Lewis dot structures for
a) SO_4^{2-}
b) HSO_4^-
c) H_2SO_4

a) SO_4^{2-}

Element	# valence electrons
S	$6e^-$
O	$4(6e^-)=24e^-$
Charge	$+2e^- \leftarrow SO_4^{2-}$ gained 2 electrons, so add $2e^-$
Σ	$32e^-$

Surviving University: First Year Chemistry

You need to place 32 electrons. Sulfur is the central atom and oxygens are the terminal atoms.

Each oxygen atom can have a maximum of 8 electrons. Put 2 electrons between each oxygen and sulfur atoms.

Form a single bond between each atom. Now each atom has a full outer shell (8 electrons).

Put brackets around the entire structure and indicate the charge.

b) HSO_4^-

Element	# valence electrons
S	$6e^-$
O	$4(6e^-) = 24e^-$
H	$1e^-$
Charge	$+1e^- \leftarrow HSO_4^-$ is an anion $\rightarrow$ it gained 1 electron, so add $1e^-$
Σ	$32e^-$

Surviving University: First Year Chemistry

You need to place 32 electrons. Sulfur is the central atom and oxygens are the terminal atoms. The hydrogen atom needs to be attached to one of the oxygen atoms.

Each oxygen atom can have a maximum of 8 electrons. The hydrogen atom can have a maximum of 2 electrons. Put 2 electrons between each oxygen and sulfur atoms. Put 2 electrons between the hydrogen atom and one of the oxygen atoms.

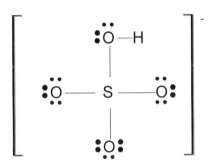

Form a single bond between each atom. Now each atom has a full outer shell (8 electrons for S and O atoms and 2 electrons for H atom). Put brackets around the entire structure and indicate the charge.

c) H_2SO_4

Element	# valence electrons
S	6e⁻
O	4(6e⁻)=24e⁻
H	2(1e⁻)=2e⁻
Σ	32e⁻

You need to place 32 electrons. Sulfur is the central atom and oxygens are the terminal atoms. Each hydrogen atom needs to be attached to an oxygen atom.

Each oxygen atom can have a maximum of 8 electrons. Each hydrogen atom can have a maximum of 2 electrons. Put 2 electrons between each oxygen and sulfur atoms. Put 2 electrons between each hydrogen and oxygen atoms.

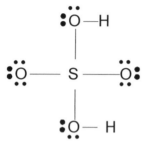

Form a single bond between each atom.

Now each atom has a full outer shell (8 electrons for S and O atoms and 2 electrons for H atoms).

Isoelectronic molecules/ions

Isoelectronic- ions/molecules that have the same number of electrons, but have different number of protons (ex. Cl^- and S^{2-})

- Isoelectronic molecules have same overall Lewis structure
- Here are some common isoelectronic molecules

Molecules/ ions	Overall Lewis structure
CO_2, OCN^-, SCN^-, N_2O, NO_2^+, OCS, CS_2	$[\ddot{O}=N=\ddot{O}]^+$
NH_3, H_3O^+	H—N—H with H below
CO_3^{2-}, NO_3^-	$[\ddot{O}—N=O$ with O below$]^-$

Surviving University: First Year Chemistry

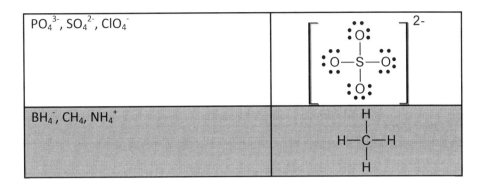

PO_4^{3-}, SO_4^{2-}, ClO_4^-	
BH_4^-, CH_4, NH_4^+	

Exceptions to the octet rule

There are 3 exceptions to the octet rule
1. Incomplete octet
2. Expanded octet
3. Odd number of electrons (radicals)

Incomplete Octet

- Incomplete octet occurs when the central atom has fewer than 8 electrons
    - This is common in boron and beryllium

Example of an incomplete octet→ BF₃
The boron atom does not have a complete octet→ boron atom has 6 electrons instead of 8 electrons.

- Since the central atom does not have 8 electrons, it is highly reactive
    - The central atom can bond to another molecule via a **coordinate covalent bond**
        - The central atom receives 2 electrons from another atom→ electrons are shared between 2 atoms

Surviving University: First Year Chemistry

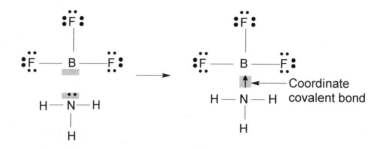

Expanded Octet
- Expanded octet occurs when the central atom has more than 8 electrons
  - This is common when the central atom is bonded to F, O, or Cl
  - Only elements in third period or higher can have an expanded octet→ these elements have a d orbital that can hold 10 electrons

Example of an expanded octet→ SF$_4$
The sulfur atom has more than a complete octet→ sulfur atom has 10 electrons instead of 8 electrons.

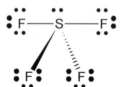

Odd number of electrons
- Molecules with odd number of electrons have at least 1 unpaired electron
  - These molecules are called **free radicals**→ they are very reactive

Example of odd number of electrons→ H and Cl radicals

H• and Cl•

These free radicals can combine to form HCl, H$_2$, Cl$_2$

H• + •H → H-H

H• + •Cl → H-Cl

$$Cl \bullet + \bullet Cl \rightarrow Cl{-}Cl$$

Formal charges in covalent molecules

Formal charge- a charge that an atom has in a molecule or in a polyatomic ion

$$Formal\ charge\ of\ atom = Group\ \#\ of\ atom - \left[LPE + \frac{1}{2}(BE) \right]$$

The sum of formal charges of atoms in a molecule is equal to the overall charge of a molecule

Note: Group # refers to the number of valence electrons present in an atom, LPE= number of electrons which are not bonded in an atom (called lone electrons), BE= number of electrons which are bonded (called bonded electrons)

Note: formal charge is not the same thing as oxidation states!

Lone electrons

Bonded electrons

(2 electrons in a single bond)

Bond	# of bonded electrons
Single	2
Double	4
Triple	6

Example 1
What is the formal charge of each atom in SO_4^{2-}? What is the sum of formal charges?
Steps
1. Draw a Lewis structure
2. Find the formal charge of each atom
3. Add the formal charges of each atom to find the formal change of the entire molecule. The sum of formal charges should be equal to the overall charge of the molecule (-2).

From example 1 of Lewis structures of oxoacids,

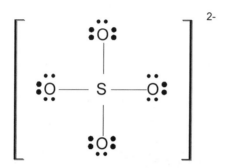

Formal charge of each oxygen atom

$$= Group\ \#\ of\ oxygen - [LPE + \frac{1}{2}(BE)]$$

Formal charge of each oxygen atom $= 6 - [6 + \frac{1}{2}(2)]$

Formal charge of each oxygen atom $= -1$

Formal charge of sulfur $= Group\ \#\ of\ sulfur - [LPE + \frac{1}{2}(BE)]$

Formal charge of sulfur $= 6 - [0 + \frac{1}{2}(8)]$

Formal charge of sulfur $= 2$

Formal charge of the molecule $= (4)(-1) + (1)(2)$

(Since there are 4 oxygen atoms, multiply -1 by 4)

Formal charge of the molecule $= -2$

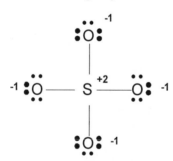

The formal charges of oxygen and sulfur atoms were -1 and 2 respectively. The sum of formal charges was -2.

Preference in nature

The molecular structure with the smallest formal charge separation (smallest difference between formal charges) is preferred in nature

Example 1

Which molecular structure of NH_3O is preferred in nature: NH_2OH or OH_2NH?

Steps

1. Draw a Lewis structure for each molecule
2. Find the formal charge of each atom in each molecule
3. See which molecule has the least separation between formal charges→ that molecular structure is preferred in nature

$\underline{NH_2OH}$

$$H - \overset{\cdot\cdot}{N} - \overset{\cdot\cdot}{\underset{\cdot\cdot}{O}} - H$$
$$\underset{\underset{H}{|}}{}$$

Atom	Formal charge
N	$5 - \left[2 + \dfrac{1}{2}(6)\right] = 0$
O	$6 - \left[4 + \dfrac{1}{2}(4)\right] = 0$
H	$1 - \left[0 + \dfrac{1}{2}(2)\right] = 0$

$\underline{OH_2NH}$

$$\overset{+1}{} \quad \overset{-1}{}$$
$$H - \overset{\cdot\cdot}{O} - \overset{\cdot\cdot}{\underset{\cdot\cdot}{N}} - H$$
$$\underset{\underset{H}{|}}{}$$

Atom	Formal charge
N	$5 - \left[4 + \dfrac{1}{2}(4)\right] = -1$
O	$6 - \left[2 + \dfrac{1}{2}(6)\right] = 1$
H	$1 - \left[0 + \dfrac{1}{2}(2)\right] = 0$

NH_2OH is preferred since it has less charge separation (there is no separation between formal charges→ all formal charges are 0)

Resonance structures

- Generally occur in molecules that have double or triple bonds
- A molecule can have 1 or more correct Lewis structures
    - Position of atoms is the same→ only electrons move!
        - Ex. to have a double or a triple bond on one side of the molecule or to have a double or a triple bond on another side of the molecule
    - **Electron pushing arrows** (curved arrows) are used to show the movement of electrons
    - Formal charges for all atoms in each resonance structure need to be calculated

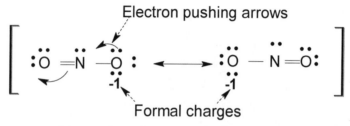

Atoms do not move, electrons move

- None of the resonance structures correctly describes the molecule
    - The actual structure of the molecule is a mix of all possible structures→ called the **resonance hybrid**
    - Electrons are delocalized (distributed) over the atoms
        - This is indicated by dotted lines
- Some molecules which have resonance structures: O_3 (ozone), CO_3^{2-}, NO_2^-, NO_3^-, HCO_3^{2-}

Drawing resonance structures

Steps
1. Draw Lewis structure of the molecule
2. Move a pair of electrons
    - Show movement of electrons using curved arrows
    - Ex. to form a double bond from a single bond
3. Calculate the formal charge for each atom for all resonance structures
4. Draw the resonance hybrid
5. Calculate the formal charge of each atom in the resonance hybrid using

Surviving University: First Year Chemistry

$$\text{Formal charge of atom in the resonance hybrid}$$
$$= \frac{\textit{Formal charge of atom in structure \#1} + \textit{Formal charge of atom in structure \#2} + \cdots}{\# \textit{ resonance structures}}$$

Example 1

Draw all possible resonance structures for ozone (O_3). What are the formal charges of each atom? What is the formal charge of each atom in the resonance hybrid?

═══ is on the left

+1   -1

$:O == \ddot{O} - \ddot{O}:$

Atom	Formal charge
O_{center}	$6 - \left[2 + \frac{1}{2}(6)\right] = 1$
O_{right}	$6 - \left[6 + \frac{1}{2}(2)\right] = -1$
O_{left}	$6 - \left[4 + \frac{1}{2}(4)\right] = 0$

══ is on the right

-1   +1

$:\ddot{O} - \ddot{O} == O:$

Atom	Formal charge
O_{center}	$6 - \left[2 + \frac{1}{2}(6)\right] = 1$
O_{right}	$6 - \left[4 + \frac{1}{2}(4)\right] = 0$
O_{left}	$6 - \left[6 + \frac{1}{2}(2)\right] = -1$

-1/2   +1   -1/2

$:\ddot{O} \cdots O \cdots \ddot{O}:$

Resonance hybrid

Atom	Formal charge
O_{center}	$\frac{1+1}{2} = 1$

O_{right}	$\dfrac{-1+0}{2} = -\dfrac{1}{2}$
O_{left}	$\dfrac{-1+0}{2} = -\dfrac{1}{2}$

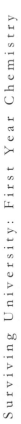

Resonance hybrid

Example 2
Draw all possible resonance structures for NO_2^-. What are the formal charges of each atom? What is the formal charge of each atom in the resonance hybrid?

=== is on the left

-1

Atom	Formal charge
N	$5 - \left[2 + \dfrac{1}{2}(6)\right] = 0$
O_{right}	$6 - \left[6 + \dfrac{1}{2}(2)\right] = -1$
O_{left}	$6 - \left[4 + \dfrac{1}{2}(4)\right] = 0$

=== is on the right

-1

Atom	Formal charge
N	$5 - \left[2 + \dfrac{1}{2}(6)\right] = 0$
O_{right}	$6 - \left[4 + \dfrac{1}{2}(4)\right] = 0$

O_{left}	$6 - \left[6 + \frac{1}{2}(2)\right] = -1$

$$\overset{-1/2}{\underset{\cdot\cdot}{:O}} = N \overset{-1/2}{\underset{\cdot\cdot}{=O:}}$$

Resonance hybrid

Atom	Formal charge
N	$\dfrac{0 + 0}{2} = 0$
O_{right}	$\dfrac{-1 + 0}{2} = -\dfrac{1}{2}$
O_{left}	$\dfrac{-1 + 0}{2} = -\dfrac{1}{2}$

$$\left[\quad :O = N - O: \quad \longleftrightarrow \quad :O - N = O: \quad \right]$$

$$\overset{-1/2}{\underset{\cdot\cdot}{:O}} = N \overset{-1/2}{\underset{\cdot\cdot}{=O:}}$$

Resonance hybrid

Bond order

- Number of bonded electrons which are shared between 2 atoms in a molecule
- Bond order measures the strength of a bond between 2 atoms in a molecule

	Bond order
Single bond	1
Double bond	2
Triple bond	3

$$Bond\ order = \frac{1}{2} \times \frac{\#\ of\ delocalized\ e^-}{\#\ of\ bonds\ over\ which\ e^-\ are\ delocalized}$$

Surviving University: First Year Chemistry

Example 1
What is the bond order for the S-O bond in SO₄²⁻?

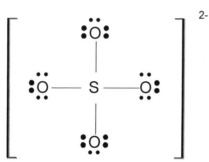

There are 2 electrons in each S-O bond. These 2 electrons are located within 1 bond.

$$Bond\ order = \frac{1}{2} \times \frac{\#\ of\ delocalized\ e^-}{\#\ of\ bonds\ over\ which\ e^-\ are\ delocalized}$$

$$Bond\ order = \frac{1}{2} \times \frac{2}{1}$$

$$Bond\ order = 1$$

The bond order of each S-O bond in SO_4^{2-} is 1.

Example 2
What is the bond order for each O-O bond in ozone (O₃)?

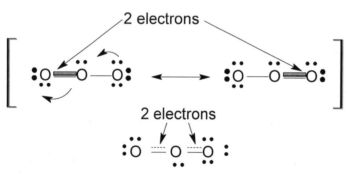

Resonance hybrid

2 electrons are spread over 2 bonds.

$$Bond\ order = \frac{1}{2} \times \frac{\#\ of\ delocalized\ e^-}{\#\ of\ bonds\ over\ which\ e^-\ are\ delocalized}$$

$$Bond\ order = \frac{1}{2} \times \frac{2}{2}$$

$$Bond\ order = \frac{1}{2}$$

The bond order of each O-O bond in ozone is ½.

Surviving University: First Year Chemistry

Bond length

- Distance between 2 nuclei of 2 bonded atoms in a molecule
- As bond order ↑, bond length ↓
    - Ex. Double bonds are shorter than single bonds

Ex. Cl_2

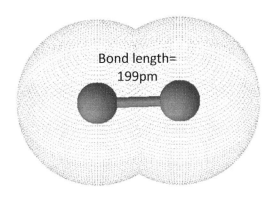

Bond length=
199pm

Valence shell electron-pair repulsion model (VSEPR)

- Electrons which are located in the valence shell of an element repel each other
    - Orbitals which contain valence electrons are positioned as far away from each other as possible
    - Repulsion of electrons causes specific angles to be formed between bonds in a molecule
        - **Bond angle**- angle between 2 bonds in a molecule
- VSEPR model is used to predict the structures of molecules made up of main group elements
    - The model is not effective for transition metals

Strength of repulsions

- Lone electrons occupy more volume than bonded electrons
    - Bonded electrons are squished together

Lone electrons

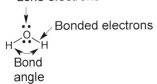

Bonded electrons

Bond angle

Amount of volume occupied by electrons in a molecule:
$$Lone \leftrightarrow lone > lone \leftrightarrow bonded > bonded \leftrightarrow bonded$$
More volume   Less volume

Structures of molecules

	Shows bonded e⁻	Shows lone e⁻	Shows shape of a molecule	Example
Lewis structure	☑	☑	☐	H—N—H with lone pair and H below
Molecular geometry	☑	☐	☑	Describes how atoms are arranged in a molecule (in 3D)→ does not consider lone pairs of electrons
Electron-pair geometry	☑	☑	☑	Describes how both atoms and lone pairs of electrons are arranged in a molecule (in 3D)

Axial and equatorial positions

- Atoms which are in the **equatorial position** are on the same plane
- Atoms which are in the **axial position** are on the same plane
- The equatorial plane is 90° from the axial plane

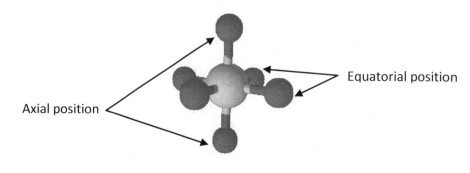

Axial position

Equatorial position

Surviving University: First Year Chemistry

Molecular shapes using VSEPR model

Note: see part 10 of this book for hybridization

Electron pair geometry	Molecular geometry	# of groups attached to the central atom	# of lone e⁻ pairs	Angle	Polar	Example
Linear	Linear	2	0	180°	No	F—Be—F
Trigonal planar	Trigonal Planar	3	0	120°	No	F—B (with three F)
	Bent	2	1	<120°	Yes	F—Ge—F
Tetrahedral	Tetrahedral	4	0	109.5°	No	Si (with four H)
	Trigonal pyramidal	3	1	<109. .5°	Yes	N (with three H)
	Bent	2	2	<109. .5°	Yes	O (with two H)
Trigonal bipyramidal	Trigonal bipyramidal	5	0	120° in horizontal plane, 90° in vertical plane	No	P (with five Cl)

Surviving University: First Year Chemistry

	Seesaw	4	1	<120° in horizontal plane, <90° in vertical plane	Yes	
	T-shaped	3	2	<120° in horizontal plane, <90° in vertical plane	Yes	
	Linear	2	3	180°	No	
Octahedral	Octahedral	6	0	90°	No	
	Square pyramidal	5	1	<90°	Yes	
	Square planar	4	2	<90°	No	

Part 10

Orbital Hybridization and Molecular Orbitals

Valence bond theory

Hybridization

Sigma and pi bonds

Molecular orbital theory

Bond order

Orbital Hybridization and Molecular Orbitals

- There are 2 theories of how atoms are bonded within molecules
  - 1. **Valence bond theory**
    - This theory is used for qualitative analysis (picturing molecules) and for describing molecules in their ground state
  - 2. **Molecular orbital theory**
    - This theory is used for quantitative analysis (calculations) and for describing molecules in excited states

Valence bond theory

- Valence bond theory states that a covalent bond consists of an orbital containing $2e^-$
  - The electrons have an opposite spin
- In order for an atom to form a covalent bond, it must have unpaired electron(s)
  - The number of unpaired electrons determines the number of bonds that can be made

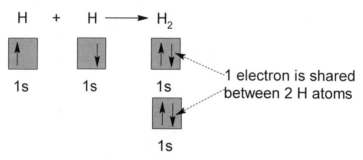

There are 2 electrons in the orbital of each atom (1 spins clockwise, 1 spins counterclockwise)

Example 1
How many bonds can oxygen atom make?
The electron configuration for oxygen atom is $1s^2 2s^2 2p^4$

Oxygen has 2 unpaired electrons→ can form 2 bonds.

Surviving University: First Year Chemistry

Orbital overlap

- 2 orbitals need to overlap in order to create a bond
  - The orbitals are waves
    - Orbitals must be in phase in order to combine (they form constructive interference)

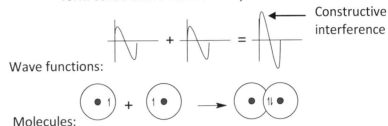

Wave functions:

Constructive interference

Molecules:

  - There is a high probability of finding the electrons which form a bond in the overlapping region
    - The 2 electrons have an opposite spin
      - Repulsion of 2 positive nuclei causes 1 electron to spin counterclockwise
      - 1 electron spins clockwise, 1 electron spins counterclockwise

Types of orbitals overlapping	Visual representation
s+s	
s+p	
p+p	

Note: ^{1} represents an electron; $^{1\downarrow}$ represents 2 electrons which are found in the region where orbitals overlap→ 1 electron spins clockwise, the other spins counterclockwise

Hybridization

- When atomic orbitals (s, p, and d) combine, new sets of orbitals are created→ these are called **hybrid orbitals**
  - The number of hybrid orbitals is the same as the number of the original atomic orbitals
  - Hybrid orbitals do not have a direction in space

- o Hybrid orbitals match the electron pair geometry of the original atomic orbitals (in part 9 on this book)
- Hybrid orbitals are created by transferring electron(s) to a higher energy level
  - o Ex. transferring an electron from an s energy level to a p energy level
- Hybrid orbitals result in higher bonding capacity, better orbital overlap, and stronger bonds between atoms

Hybrid orbital type	Atomic orbitals which combine	# e⁻ pairs	Geometry	Angle	Examples
sp	s orbital p orbital	2	linear	180°	BeF_2 CO_2
sp²	s orbital 2 p orbitals	3	trigonal planar	120°	BF_3 SO_3
sp³	s orbital 3 p orbitals	4	tetrahedral	109.5°	CH_4 H_2O
sp³d	s orbital 3 p orbitals d orbital	5	trigonal-bipyramidal	107.5°	PCl_5 ClF_3
sp³d²	s orbital 3 p orbitals 2 d orbitals	6	octahedral	90°	SF_6 ClF_5

Sigma and Pi bonds

- A molecule can rotate if it has a single bond, but cannot rotate if it has double or triple bonds

Sigma bond (σ)-an overlap between s-s, s-p, or p-p orbitals

- A sigma bond is formed when electrons are shared between 2 nuclei (covalent bond)→ electrons are attracted to both nuclei simultaneously

Pi bond (π)- an overlap between 2 p orbitals

- The p orbitals are not hybridized
- The π bond is positioned above/below the σ bond
  - o The electron density is parallel to the σ bond

Type of a bond	# σ bonds	# π bonds	
Single bond	1	0	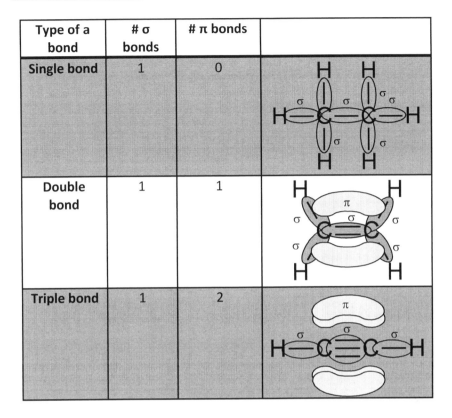
Double bond	1	1	
Triple bond	1	2	

Molecular orbital theory

Molecular orbitals

- Atomic orbitals of 2 atoms must overlap for a bond to be created
- When atomic orbitals (s, p, and d) combine, new sets of orbitals are created→ these are called **molecular orbitals**
    - The number of molecular orbitals is the same as the number of the original atomic orbitals
- Valence electrons of all atoms in a molecule are located in the molecular orbitals
    - Each molecular orbital can hold a maximum of 2 electrons
    - Molecular orbitals are spread out over the entire atom or molecule
- Molecular orbitals are arranged in order of ↑ energy
    - Electrons are placed into the lower energy orbitals first

Principles of molecular orbital theory

Principle	Description
First	<ul><li>Atomic orbitals combine to form molecular orbitals<ul><li>Atomic orbitals are wave functions→ 2 waves can combine in phase (constructive interference) or out of phase (destructive interference)</li></ul></li></ul>**Bonding molecular orbital (σ or π)**- atomic orbitals combine constructively→ there is a high probability of finding electrons along the bond axis (between 2 nuclei) Wave functions: Molecules: **Antibonding molecular orbital (σ* or π*)**- atomic orbitals combine destructively→ nuclei repel each other→ there is a low probability of finding electrons between 2 nuclei Wave functions: Molecules: <ul><li># atomic orbitals= # molecular orbitals</li><li>It takes more energy to produce σ* molecular orbital than to produce σ molecular orbital</li></ul>
Second	<ul><li>σ molecular orbital has less energy than the original atomic orbital<ul><li>The system is stable when electrons are in bonding molecular orbitals→ ↓ energy= stable system</li></ul></li><li>σ* molecular orbital has more energy than the original atomic orbital</li></ul>
Third	<ul><li>Electrons are placed into molecular orbitals from lower to higher energy levels according to<ul><li>**Pauli's Exclusion Principle**- no 2 electrons can have the same set of 4 quantum numbers, no 2</li></ul></li></ul>

In the First principle cell, the following labels and diagrams appear:
- Constructive interference (labelled with arrow)
- Destructive interference (labelled with arrow)
- Nodal plane (labelled with arrow)

	electrons can have the same spin ○ **Hund's Rule**- 1 electron must occupy each of several orbitals of the same energy level before a second electron can occupy the same orbital ▪ Within a molecular orbital, 1 electron spins clockwise and 1 electron spins counterclockwise
Fourth	▪ When atomic orbitals have a similar energy level, they can combine to form molecular orbitals

Electron configurations

- Atomic orbitals have electron configurations
  - From part 7, the filling order for atomic orbitals is
    - 1s, 2s, 2p, 3s, 3p, 4s, etc.
- Molecular orbitals also have electron configurations
  - The possible molecular orbitals are σ, σ*, π, and π*
    - Each molecular orbital holds a certain amount of valence electrons

σ orbital holds 2 valence electrons
π orbital holds 4 valence electrons

- The filling order for molecular orbitals is

$$Order\ of\ MO = \sigma_{1s}, \sigma*_{1s}, \sigma_{2s}, \sigma*_{2s}, \pi_{2p}, \sigma_{2p}, \pi*_{2p}, \sigma*_{2p}$$

Molecular orbital	# valence e$^-$
$\sigma*_{2p}$	2
$\pi*_{2p}$	4
σ_{2p}	2
π_{2p}	4
$\sigma*_{2s}$	2
σ_{2s}	2
$\sigma*_{1s}$	2
σ_{1s}	2

Example 1
Draw the molecular orbital occupations for O_2 and show its electron configuration.
You need to find out how many valence electrons are in O_2.

	# valence e⁻
O	2(6e⁻)
Total	12e⁻

Looking at the periodic table, oxygen has atomic number 8 and is located in the 2p box. This means that the valence electrons are located in the 2s ($\sigma_{2s}, \sigma*_{2s},$) and 2p ($\pi_{2p}, \sigma_{2p}, \pi*_{2p}, \sigma*_{2p}$) molecular orbitals.

1s			Oxygen	1s
2s			2p	
3s			3p	
4s	3d		4p	
5s	4d		5p	
6s	5d		6p	
7s	6d			

4f
5f

12 electrons need to be placed

	O₂
$\sigma*_{2p}$	__
$\pi*_{2p}$	↑ ↑
σ_{2p}	↑↓
π_{2p}	↑↓ ↑↓
$\sigma*_{2s}$	↑↓
σ_{2s}	↑↓

Note: ↑↓ represents 2 electrons. 1 electron is spinning clockwise, the other electron is spinning counterclockwise.

Electron configuration for O₂ is:

[core e⁻] $(\sigma_{2s})^2, (\sigma*_{2s})^2, (\pi_{2p})^4, (\sigma_{2p})^2, (\pi*_{2p})^2$

Note: the numbers that are superscripted represent the number of electrons that are present in a molecular orbital.

Example 2
Draw the molecular orbital occupations for NO and show its electron configuration.

You need to find out how many valence electrons are in NO.

Surviving University: First Year Chemistry

	# valence e⁻
N	5e⁻
O	6e⁻
Total	11e⁻

Looking at the periodic table, oxygen has atomic number 8 and nitrogen has atomic number 7. They are both located in the 2p box. This means that the valence electrons are located in the 2s ($\sigma_{2s}, \sigma*_{2s,}$) and 2p ($\pi_{2p}, \sigma_{2p}, \pi*_{2p}, \sigma*_{2p}$) molecular orbitals.

You need to place 11 electrons.

	NO
$\sigma*_{2p}$	—
$\pi*_{2p}$	__ ↑
σ_{2p}	↑↓
π_{2p}	↑↓ ↑↓
$\sigma*_{2s}$	↑↓
σ_{2s}	↑↓

Note: ↑↓ represents 2 electrons. 1 electron is spinning clockwise, the other electron is spinning counterclockwise.

NO MO configuration: [core e⁻] $(\sigma_{2s})^2, (\sigma*_{2s})^2, (\pi_{2p})^4, (\sigma_{2p})^2, (\pi*_{2p})^1$

Note: the numbers that are superscripted represent the number of electrons that are present in a molecular orbital.

Bond order

Bond order- the total number of bonding pairs of electrons in a molecule

$$Bond\ order = \frac{1}{2}(\#\ e^- \ in\ bonding\ MO - \#\ e^-\ in\ antibonding\ MO)$$

Note: MO stands for molecular orbitals

- As bond order ↑, the bond length ↓, and the energy needed to break a bond ↑

Example 1
Find the bond order for O_2.
From example 1 of electron configurations section,
Electron configuration for O_2 is:
[core e⁻] $(\sigma_{2s})^2, (\sigma*_{2s})^2, (\pi_{2p})^4, (\sigma_{2p})^2, (\pi*_{2p})^2$

	# of electrons
Bonding MO	8
Antibonding MO	4

$$Bond\ order = \frac{1}{2}(\#\ e^- \ in\ bonding\ MO\ - \ \#\ e^- \ in\ antibonding\ MO)$$

$$Bond\ order = \frac{1}{2}(8 - 4)$$

$$Bond\ order = 2$$

The bond order in O_2 is 2.

Example 2

Find the bond order for NO.

From example 2 of electron configurations section,

NO MO configuration: [core e⁻] $(\sigma_{2s})^2, (\sigma *_{2s})^2, (\pi_{2p})^4, (\sigma_{2p})^2, (\pi *_{2p})^1$

	# of electrons
Bonding MO	8
Antibonding MO	3

$$Bond\ order = \frac{1}{2}(\#\ e^- \ in\ bonding\ MO\ - \ \#\ e^- \ in\ antibonding\ MO)$$

$$Bond\ order = \frac{1}{2}(8 - 3)$$

$$Bond\ order = 2.5$$

The bond order in NO is 2.5.

Part 11

Classifying Substances

Intermolecular forces

Intramolecular forces

Molecular solids

Covalent network solids

Ionic solids

Metallic solids

Summary of physical

properties of solids

Water

Solubility in water

Surviving University: First Year Chemistry

Classifying Substances

- Atomic composition and arrangement of atoms dictate physical properties of substances
- Physical properties include state, melting and boiling points, density, and colour
    - **Melting point**- temperature at which solid changes into a liquid
        - Intermolecular forces are broken, intramolecular forces are not broken
    - **Boiling point**- temperature at which liquid changes into a gas
        - Intermolecular forces are broken, intramolecular forces are not broken

Intermolecular forces

- Intermolecular forces are forces which exist between molecules
    - All substances have intermolecular forces
    - *Think: intErmolecular= between*
- Intermolecular forces are involved with physical changes

Strength of intermolecular forces
- Strength of intermolecular forces dictate physical properties
    - State of a substance, its melting point, and its boiling point
    - Stronger intermolecular forces result in ↑ melting points and ↑ boiling points
        - More energy is required to separate molecules

Strength of intermolecular forces increases

Gas <	Liquid <	Solid
▪ Molecules can move freely ▪ There is much space between molecules	▪ Molecules can move freely ▪ There is little space between molecules	▪ Molecules are fixed (cannot move freely). Molecules can vibrate. ▪ There is little space between molecules

Surviving University: First Year Chemistry

Types of intermolecular forces

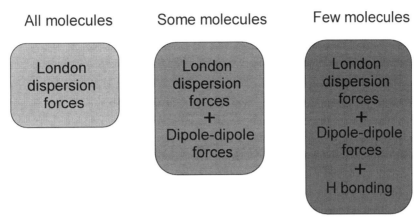

All molecules	Some molecules	Few molecules
London dispersion forces	London dispersion forces + Dipole-dipole forces	London dispersion forces + Dipole-dipole forces + H bonding

Strength of intermolecular forces increases

London dispersion (van der Waals)	<	Dipole-dipole	<	Hydrogen bonding	<	Ion-dipole

Type of force	Description	Example
London dispersion	▪ Occurs between all molecules ▪ Temporary attraction between nucleus of 1 molecule and electrons of another molecule→ this results in **polarizability** (distortion of e⁻ cloud of a molecule) ▪ Larger molecules have stronger London dispersion forces	Nucleus e⁻ He e⁻ e⁻ He e⁻ 2 atoms move towards each other. Nucleus of 1 atom is repelled by nucleus of another atom (both are +ive). e⁻ of 1 atom are repelled by e⁻ of another atom (both are -ive). e⁻ of 1 atom are attracted to nucleus of another atom. This results in distortion of e⁻ clouds.

Surviving University: First Year Chemistry

	↑ amount of e⁻, ↑ polarizability	

As molecules move apart, their e⁻ clouds go back to normal state.

Dipole-dipole	▪ Occurs between polar molecules (have unequal sharing of electrons) ○ More electronegative atom is δ- ▪ Electrons spend more time around δ⁻ atom ▪ δ+ end of one molecule is attracted to δ- end of another molecule	
H bonding	▪ H which is attached to O, N, or F is attracted to O, N, F, or S	

Ion-dipole	<ul><li>Cation (+ive ion) is attracted to δ- end of a molecule</li><li>Anion (-ive ion) is attracted to δ+ end of a molecule</li></ul>	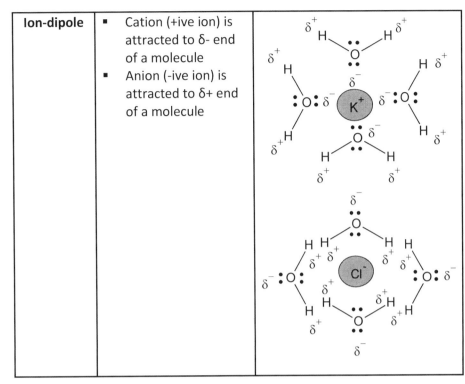

Example 1
Based on intermolecular forces, which of the following has the highest boiling point?

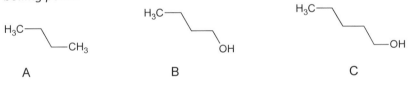

Molecule	# of C atoms	Intermolecular forces present
A	4	<ul><li>London dispersion</li></ul>
B	4	<ul><li>London dispersion</li><li>Dipole-dipole</li><li>H bonding</li></ul>
C	5	<ul><li>London dispersion</li><li>Dipole-dipole</li><li>H bonding</li></ul>

Since molecules B and C have dipole-dipole and H bonding forces, they have higher boiling points than molecule A. Molecule C is longer than molecule B. Thus, molecule C has ↑ amount of e⁻, ↑ polarizability, and

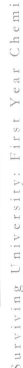Surviving University: First Year Chemistry

stronger London-dispersion forces. More energy is needed to break apart its intermolecular forces and convert molecule C from liquid state to gas state. Thus, Molecule C has the highest boiling point.

Intramolecular forces

- Intramolecular forces are forces which exist between atoms within a molecule
- Intramolecular forces are involved with chemical changes
- Types of intramolecular forces

Type	Description	Example
Covalent bonding	<ul><li>Between non-metals</li><li>Each atom donates 1 e⁻ to form a bond (1 bond= 2e⁻)</li><li>Each atom achieves an octet</li><li>Electrons are <u>shared equally</u> between atoms→ electrons are equally attracted to both nuclei of atoms</li></ul>	:C̈l—C̈l: :Ö=Ö:
Polar covalent bonding	<ul><li>Between non-metals</li><li>Each atom donates 1 e⁻ to form a bond (1 bond= 2e⁻)</li><li>Each atom achieves an octet</li><li>Electrons are <u>not shared equally</u> between atoms→ electrons are attracted more to nucleus of 1 atom (that atom is δ-)</li></ul>	δ^+ H—F δ^-

Coordinate covalent bond	▪ Between non-metals ▪ Each atom achieves an octet ▪ 1 atom (**Lewis base**) donates 2 e⁻ to form a bond→ the other atom (**Lewis acid**) does not donate e⁻ for the bond ▪ Electrons are <u>shared</u> <u>equally</u> between atoms	(Lewis structure diagrams of BF_3 with NH_3 showing coordinate covalent bond formation)
Ionic bonding	▪ This type of bonding is often between a metal and a non-metal ▪ Each atom achieves an octet ▪ 1 atom loses electron(s) (metal)→ becomes a cation (+ively charged ion) ▪ The other atom gains electron(s) (non-metal) → becomes an anion (-ively charged ion) ▪ Atoms are held together via electrostatic forces→ +ive and −ive ions attract each other	Na^+ :$\overset{..}{\underset{..}{Cl}}$: ⁻

Types of solids

1. Molecular solids
2. Covalent network solids
3. Ionic solids
4. Metallic solids

1) Molecular Solids

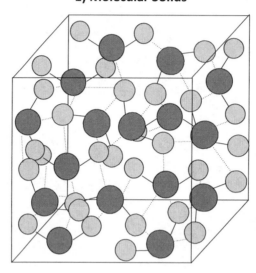

About

- Solids are composed of separate molecules
  - All molecules are identical to each other (ex. all are $C_6H_{12}O_6$)
  - Molecules consist of atoms
    - Atoms are typically non-metals
    - Atoms can be identical (ex. Cl in Cl_2) or different (C, H, and O in $C_6H_{12}O_6$)
- Examples
  - $C_6H_{12}O_6$ (glucose)
  - H_2O
  - Cl_2

Forces in molecular solids

- Atoms within molecules are held together via intramolecular forces
  - Covalent bonding
- Molecules are held together via intermolecular forces
  - London dispersion

Surviving University: First Year Chemistry

- Dipole-dipole if molecules are polar
- H bonding (if have H which is attached to O, N, or F is attracted to O, N, F, or S)

Physical properties

- State
  - Are typically gases or liquids at room temperature→ are solids at low temperatures
  - Large molecules (ex. $C_{10}H_8$) are solids at room temperature
- Most are soft
  - Atoms can be easily displaced
- Low melting and boiling points
  - Since intermolecular forces are weak, it does not take much energy to convert solid to liquid or from liquid to gas
- Do not conduct electricity
  - Do not have a charge
  - When placed into a solvent (ex. water), molecules separate from each other, but do not form ions
  - In order to conduct electricity, solution needs to have ions which can move in presence of electric field

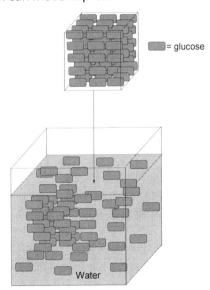

- Solubility in water
  - Many molecular solids (ex. $CH_3CH_2CH_2CH_3$) do not dissolve in water→ they form a separate layer

    o   Solubility of glucose (sugar) in water is due to London dispersion forces, dipole-dipole forces, and hydrogen bonding

Example 1

State intermolecular forces present in each of the following molecular solids. Which of these molecular solids will have highest melting point, boiling point?

CH_4 H_3C—OH H_3C——————OH

A   B   C

Molecule	# C atoms	Intermolecular forces
A	1	London dispersion
B	1	London dispersion Dipole-dipole • O atom is more electronegative than C atom→ electrons spend more time around oxygen atom (δ^-) than C atom (δ^+) H bonding
C	3	London dispersion Dipole-dipole • O atom is more electronegative than C atom→ electrons spend more time around oxygen atom (δ^-) than C atom (δ^+) H bonding

- The molecule with highest melting and boiling point will have the strongest intermolecular forces.
- Molecule A has the least amount of intermolecular forces→ little energy will be needed to break apart the forces between molecules.
- Both molecules B and C have 3 types of intermolecular forces. However, molecule C has more C atoms→ has ↑ amount of e⁻, ↑ polarizability, and stronger London-dispersion forces. More energy is needed to break apart its intermolecular forces

Thus, Molecule C has the highest boiling and melting points.

Surviving University: First Year Chemistry

2) Covalent Network Solids

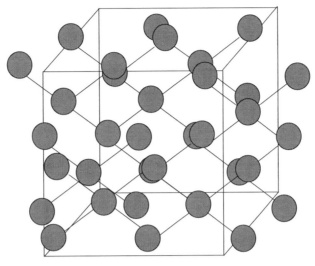

<u>About</u>

- The entire structure (the solid) can be considered a giant molecule
- Solid is composed of many atoms held together via covalent bonding
    - Many of the atoms are non-metals
    - Atoms can be identical (ex. C in diamond) or different (Si, O in SiO_2)
- Examples
    - Diamond (C)
    - Graphite (C)
    - Silica (SiO_2)
    - Titania (TiO_2)
    - Alumina (Al_2O_3)
- Chemical formula indicates proportion of each type of atom present in a solid

Example 1
TiO_2 is a covalent network solid. What does the formula indicate about the structure of the solid?
A solid does not contain just 1 Ti and 2 O atoms. There are many Ti and O atoms bonded together via covalent bonds. There are twice as many O atoms as Ti atoms in a solid.

Forces in covalent network solids

- Atoms are held together via intramolecular forces
    - Covalent bonding

Physical properties

- State
    - Solids at room temperature
- Are hard and very durable
    - Atoms cannot be easily displaced due to many covalent bonds
    - Exception: graphite
- Very high melting and boiling points
    - Covalent bonds must be broken in order to change state (requires much more energy than to break intermolecular forces in molecular solids)
    - Ex. Diamond, SiO_2
- Do not conduct electricity
    - Atoms are not charged
    - When placed into a solution (ex. water), atoms remain bonded via covalent bonds→ do not dissociate to form ions
- Solubility in water
    - Most are insoluble in water→ much energy is needed to break apart covalent bonds
        - The bonds between adjacent atoms are very strong→ hydration is not enough to break apart covalent bonds

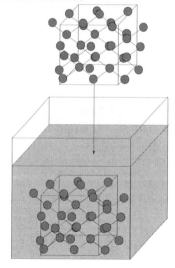

3) Ionic Solids

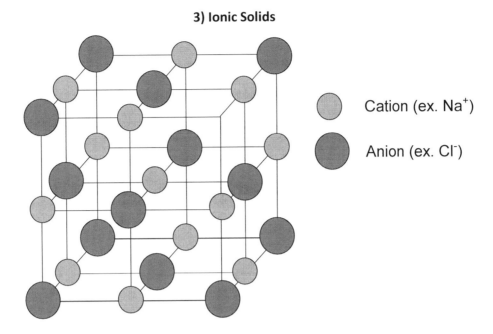

Cation (ex. Na$^+$)

Anion (ex. Cl$^-$)

About

- Solids are composed of ions
    - Ionic solids contain anions (-ive) and cations (+ive)
        - Anions can be polyatomic (ex. SO_4^{2-})
    - Most cations are metals, most anions are non-metals
- Overall, the solid is neutral
    - **Electroneutrality principle-** +ive charge of cations and –ive charge of anions cancel out
- Examples
    - NaCl
    - $CaCl_2$
    - $BaCO_3$
    - NaOH

Forces in ionic solids

- Ions are held together by **electrostatic forces**
    - Same charges repel each other
        - Cations repel cations
        - Anions repel anions
    - Opposite charges attract each other
        - Cations attract anions

- Each atom in crystal lattice experiences attraction by 6 other atoms, and repulsion by 4 other atoms
  - This results in a net energy (called **lattice energy**) which holds the structure together

Physical properties

- State
  - Solids at room temperature
- Are hard
  - The structure is strong because it is held together by electrostatic forces
  - When ions are displaced from their locations, structure becomes brittle
- Very high melting and boiling points
  - Much energy is needed to overcome electrostatic forces
- When are not in a solution, ionic solids do not conduct electricity
  - Ions are fixed→ there are no mobile ions
- Conduct electricity when in molten state (are melted→ liquid form)
- Conduct electricity when placed into water
  - When ionic solid is placed into a solution, it dissociates into its ions
    - The hydration is strong enough to break apart ionic solids
      - Water surrounds the ionic solid and overcomes the lattice energy
  - Ions which can move in presence of electric field→ can conduct electricity

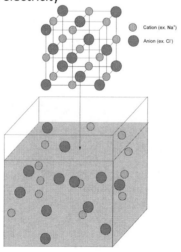

Surviving University: First Year Chemistry

4) Metallic Solids

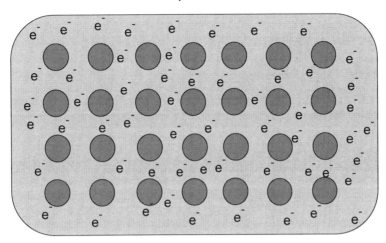

About

- Solid is composed of many positive atoms (cations) surrounded by mobile valence electrons ("sea" of electrons)
    - Atoms are metals
    - Atoms can be identical (ex. Zn) or different (ex. in alloys)
        - Ex. stainless steel→ mixture of Fe and Cr
- Examples
    - Cu
    - Zn
    - Na
    - Cr
    - Au

Forces in metallic solids

- Atoms are held together via **delocalized bonding**
    - Valence electrons can move between atoms
        - These electrons are **delocalized**
- Atoms are cations→ are surrounded by a sea of valence electrons
- ↑ amount of mobile electrons (valence electrons)= stronger forces

Physical properties

- State
    - Solids at room temperature
    - Mercury is liquid at room temperature
- Are malleable and ductile

- When solid is bent, atoms and electrons are displaced→ delocalized bonding remains
- Have high density
- Are lustrous (able to reflect light)
- Very high melting and boiling points
    - Group 1 metals have low melting and boiling points
        - Each atom can give only 1 e⁻ for delocalized bonding
    - Transition metals have high melting and boiling points
        - Atoms can give 2 e⁻ from s orbital and several e⁻ from d orbital

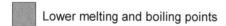
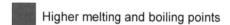

Lower melting and boiling points

Higher melting and boiling points

- Conduct electricity
    - Atoms are positively charged (cations)
    - Electrons are mobile

Summary of Physical Properties of Solids

Forces in solids

Type of a solid	Forces present
Molecular solid	<ul><li>Covalent bonding</li><li>London dispersion</li><li>Dipole-dipole if polar substance</li><li>H bonding (if have H which is attached to O, N, or F is attracted to O, N, F, or S)</li></ul>
Covalent network solid	<ul><li>Covalent bonding</li></ul>
Ionic solid	<ul><li>Electrical forces</li></ul>
Metallic solid	<ul><li>Delocalized bonding</li></ul>

Melting and boiling points

Melting and boiling points increase
Strength of forces increases

Low	<	High	<	Very high	<	Even higher
Molecular solids		Metallic solids		Covalent network solids		Ionic solids

- Melting and boiling points of metallic solids varies between different metals (depends on number of mobile electrons)

Example 1
Which of the following has the lowest and highest melting point? CaO, TiO_2, Zn, HF

Low	<	High	<	Very high	<	Even higher
HF		Zn		TiO_2		CaO
Molecular solid		Metallic solid		Covalent network solid		Ionic solid

Surviving University: First Year Chemistry

A Special Case: Water

Intramolecular forces

- Atoms within water molecule are held together by intramolecular forces
  - Water molecule is polar
    - Electrons are shared unequally between H and O atoms
      - O is more electronegative than H→ pulls e⁻ towards itself→ → electrons spend more time around oxygen atom (δ^-) than H atom (δ^+)
  - Each water molecule has 2 polar covalent bonds

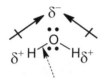

Polar covalent bond

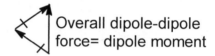

Line up the dipole-dipole forces tip to tail

Overall dipole-dipole force= dipole moment

Intermolecular forces

- Molecules of water are held together by intermolecular forces→ these forces are very strong
  - Dipole-dipole
    - **Dipole moment** is the overall dipole-dipole force in a molecule
    - δ^+ end of one molecule is attracted to δ^- end of another molecule
  - London dispersion
  - H bonding
    - H which is attached to O is attracted to another O atom
    - H bonding is stronger than covalent bonding
    - H bonding is abnormally strong for water

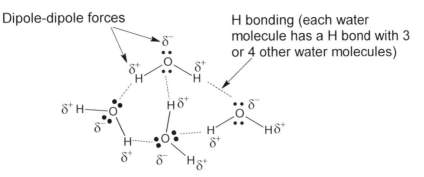

Dipole-dipole forces

H bonding (each water molecule has a H bond with 3 or 4 other water molecules)

Physical properties of water

- High boiling point
    - Since intermolecular forces are strong, much energy is needed to break the forces between water molecules

Clathrate hydrates

- Water molecules can form cage-like structures and surround substances
    - Water can trap CO_2, methane, small C compounds, and other molecules

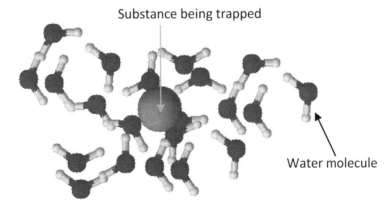

Substance being trapped

Water molecule

Solubility of molecular substances in water

- "Like dissolves like"
    - Polar substances dissolve in polar substances
        - **Polar substance**- its molecules have a dipole moment

- Ex. HBr, H_2O, HCl, CH_3CH_2OH
  - Water is a polar substance
- Non-polar substances dissolve in non-polar substances
  - **Non-polar substance**- its molecules do not have a dipole moment
    - Ex. CH_4, $CH_3CH_2CH_3$, CO_2, CBr_4
- The higher the amount of intermolecular forces that a substance can form with water, the higher the solubility
  - Substance that best dissolves in water has the same intermolecular forces as H_2O

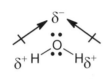 Line up the dipole-dipole forces tip to tail

 Dipole moment

Water is a polar substance

Example 1
Will the following molecules be soluble in water?
a) CH_4
b) CH_3OH
c) NH_3
d) $CH_3CH_2CH_2CH_2CH_2CH_2CH_2CH_2OH$

Molecule	Structre	Dipole moment	Intermolecular forces	Soluble in water?
CH_4	Non-polar	No	▪ London dispersion	No
CH_3OH	Polar	Yes	▪ London dispersion ▪ Dipole-dipole ▪ H bonding	Yes

Surviving University: First Year Chemistry

NH$_3$		Yes	<ul><li>London dispersion</li><li>Dipole-dipole</li><li>H bonding</li></ul>	Yes
	Polar			
C$_8$H$_{18}$O	Both polar and nonpolar→ most of the molecule is nonpolar	Very small	<ul><li>Mostly London dispersion</li><li>Small amount of dipole-dipole</li><li>Small amount of H bonding</li></ul>	No

Solubility of ionic substances in water

- When a salt (ionic compound) is placed into water, it breaks apart into its ions

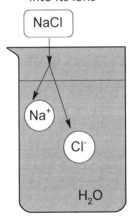

- Water surrounds ions→ ion-dipole force exists between water and ions
    - δ^+ part of water molecule is attracted to anions (-ive)
    - δ^- part of water molecule is attracted to cations (+ive)

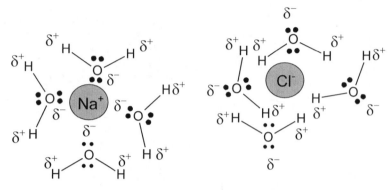

- If attraction of water molecules to ions is strong enough, then salt will dissolve (break apart into its ions)
    - If attraction is not strong enough, then ions will remain together
    - To know whether a substance will dissolve in water, use solubility rules (part 3 of this book)

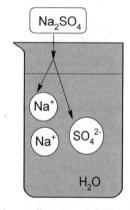

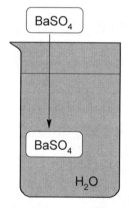

According to solubility rules, Na_2SO_4 is soluble in water (so it dissociates into its ions)

The attraction is strong enough to break up the ionic compound

According to solubility rules, $BaSO_4$ is not soluble in water (it does not dissociates into its ions)

The attraction is not strong enough to break up the ionic compound

Solvation- polar molecules surround an ion
Hydration- water molecules surround an ion
Hydrated ion- ion is surrounded by a solvation layer (a layer of water molecules)

Surviving University: First Year Chemistry

Part 12

Colligative Properties

Vapor-pressure depression

Boiling-point elevation

Freezing-point depression

Osmotic pressure

Surviving University: First Year Chemistry

Colligative Properties

Colligative properties- properties which depend on the number of solute particles present in a solution

- Colligative properties do not depend on the type of particles present in a solution
    - They do not depend on the identity, charge, mass, or size of particles
- Types of colligative properties
    1. Vapor-pressure depression
    2. Boiling-point elevation
    3. Freezing-point depression
    4. Osmotic pressure

1) Vapor-pressure depression

- There is a dynamic equilibrium between molecules in a liquid phase and molecules in a gas phase

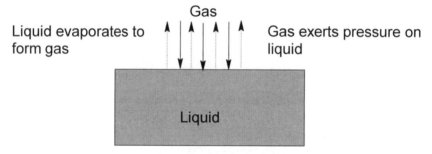

Vapor pressure- the pressure which gas exerts on a liquid (gas applies a force over the exposed surface of a liquid)

- Vapor pressure is a result of a liquid evaporating to form a gas
- As the amount of intermolecular forces present in the liquid $\downarrow$, vapor pressure $\uparrow$
    - The liquid evaporates more easily

Volatile liquids- liquids have high vapor pressure and as a result evaporate more easily

Liquids which contain a dissolved solute

- When a solute is dissolved in a solvent, solvent molecules surround solute molecules
    - Energy is needed to break apart intermolecular forces→ more energy is needed for solution to evaporate (than

would be needed if solute molecules were not present in the solution)
- If a solute is added to a solvent, the vapor pressure $\downarrow$
  - More energy is needed for vapor pressure to reach the atmospheric pressure

Dalton's law of partial pressures
- The total pressure of a solution which contains 2 liquids (liquid A and liquid B) is the sum of partial pressures of each liquid

$$P_T = P_A + P_B$$

Note: P_T = total pressure created by all liquids (atm), P_A= pressure created by liquid A (atm), P_B= pressure created by liquid B (atm)

Raoult's law (aka **the ideal solution law**)
- Use this law to find the partial pressures of each liquid

$$P_A = X_A P_A^\circ$$
$$\Delta P_A = -X_B P_A^\circ$$
$$\text{where } X_A = \frac{n_A}{n_T} = 1 - X_B$$
$$\text{Where } n_T = n_A + n_B + \cdots$$
So the Dalton's law becomes
$$P_T = P_A + P_B = X_A P_A^\circ + X_B P_B^\circ$$

Note: P°_A= pressure created by pure liquid A (atm), P_A= partial vapor pressure created by pure liquid A (atm), X_A= mole fraction of liquid A, X_B= mole fraction of liquid B, ΔP_A= change in partial vapor pressure created by pure liquid A (atm), n_A= # moles of liquid A (mol), n_B= # moles of liquid B (mol)

Mole fraction (X)- the # of moles of 1 type of a liquid divided by the total # of moles of liquid in a solution

Example 1
151g of 2-propanol (C_3H_8O) is dissolved in 542g of water. Find the vapor pressure of water at 90°C (vapor pressure of pure water= 70.10kPa).
The 2 solutions are propanol and water.
Steps
1. Find the # moles of propanol using $n = \frac{m}{M}$
2. Find the # moles of water using $n = \frac{m}{M}$
3. Find mole fraction of water using $X_A = \frac{n_A}{n_T}$
4. Find the vapor pressure of water using $P_A = X_A P_A^\circ$

m_{H_2O}	542g
$m_{C_3H_8O}$	151g

Surviving University: First Year Chemistry

M_{H_2O}	?g/mol
$M_{C_3H_8O}$	?g/mol
n_{H_2O}	?mol
$n_{C_3H_8O}$	?mol
n_{Total}	?mol
X_{H_2O}	?
P_{H_2O}	?atm
$P^{\circ}_{H_2O}$	70.10kPa

$$M_{H_2O} = 2(1.01g/mol) + 16.00g/mol = 18.02g/mol$$
$$M_{C_3H_8O} = 3(12.01g/mol) + 8(1.01g/mol) + 16.00g/mol$$
$$M_{C_3H_8O} = 60.11g/mol$$
$$n_{H_2O} = \frac{m}{M} = \frac{542g}{18.02g/mol} = 30.1mol$$
$$n_{C_3H_8O} = \frac{m}{M} = \frac{151g}{60.11g/mol} = 2.51mol$$
$$n_{Total} = n_{H_2O} + n_{C_3H_8O} = 30.1mol + 2.51mol = 32.61mol$$
$$X_{H_2O} = \frac{n_{H_2O}}{n_{Total}} = \frac{30.1mol}{32.61mol} = 0.92$$
$$P_{H_2O} = X_{H_2O}P^{\circ}_{H_2O} = 0.92(70.10kPa) = 64.7kPa$$
The vapor pressure of water in the solution was 64.6kPa.

2) Boiling-point elevation

Boiling point- the temperature at which the vapor pressure is equal to the atmospheric pressure

Atmospheric pressure- pressure which the Earth's atmosphere exerts on a solution (101.325Pa)

- If a solute is dissolved in a solvent, boiling point ↑
  - Energy is needed to break apart intermolecular forces between solute and solvent molecules→ more energy is needed for solution to evaporate (than would be needed if solute molecules were not present in the solution)
  - The solution will boil at a higher temperature
  - As the number of particles in a solution ↑, boiling point ↑

$$\Delta T_B = k_b \times m_{solute}$$
$$k_b \; for \; water = 0.5°C/m$$

Note: ΔT_B= difference in boiling point between the solvent and the dissolved solution (°C or K), k_b= the solvent's boiling-point elevation constant (°C/m), m_{solute}= molal concentration of a solution (mol/kg)

Surviving University: First Year Chemistry

Note: k_b values are usually provided at the back of your chemistry textbook.

Molality (m)- how much solute (kg) is dissolved per 1L of a solution

$$molality_{solute} = \frac{n_{solute}}{mass_{solvent}}$$
Note: mass must be in kg

Note: molality= molality of solute (mol/kg or m), n= # moles (mol), m= mass of solvent (kg)

3) Freezing-point depression

Freezing point- the temperature at which liquid turns into solid
- The solid and liquid phases are in equilibrium with the atmospheric pressure
- If a solute is dissolved in a solvent, freezing point ↓ (solution's melting point also ↓)
  - When a solution freezes, molecules assemble into an orderly structure
    - Solute particles interfere with solution's assembly into a solid lattice structure
  - As the number of particles in a solution ↑, freezing point ↓

$$\Delta T_f = -k_f \times m_{solute}$$
The negative sign is because freezing point ↓
$$k_f \; for \; water = 1.9°C/m = 1.86K/m$$

Note: ΔT_f= difference in freezing point between the solvent and the dissolved solution (°C or K), k_f= the solvent's freezing-point depression constant (°C/m or K/m), m_{solute}= molal concentration of a solution (mol/kg)

Note: k_f values are usually provided at the back of your chemistry textbook.

Example 1
A solution contains ethylene glycol (M= 62.07g/mol) dissolved in 0.0525kg of water. The freezing point of water changes from 273.15K to 260K. Find the mass of ethylene glycol present in the solution.
Steps
1. Find ΔT_f using $\Delta T_f = T_{f \; final} - T_{f \; initial}$
2. Find molality using $\Delta T_f = -k_f \times m_{solute}$

Find the # of moles of ethylene glycol using $molality_{solute} = \frac{n_{solute}}{mass_{solvent}}$

3. Find the mass of ethylene glycol using $n = \frac{m}{M}$

m_{H_2O}	52.5g
$T_{f\ initial}$	273.15K
$T_{f\ final}$	260K
ΔT_f	?K
k_f	1.86K/m
m (molality)	?mol/kg
$n_{ethylene\ glycol}$	?g
$m_{ethylene\ glycol}$	?g
$M_{ethylene\ glycol}$	62.07g/mol

$$\Delta T_f = T_{f\ final} - T_{f\ initial} = 260K - 273.15K = -13.15K$$

$$\Delta T_f = -k_f \times m_{solute}$$

$$m_{solute} = -\frac{\Delta T_f}{k_f}$$

$$m_{solute} = -\frac{(-13.15K)}{1.86K/m}$$

$$m_{solute} = 7.07m = 7.07mol/kg$$

Now you need to find the # of moles of ethylene glycol.

$$molality_{solute} = \frac{n_{solute}}{mass_{solvent}}$$

$$n_{ethylene\ glycol} = molality_{solute} \times mass_{solvent}$$

$$n_{ethylene\ glycol} = \frac{7.07mol}{kg} \times 0.0525kg$$

$$n_{ethylene\ glycol} = 0.371mol$$

Now you need to find the mass of ethylene glycol.

$$n = \frac{m}{M}$$

$$m_{ethylene\ glycol} = n \times M$$

$$m_{ethylene\ glycol} = 0.371mol \times 62.07g/mol$$

$$m_{ethylene\ glycol} = 23.04g$$

23.04g of ethylene glycol were present in the solution.

4) Osmotic Pressure

Osmosis- the net movement of water across a semipermeable membrane

- **Semipermeable membrane**- allows some substances to pass through, but not others
- Water flows from a region of low solute concentration to a region of high solute concentration

H₂O → Semipermeable membrane →

Low solute concentration (few solute molecules)

High solute concentration (many solute molecules)

Osmotic pressure- the pressure (a force applied over an area) that would be needed in order to prevent osmosis from occurring

$$\Pi = CRT$$
$$\text{where } C = \frac{n}{V}$$
$$\text{and } R = 8.314 \frac{L \cdot kPa}{K \cdot mol}$$

Note: ∏= osmotic pressure (atm), C= concentration of solution (mol/L or M), n= # moles (mol), V= volume (L), R= gas constant, T= temperature (K)
Note: temperature must be in Kelvin

Part 13

Nuclear Chemistry

Surviving University: First Year Chemistry

Units of radiation

Radiation types

Penetrating ability

Nuclear reaction types

Radioactive decay series

Nuclear stability and energetics

Nuclear binding energy

Activity

Half-life

Carbon dating

Nuclear Chemistry

Nuclear chemistry- deals with changes in the nucleus of an atom

- Nucleus is unstable→ nucleus has an undesirable neutron to proton ratio
    - There are many repulsions in the nucleus
    - Nucleus decays naturally→ particles and energy are released
    - Released energy can remove electrons from other atoms

Transmutation- formation of a new element from a radioactive element

Units of radiation

- Radiation is measured in Becquerel
    - The Becquerel is based on individual nuclear decays

$$1 Bq = 1 \ disintegration/second$$

- Exposure to radiation is measured in Gray
    - **Gray**- 1 J of energy deposited per kg of material
- Exposure to radiation in living tissue is measured in Sievert
    - **Sievert**- 1 J of energy deposited per kg of tissue
- Masses and mass differences are measured in atomic mass units (amu)

$$1 \ amu = 1.66058 \times 10^{-27} kg$$

- Energy is measured in electron-volts (eV)
    - 1 volt multiplied by the charge of an electron

$$1 eV = 1.6029 \times 10^{-19} J$$

Radiation types

Mass number (# of protons+ # of neutrons)

$^{4}_{2}\alpha \longleftarrow$ **Symbol**

Atomic number (# of protons)

Radiation type	Symbol	Charge	Mass (amu)	Composition
Alpha (α)	$^{4}_{2}He, \ ^{4}_{2}\alpha$	+2	4	helium nucleus

Surviving University: First Year Chemistry

Beta (negatron, β⁻)	$_{-1}^{0}e, \, _{-1}^{0}\beta$	-1	1/1837	fast electron
Beta (positron, β⁺)	$_{+1}^{0}e, \, _{+1}^{0}\beta$	+1	1/1837	fast electron
Gamma (γ)	γ	none	none	high energy photon
X-ray	X-ray	none	none	high energy photon
Neutron (n)	$_{0}^{1}n$	none	1	fast neutron

- Gamma radiation involves rearrangement of the nucleus→ there is no transmutation (no new elements are created)
- Gamma radiation and X-rays are the same type of radiation except for the energy range

Penetrating ability

- Ability for radiation to go through material
- A neutron has the highest penetrating ability, alpha radiation has the lowest penetrating ability

> ### Penetrating ability increases
> ⟵
> $n > \gamma > \beta > \alpha$

Nuclear reaction types

Nuclear reaction- spontaneous decay of a nucleus of an atom

> In any reaction, the total mass of reactants has to be equal to the total mass of products (mass must be balanced)
> The sum of atomic numbers and atomic masses of reactants is equal to the sum of atomic numbers and atomic masses of products
> (# of protons and neutrons are conserved)

- If an element loses protons, it transforms into a different element→ the new element is called the **daughter product**
  - Ex. during alpha decay, an alpha particle ($_{2}^{4}\alpha$) is released→ a new element is formed

Reaction type	Example
Alpha decay	$^{226}_{88}Ra \rightarrow ^{4}_{2}\alpha + ^{222}_{86}Rn$
Beta decay	$^{239}_{92}U \rightarrow ^{0}_{-1}\beta + ^{239}_{93}Np$
Positron emission	$^{207}_{84}Po \rightarrow ^{0}_{+1}\beta + ^{207}_{83}Bi$
Electron capture	$^{7}_{4}Be + ^{0}_{-1}e \rightarrow ^{7}_{3}Li$
Nuclear fission	$^{235}_{92}U + ^{1}_{0}n \rightarrow 3^{1}_{0}n + ^{141}_{56}Ba + ^{92}_{36}Kr$

Example 1
Balance the following reaction. What are the symbol, atomic number, and mass number for X and Y?

$$^{236}_{92}U + ^{1}_{0}n \rightarrow ^{?}_{?}X + ^{237}_{93}Y$$

Steps
1. Balance masses
2. Balance the # of protons
3. Identify X and Y

First, you need to make sure that the mass is balanced. Add the mass numbers on each side of the equation.

Mass number (# of ⟶ $^{1}_{0}n$
protons+ # of neutrons)

	$^{236}_{92}U + ^{1}_{0}n \rightarrow$	$X + ^{237}_{93}Y$
Mass	236+1= 237	237

The masses are the same on both sides. This means that the mass number of X is 0 ($^{0}_{?}X$).
Now you need to balance the atomic numbers (# of protons). Add the atomic numbers on each side of the equation.

Atomic number ⟶ $^{1}_{0}n$
(# of protons)

	$^{236}_{92}U + ^{1}_{0}n \rightarrow$	$X + ^{237}_{93}Y$
Atomic number	92+ 0= 92	93 If $^{0}_{-1}X$, then -1+ 93= 92

The atomic numbers on each side are not the same. If the atomic number of X is -1, then the atomic numbers balance.
Now you know that $^{236}_{92}U + ^{1}_{0}n \rightarrow ^{0}_{-1}X + ^{237}_{93}Y$.
$^{0}_{-1}X$ corresponds to $^{0}_{-1}\beta$.
From periodic table, the element with atomic number of 93 is Np.

Surviving University: First Year Chemistry

Thus, $^{236}_{92}U + ^{1}_{0}n \rightarrow ^{0}_{-1}\beta + ^{237}_{93}Np$

Radioactive decay series

- Radioactive isotopes are unstable. They may decay into other radioactive isotopes, which could then decay into other radioactive isotopes
    - With each decay, the daughter radioactive isotopes become more stable
    - After a series of decays, the final isotope will eventually be stable

Example 1

Radon-218 is unstable and it will eventually decay into a stable element X whose mass number is 206. During these decays, 3 alpha particles and 2 negatron particles were emitted. Which element is X?

Steps

1. Write a chemical equation
2. Balance masses
3. Balance the # of protons
4. Identify X and Y

From the periodic table, the atomic number for radon is 86.

$$^{218}_{86}Rn \rightarrow ^{206}_{?}X + 3\ ^{4}_{2}\alpha + 2\ ^{0}_{-1}\beta$$

Now you need to make sure that the mass is balanced. Add the mass numbers on each side of the equation.

Mass number (# of $\longrightarrow$ $^{4}_{2}\alpha$
protons+ # of neutrons)

	$^{218}_{86}Rn \rightarrow$	$^{206}_{?}X + 3\ ^{4}_{2}\alpha + 2\ ^{0}_{-1}\beta$
Mass	218	206+ 3(4)+ 2(0)= 218

The masses are the same on both sides.

Now you need to balance the atomic numbers (# of protons). Add the atomic numbers on each side of the equation.

Atomic number
(# of protons) $\longrightarrow$ $^{4}_{2}\alpha$

	$^{218}_{86}Rn \rightarrow$	$^{206}_{?}X + 3\ ^{4}_{2}\alpha + 2\ ^{0}_{-1}\beta$
Atomic number	86	3(2)+2(-1)= 4 If $^{206}_{82}X$, then 82+1= 86

The atomic numbers on each side are not the same. If the atomic number of X is 82, then the atomic numbers balance.

Now you know that $^{218}_{86}Rn \rightarrow {}^{206}_{82}X + 3\,{}^{4}_{2}\alpha + 2\,{}^{0}_{-1}\beta$

From periodic table, the element with atomic number of 82 is Pb. Thus, $^{218}_{86}Rn \rightarrow {}^{206}_{82}Pb + 3\,{}^{4}_{2}\alpha + 2\,{}^{0}_{-1}\beta$

Nuclear stability and energetics

- It has been observed that atoms with even # of protons or neutrons are more stable than atoms with odd # of protons or neutrons

	# of elements
Even number of protons and neutrons	168
Odd number of protons, even number of neutrons	50
Even number of protons, odd number of neutrons	57
Odd number of protons and neutrons	4

- It has also been observed that unstable radioactive isotopes decay into stable elements or long-lived radioisotopes
    - These stable elements or long-lived radioisotopes follow a band of stability
        - **Band of stability**- the range of isotopes that are stable and will not decay)
- The most stable isotopes are in the middle of the periodic table
    - Mn, Fe, Co
- As the atomic mass $\uparrow$, isotopes become more unstable
    - Isotopes lose mass in order to become more stable
    - **Alpha emission** occurs when an isotope loses mass to reach the band of stability
- $^{1}_{1}H$ and $^{3}_{2}He$ are the only 2 stable isotopes that have more protons than neutrons
- Up to Ca, isotopes have # protons = # neutrons
- After Ca, neutron-proton ratio > 1
    - There are more neutrons than protons
    - **Beta emission** occurs when the neutron-proton ratio in an atom is high$\rightarrow$ the atom emits a beta particle in order to decrease the neutron-proton ratio
- **Positron emission** or **electron capture** occurs when neutron-proton ratio is low

Nuclear binding energy

Nuclear binding energy (E_b)- the energy needed to break down a nucleus into protons and neutrons

Sign of E_b	Reaction
+ive	• Not spontaneous • Net energy would be needed to break down the nucleus
-ive	• Spontaneous • Net energy would be released to break down the nucleus

Mass difference- the difference between the sum of all protons and neutrons in an atom and the observed atomic mass
- The missing or excess mass of an atom is converted into its **binding energy**
  - Nuclear binding energy measures the energy needed to keep protons and neutrons in the nucleus

$$\Delta m = \Sigma mass\ of\ products - \Sigma mass\ of\ reactants$$
Note: Δm= mass defect or excess mass (kg or amu)

$$E_b = \Delta mc^2$$
Note: Δm= mass difference (kg/mol), c= 3.00×10^8 m/s (the speed of light), E_b= nuclear binding energy (Δm x (speed)^2 gives units of kg x m^2/s^2 per mol, or J/mol)
- To convert E_b from J/amu to MeV/amu

$$E_b\ in\ MeV/amu = \left(\frac{E_b\ in\ J/amu}{1.6029 \times 10^{-19} J/eV}\right)$$
$$E_b = \Delta m \times 931.5\ MeV/amu$$
Note: Δm= mass difference (kg/mol), E_b= nuclear binding energy (J/mol)

Nucleon- a nuclear particle (a proton or a neutron)
- Nucleons are used to calculate the mass of a nucleus
  - Remember that mass number= # of protons + # of neutrons

Mass number
$^4_2$He ← Symbol of element
Atomic number

Example 1

Find the binding energy for carbon-12 in kJ/mol and kJ/mol nucleon.

Steps

1. Find mass difference using $\Delta m = \Sigma mass\ of\ products - \Sigma mass\ of\ reactants$
2. Plug mass difference into $E_b = \Delta mc^2 \rightarrow$ find E_b
3. Divide E_b by the number of nucleons in carbon-12

Step 1

Carbon-12 has an atomic number of 6 and a mass number of 12.

Atomic number= # of protons= 6

Mass number= # of protons+ # of neutrons= 12

# of neutrons= Mass number- # of protons= 12-6= 6

So carbon-12 is made up of 6 protons and 6 neutrons

$^{12}_{6}C \rightarrow 6\ ^{1}_{0}n + 6\ ^{1}_{1}p$

$^{1}_{1}p$ can be replaced with $^{1}_{1}H$ because hydrogen also has 1 proton and 0 neutrons. Hydrogen ($^{1}_{1}H$) has an atomic number of 1 and a mass of 1.007825 g/mol. Hydrogen also includes the electrons that must be accounted for in ^{12}C. The exact mass of a neutron ($^{1}_{0}n$) is 1.008665 g/mol.

$\Delta m = \Sigma mass\ of\ products - \Sigma mass\ of\ reactants$

$\Delta m = (6 \times mass\ ^{1}_{1}H + 6 \times mass\ ^{1}_{0}n) - mass\ ^{12}_{6}C$

$\Delta m = (6 \times 1.007825 g/mol + 6 \times 1.008665 g/mol) - 12.000000 g/mol$

$\Delta m = 9.8940 \times 10^{-2} g/mol\ nuclei$

Step 2

Note: in order to use Δm in $E_b = \Delta mc^2$, you need to convert Δm into kg.

$\Delta m = 9.8940 \times 10^{-2} g/mol\ nuclei \times \dfrac{1 kg}{1000 g}$

$\Delta m = 9.8940 \times 10^{-5} kg/mol\ nuclei$

$E_b = \Delta mc^2$

$E_b = (9.8940 \times 10^{-5} kg/mol\ nuclei)(3.00 \times 10^8 m/s)^2$

$E_b = 8.89 \times 10^{12} J/mol\ nuclei$

Step 3

# of nucleons= # of protons+ # of neutrons= 6+6= 12

$E_b = 8.89 \times 10^{12} J/mol\ nuclei \div 12\ nucleons/mol\ nuclei$

$E_b = 7.41 \times 10^{11} J/nucleon$

The binding energy of carbon-12 is $7.41 \times 10^{11} J/nucleon$.

Example 2

Find the binding energy for hydrogen-2 (deuterium) in MeV and MeV/nucleon.

Steps

1. Find mass difference using $\Delta m = \Sigma mass\ of\ products - \Sigma mass\ of\ reactants$

2. Plug mass difference into

$E_b = \Delta m \times 931.5 \frac{MeV}{amu} \rightarrow$ find E_b

3. Divide E_b by the number of nucleons in carbon-12

Step 1

Hydrogen-2 has an atomic number of 1 and a mass number of 2.

Atomic number= # of protons= 1

Mass number= # of protons+ # of neutrons= 2

# of neutrons= Mass number- # of protons= 2-1= 1

So hydrogen-2 is made up of 1 proton and 1 neutron

$^2_1H \rightarrow {}^1_0n + {}^1_1p$

^1_1p can be replaced with ^1_1H (mass of 1.007825amu). The mass of a neutron (^1_0n) is 1.008665amu.

$^2_1H \rightarrow {}^1_0n + {}^1_1H$

$\Delta m = \Sigma mass\ of\ products - \Sigma mass\ of\ reactants$

$\Delta m = (1 \times mass\ {}^1_1H + 1 \times mass\ {}^1_0n) - mass\ {}^2_1H$

$\Delta m = (1 \times 1.007825 amu + 6 \times 1.008665 amu) - 2.01410 amu$

$\Delta m = 0.00239\ amu$

Step 2

Since you are asked to find E_b in MeV/amu, use

$E_b = \Delta m \times 931.5 \frac{MeV}{amu}$

$E_b = 0.00239 amu \times 931.5 \frac{MeV}{amu}$

$E_b = 2.23 MeV$

Step 3

# of nucleons= # of protons+ # of neutrons= 1+1= 2

$E_b\ per\ nucleon = \frac{2.23 MeV}{2\ nucleons}$

$E_b\ per\ nucleon = \frac{1.11 MeV}{nucleon}$

The binding energy for hydrogen-2 is 2.23MeV or 1.11MeV/nucleon.

Activity

Activity (A)- # of disintegrations present per unit of time
- Activity is measured in Becquerels (Bq)
- Activity is proportional to the number of radioactive atoms present

$$\left(\frac{\Delta N}{\Delta t}\right) \propto N$$

ΔN= change in the number of atoms, Δt= change in time (s or min or h), N= # of atoms, α means proportional

$$ln\left(\frac{N}{N_0}\right) = -kt$$

Note: ln = natural logarithm, t= time (s or min or h), k= rate constant, N_0= number of atoms at the beginning of the decay, N= number of atoms after a specific period of time

$$ln\left(\frac{A}{A_0}\right) = -kt$$

Note: A_0= activity of the sample at the beginning of decay (Bq), A= activity after a specific period of time (Bq), k= rate constant, t= time (s or min or h)

Half-life

Half life- the time it takes for a radioisotope to lose half of its activity
- Ex. it takes 29.1 years for strontium-90 to decrease in activity from, say 10 Bq to 5 Bq→ the half-life is 29.1 years
- There are 2 methods to calculate the half-life

Method #1: $$t_{1/2} = \frac{ln\,2}{k}$$

Note: $t_{1/2}$= half life (s or min or h or days), k=rate constant (will be given in the problem or will be able to calculate)

Method #2: $$A = A_0 \times \left(\frac{1}{2}\right)^n$$
$$\text{where } n = \frac{t}{t_{1/2}}$$

Note: A_0= activity of the sample at the beginning of decay (Bq), A= activity after a specific period of time (Bq), n= # of half-lives (can be a fraction), t= time (s or min or h or days), $t_{1/2}$= half life (s or min or h or days)

Example 1→ using method #1
A sample of Strontium-90 has an activity of $1.0x10^3$ Bq. 1 year later the activity is 975 Bq.

Surviving University: First Year Chemistry

a) What is the half-life of strontium-90?

b) How much time is needed for the activity to decrease to 1.0% of its original value?

a) What is the half-life of strontium-90?

Steps

1. Find k using $-kt = \ln\left(\frac{A}{A_0}\right)$

2. Find $t_{1/2}$ using $t_{1/2} = \frac{\ln 2}{k}$

	^{90}Sr
A_0	1.0×10^3 Bq
A	975 Bq
t	1 a
$t_{1/2}$	? a
k	?1/ a

Note: the symbol for a year is annum (a)

Find k using $-kt = \ln\left(\frac{A}{A_0}\right)$

$$k = \ln\left(\frac{A}{A_0}\right) \div (-t)$$

$$k = \ln\left(\frac{975 Bq}{1.0 \times 10^3 Bq}\right) \div (-1a)$$

$$k = 0.025\frac{1}{a}$$

Now find $t_{1/2}$

$$t_{1/2} = \frac{\ln 2}{k}$$

$$t_{1/2} = \frac{\ln 2}{0.025a^{-1}}$$

$$t_{1/2} = 27a$$

The half-life of strontium-90 was calculated to be 27 years.

b) How much time is needed for the activity to decrease to 1.0% of its original value?

Steps

1. Find 1.0% of original activity value

2. Find t using $-kt = \ln\left(\frac{A}{A_0}\right)$

The original activity value is 1.0×10^3 Bq. You need to find what 1.0% of that value is.

$$A = A_0 \times \frac{1.0\%}{100\%}$$

Surviving University: First Year Chemistry

$$A = 1.0 \times 10^3 Bq \times \frac{1.0\%}{100\%}$$

$$A = 10 Bq$$

	^{90}Sr
A_0	$1.0 \times 10^3 Bq$
A	$10 Bq$
t	$?a$
$t_{1/2}$	$27a$
k	$0.025 a^{-1}$

$$-kt = \ln\left(\frac{A}{A_0}\right)$$

$$t = \ln\left(\frac{A}{A_0}\right) \div (-k)$$

$$t = \ln\left(\frac{10 Bq}{1.0 \times 10^3 Bq}\right) \div (-0.025 a^{-1})$$

$$t = 184.2a$$

It will take 184.2 years for the activity of strontium-90 to decrease to 1.0% of its original value.

Example 2→ using method #2
The half-life of phosphorus-32 is 14 days. What % of its activity
a) After 1 half-life
b) After 2 half-lives
c) After 5 half-lives

a) After 1 half-life
Let original activity be 100%
$A_0 = 100\%$
$A = ?\%$
$n = 1$

$$A = A_0 \times \left(\frac{1}{2}\right)^n$$

$$A = 100\% \times \left(\frac{1}{2}\right)^1$$

$$A = 50\%$$

After 1 half-life, 50% of the activity remains.

b) After 2 half-lives
$A_0 = 100\%$
$A = ?\%$
$n = 2$

$$A = A_0 \times \left(\frac{1}{2}\right)^n$$

$$A = 100\% \times \left(\frac{1}{2}\right)^2$$

$$A = 100\% \times \frac{1}{4}$$

$$A = 25\%$$

After 2 half-lives, 25% of the activity remains.

c) After 5 half-lives

A_0= 100%

A= ?%

n= 5

$$A = A_0 \times \left(\frac{1}{2}\right)^n$$

$$A = 100\% \times \left(\frac{1}{2}\right)^5$$

$$A = 100\% \times \frac{1}{32}$$

$$A = 3.13\%$$

After 5 half-lives, 3.13% of the activity remains.

Example 3→ using method #2
Phosphorus-32 is commonly used in biochemical research. Every 6 months, your lab orders 37.5Bq of phosphorus-32. What is its activity when a new order is placed? The half-life of phosphorus-32 is 14 days.
Steps

1. Find the # of half-lives using $n = \dfrac{t}{t_{1/2}}$

2. Find activity after 6 months using $A = A_0 \times \left(\frac{1}{2}\right)^n$

Convert 6 months into days

$$time\ in\ days = 6months \times \frac{30days}{1month}$$

$$time\ in\ days = 180days$$

t= 180days

$t_{1/2}$= 14days

n= ?

A_0= 37.5Bq

A= ?Bq

$$n = \frac{t}{t_{1/2}}$$

Surviving University: First Year Chemistry

$$n = \frac{180 days}{14 days}$$

$$n = 12.86$$

$$A = A_0 \times \left(\frac{1}{2}\right)^n$$

$$A = 37.5 Bq \times \left(\frac{1}{2}\right)^{12.86}$$

$$A = 0.005 Bq$$

The activity of phosphorus-32 when a new order is placed is 0.005Bq.

Carbon dating

- Carbon-14 is used to find the age of artefacts
- Carbon-14 is present in carbon dioxide (CO_2)
  - Animals and plants use CO_2
  - When an organism dies, it stops taking up carbon-14
- Carbon-14 has a long half-life (5730 years)
- Activity of carbon-14 is measured to detect the age of an organism
  - Organisms of different ages will have different activities
  - Ancient organisms have lower activity of carbon-14

Example 1
In nature, the activity (A_0) of carbon is 250Bq per kg of carbon. You find a human bone. Forensic analysis reveals that the bone has a specific activity of 164Bq per kg of carbon. What is the age of this bone? The half-life of carbon-14 is 5730 years.

Steps

1. Find # of half-lives using $A = A_0 \times \left(\frac{1}{2}\right)^n$

2. Find bone's age using $n = \frac{t}{t_{1/2}}$

A= 164Bq/kg
A_0= 250Bq/kg
n= ?

$$A = A_0 \times \left(\frac{1}{2}\right)^n$$

$\frac{A}{A_0} = \left(\frac{1}{2}\right)^n$ take ln of both sides

$ln\frac{A}{A_0} = ln\left(\frac{1}{2}\right)^n$ bring n down (in front of ln)

$ln\frac{A}{A_0} = n \times ln\frac{1}{2}$ rearrange for n

$$n = \frac{ln\frac{A}{A_0}}{ln\frac{1}{2}}$$

$$n = \frac{ln\frac{164Bq/kg}{250Bq/kg}}{ln\frac{1}{2}}$$

$$n = 0.6082$$

$$n = \frac{t}{t_{1/2}}$$

You know that $t_{1/2}$ is 5730 years→ you need to find t.

$$t = n \times t_{1/2}$$

$$t = 0.6082 \times 5730 years$$

$$t = 3485 years$$

The bone was 3485 years old.

Part 14

Stereochemistry

Summary of isomers

Stereoisomers

Chirality

Stereocenters

Internal plane of symmetry

Superimposability

Enantiomers

R and S configurations

Conformational isomers

Newman projections

Stereochemistry

- Stereochemistry deals with arrangement of atoms in 3 dimensions and effect of arrangement on chemical reactions

<u>Summary of isomers</u>

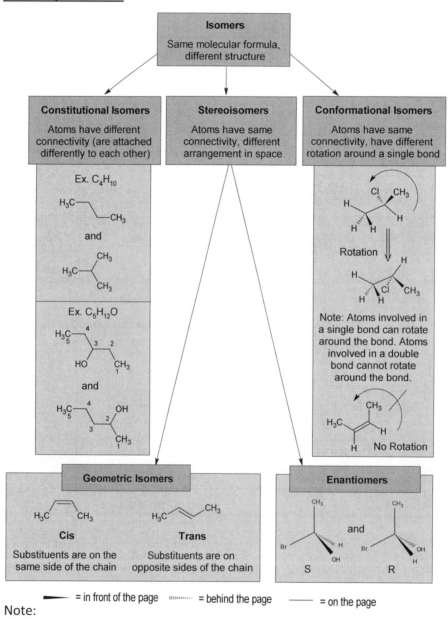

= in front of the page   = behind the page   = on the page

Note:

Surviving University: First Year Chemistry

Stereoisomers

- Stereoisomers have same chemical formula, same connectivity of atoms, but different arrangement of atoms in space
- Stereoisomers have the following properties
  - 1. Have 1 or more stereocenters
  - 2. Do not have an internal plane of symmetry
  - 3. Are non-superimposable on their mirror images

1) Stereocenters

Stereocenter- an atom which is attached to 4 different groups
- Stereocenter is usually indicated with *

For example:

Example 1
*Do the following molecules have a stereocenter? If yes, indicate stereocenter with *.*

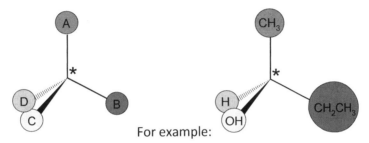

A   B   C

Look for an atom that is attached to 4 different groups.

Molecule	Are any atoms attached to 4 groups?	Indicate stereocenter with *
A	No. The 4 groups that C atom is attached to are the same.	No stereocenter. CH_4
B	All C atoms which are a part of $-CH_3$ groups are not attached to 4 different groups.	H—$\underset{CH_3}{\overset{CH_3}{\underset{|}{\overset{|}{\underset{*}{}}}}}$—H ... CH$_3$ CH$_2$OH

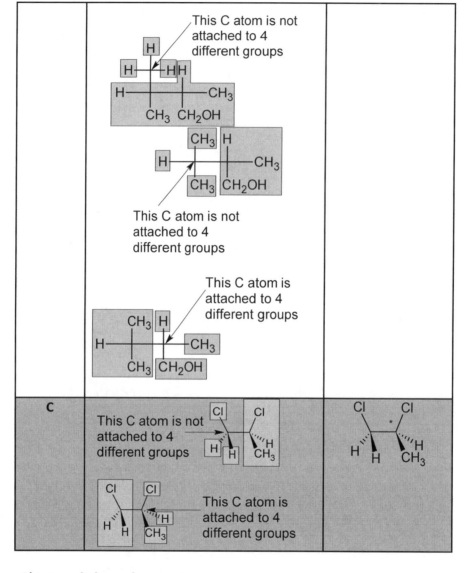

2) Internal plane of symmetry

- Internal plane of symmetry exists when a line is put through the molecule and the image is identical on both sides of the line

Surviving University: First Year Chemistry

Case #1

Case #2

Object

Object

Internal plane is then added to the object.

Internal plane is then added to the object.

Internal plane of symmetry

Internal plane of symmetry

Since the image is identical on each side of the line, the object has an internal plane of symmetry

No matter where the internal plane is placed, the images on each side of the line are not identical. Thus, the object does not have an internal plane of symmetry.

Example 1
Do the following molecules have an internal plane of symmetry?

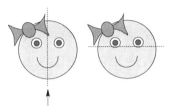

A   B   C   D

E

Start by adding internal plane to each molecule. If the images on each side of the internal plane are identical to each other, then the molecule

Surviving University: First Year Chemistry

has an internal plane of symmetry. If the images on each side of the internal plane are not identical to each other, then the molecule does not have an internal plane of symmetry.

The following are the most basic planes of symmetry→ there could be other elements of symmetry that are not shown here.

Molecule	Add internal plane	Does the molecule have internal plane of symmetry?
A	H₃C ... CH₃ — Images are not identical; H₃C ... CH₃ — Symmetrical (images are identical); H₃C ... CH₃ — Images are not identical; H₃C ... CH₃ — Images are not identical	Yes
B	H,H,C,H ... Br — Symmetrical (Images are identical); H₃C ... Br — Images are not identical; H₃C ... Br — Images are not identical; H₃C ... Br — Images are not identical	Yes

C	Symmetrical (images are identical) Images are not identical Symmetrical (images are identical) The plane of symmetry cuts through the middle of the molecule	Yes
D	Symmetrical (images are identical) Images are not identical Images are not identical Images are not identical	Yes
E	Symmetrical (images are identical) Symmetrical (images are identical) Symmetrical (images are identical) The plane of symmetry cuts through the middle of the molecule	Yes

3) Superimposability

Superimposable molecule- the object and its mirror image are identical
Non-superimposable molecule- the object and its mirror image are <u>not</u> identical

Case #1

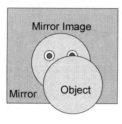

When this object looks into the mirror, he/she sees his/her mirror image

Case #2

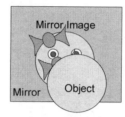

When this object looks into the mirror, she sees her mirror image

The object is then turned around and compared to his/her mirror image

Object   Mirror   Mirror Image

The object is then turned around and compared to her mirror image

Object   Mirror   Mirror Image

When you place the object and mirror image on top of each other, they are identical (are superimposable)

When you place the object and mirror image on top of each other, they are not identical (are non-superimposable)

Example 1
Is the following molecule superimposable on its mirror image?

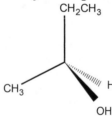

Surviving University: First Year Chemistry

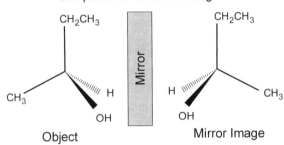

(looking from behind)

The object is then turned around and compared to its mirror image

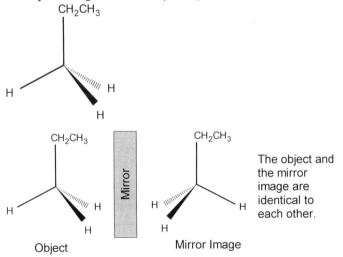

Notice that in object OH and H are on the right, CH_3 is on the left.

In mirror image, OH and H are on the left, CH_3 is on the right.

This indicates that the object and its mirror image are not identical.

Thus, the molecule is not superimposable on its mirror image.

Example 2

Is the following molecule superimposable on its mirror image?

The object and the mirror image are identical to each other.

Thus this molecule is superimposable on its mirror image.

Examples of chirality

Example 1

Is the following molecule chiral? If so, indicate the stereocenter(s) with *.

In order for a molecule to be chiral, it must satisfy these conditions
- Has 1 or more stereocenters
- Does not have an internal plane of symmetry
- Is non-superimposable on its mirror image

☑ Has 1 or more stereocenters

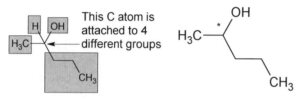

Thus, this molecule has 1 stereocenter.

☑ Does not have an internal plane of symmetry

Images are not identical   Images are not identical

Images are not identical   Images are not identical

☑ Is non-superimposable on its mirror image

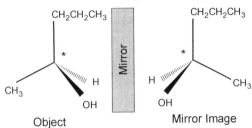

Put stereocenter (*) in the middle and attach
the 4 groups

CH₂CH₂CH₃ | Mirror | CH₂CH₂CH₃

*

CH₃

H

OH

Object

H

CH₃

OH

*

Mirror Image

Since the object and the mirror image are not
identical to each other, the molecule is not
superimposable on its mirror image.

Since this molecule satisfies the 3 conditions to be chiral, it is chiral.

Example 2
Is the following molecule chiral?

Cl⎯⎯⎯H

H

CH₃

☐ Has 1 or more stereocenters

H

Cl⎯⎯⎯H

CH₃

**This C atom is
not attached to 4
different groups**

Since the molecule does not have a stereocenter, it is not chiral.

Example 3
Is the following molecule chiral?

OH

H₃C⎯

OH

CH₃

Surviving University: First Year Chemistry

☑ Has 1 or more stereocenters

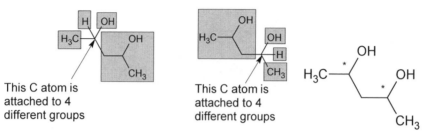

This C atom is attached to 4 different groups

This C atom is attached to 4 different groups

Thus, this molecule has 2 stereocenters.

☐ Does not have an internal plane of symmetry

Images are not identical

Images are not identical

Images are not identical

Symmetrical (Images are identical)

Since the molecule has an internal plane of symmetry, it is not chiral.

Enantiomers (R and S)

- Enantiomers are stereoisomers which are mirror images of each other and are not superimposable onto each other
  - Each stereoisomer
    - Has 1 or more stereocenters
    - Does not have an internal plane of symmetry
    - Is not superimposable on its mirror image
- See part 20 of this book for optical properties of enantiomers and polarimetry

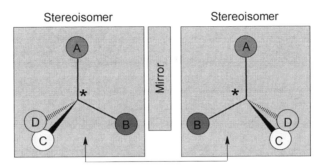

Enantiomers

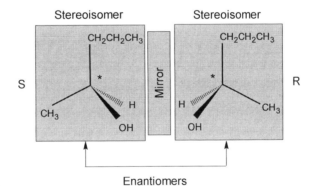

Enantiomers

Example:

R and S configurations

- R and S system of naming is used to determine the 3D structure of stereoisomer
- If 2 molecules contain the same atoms, the same connectivity, and are stereoisomers, they are differentiated using the R and S notation
  - These 2 molecules are enantiomers

Rules for naming R and S

1. Find stereocenter(s) in the molecule
- Atom at the stereocenter is attached to 4 different groups
2. Circle the 4 groups that are attached to each stereocenter
3. Assign priority (#1, #2, #3, #4) to each of the groups that are attached to each stereocenter
- #1 has the highest priority, #4 has the lowest priority
- ↑ atomic number means ↑ priority
    - Atomic number is obtained from the periodic table
    - ex. C (atomic number 6) vs H (atomic number 1)
        - Since C has ↑ atomic number than H, it has ↑ priority
    - ex. C (atomic number 6) vs O (atomic number 8)
        - Since O has ↑ atomic number than C, it has ↑ priority
    - ex. Cl (atomic number 17) vs Br (atomic number 35)
        - Since Br has ↑ atomic number than Cl, it has ↑ priority
- If the priority of 2 or more groups is the same, consider atoms which are bonded to these atoms (work outwards)

Note: C* stands for the chiral centre

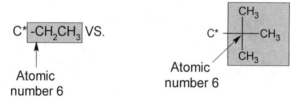

Now look at atoms which are bonded to the C atom

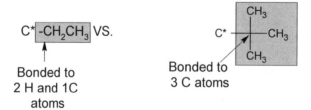

C atom has higher priority than H atom. Since the group on the right has more C atoms, it has higher priority.

Surviving University: First Year Chemistry

- In the case of a double bond

Note: C* stands for the chiral centre

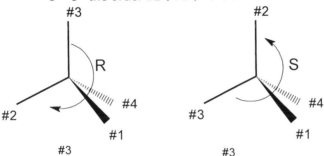

Look at as:

When looking at priorities, consider C atom to be bonded to 2 O atoms

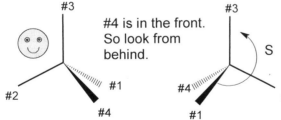

Look at as:

When looking at priorities, consider C atom to be bonded to 2 C atoms

4. Assign R or S
- If the lowest priority group (#4) is behind the page
  - R= the order #1→#2→#3 is **clockwise**
  - S= the order #1→#2→#3 is **counterclockwise**

#3
R
#2
#4
#1

#2
S
#3
#4
#1

#3
#2
#1
#4
#4 is in the front. So look from behind.

#3
S
#4
#2
#1
This is what you see when you look from behind. You see #4 in the back and #1 in the front.

Note: ▬ = in front of the page   ⅲⅲⅲⅲ = behind the page   ── = on the page

Example 1
Does the following molecule have R or S configuration?

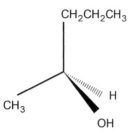

Step 1: Find stereocenter(s) in the molecule

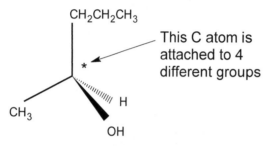

Step 2: Circle the 4 groups that are attached to each stereocenter

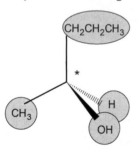

Step 3: Assign priority (#1, #2, #3, #4) to each of the groups that are attached to each stereocenter

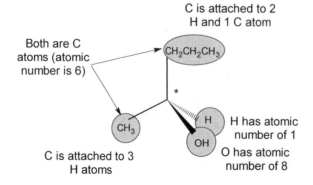

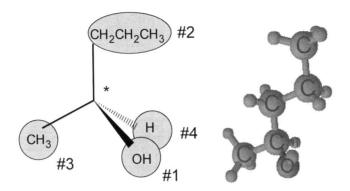

The group with the lowest priority is behind the stereocenter. You do not need to rotate the molecule.

Step 4: Assign R or S

The lowest priority group (#4) is behind the page.

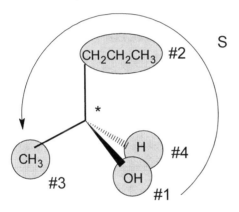

Since the order is counterclockwise, the configuration is S.

Conformational Isomers (Conformers)

- Atoms have same connectivity, but different rotation around the single bond

Newman projections

- Newman projection represents spatial arrangement of atoms around 2 bonded atoms

Look this way ⟶ Front H H Cl Back

Cl H H

Dash-wedged representation

This is the same as:

Cl Back C atom
H H
H H
Front C atom
Cl

Cl Back C atom
H H
H H
Cl

Newman projection

Look this way ⟶ Cl Cl
Front H H H H Back

Dash-wedged representation

This is the same as:

Cl Back C atom
ClH
H H
Front C atom

ClCl Back C atom
Front C atom
H H
H H

Newman projection

Surviving University: First Year Chemistry

- There are 2 conformations: **staggered** and **eclipsed**

Conformation	Newman Projection	Energy
Staggered		Lower energy
Eclipsed		Higher energy (atoms are closer together→ repulse each other)

  o In order to convert between the 2 conformations, 1 of the atoms involved in a single bond needs to be rotated by 60°

Rotate by 60°

Eclipsed   Staggered

Part 15

Hydrocarbons

Catenation

Saturated vs unsaturated

Types of hydrocarbons

Stability of hydrocarbons

Physical properties of

hydrocarbons

Benzene

Hückel's rule

Aromaticity

Derivatives of benzene

Surviving University: First Year Chemistry

Hydrocarbons

- Hydrocarbons are composed of hydrogen and carbon atoms
  - Carbon needs to have an octet→ can make 4 covalent bonds
  - Hydrogen can make 1 covalent bond

$$H\text{—}\underset{\underset{H}{|}}{\overset{\overset{H}{|}}{C}}\text{—}H$$

Ex. Methane

Catenation of carbon

Catenation- ability of an element to form long chains of covalent bonds
- Carbon is capable of catenation

Ex. Decane

Note: by convention, H atoms are not shown. Each corner represents a C atom. Some H atoms are not shown. Since C can make 4 bonds, C at each corner is bonded to 2 H atoms.

Saturated vs unsaturated

Saturated hydrocarbons- all bonds are single bonds
- Maximum amount of hydrogen atoms is present

Ex. Heptane

Unsaturated hydrocarbons- there are some double or triple bonds
- Have less than the maximum amount of hydrogen atoms

Ex. 2,5-heptadiene

Types of hydrocarbons

Type	Structure	General formula	Saturated?	Isomerism
Alkane	$R_3C\text{---}CR_3$	C_nH_{2n+2}	yes	Conformational
Alkene	$R_2C{=}CR_2$ Cis R R Trans R R	C_nH_{2n}	No	Conformational Cis/trans
Alkyne	$RC{\equiv}CR$	C_nH_{2n-2}	No	Conformational
Cycloalkane	Single bond, cyclic structure	C_nH_{2n}	Yes	Conformational
Cycloalkene	1 or more double bonds, cyclic structure	-	No	Conformational Cis/trans
Cycloalkyne	1 or more triple bonds, cyclic structure	-	No	Conformational
Aromatic	Alternating - and = bonds Ex. Benzene (C_6H_6)	-	No	Conformational Cis/trans

Surviving University: First Year Chemistry

Stability of hydrocarbons

- Hydrocarbons are stable molecules
    - Much energy is needed to break apart C-C and C-H covalent bonds
    - Hydrocarbons are nonpolar molecules and have low reactivity
        - Since hydrocarbons are less likely to react, they are stable

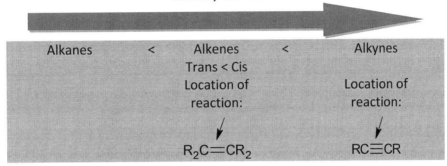

Reactivity increases
Stability decreases

Alkanes	<	Alkenes	<	Alkynes
		Trans < Cis		
		Location of reaction:		Location of reaction:
		$R_2C = CR_2$		$RC \equiv CR$

- Trans vs Cis
    - Cis alkenes are less stable than trans alkenes due to steric strain
        - **Steric strain**- unfavourable repulsion of electrons of substituent groups
            - Causes molecule to become less stable→ less energy is needed to break apart the covalent bonds→ molecule is more reactive

Cis

Electrons of substituents are close together- repulse each other

Trans

Electrons of substituents are far away- do not repulse each other as much

Physical properties of hydrocarbons

- Strength of intermolecular forces dictate physical properties
  - State of a substance, its melting point, and its boiling point
- Intermolecular forces present in hydrocarbons
  - London dispersion forces
    - Temporary attraction between nucleus of 1 molecule and electrons of another molecule
    - This results distortion of e⁻ cloud of a molecule
  - Smaller molecules have weaker intermolecular forces
    - There are fewer electrons to be distorted→ weaker London dispersion forces
  - Larger molecules have stronger intermolecular forces
    - There are more electrons to be distorted→ stronger London dispersion forces
- State
  - Smaller molecules= weaker intermolecular forces= gas state at room temperature

# C	
1	Methane
2	Ethane
3	Propane
4	Butane

  - Larger molecules= stronger intermolecular forces (London dispersion forces)= liquid state at room temperature

# C	
5	Pentane
6	Hexane
7	Heptane
8	Octane
9	Nonane
10	Decane

  - Long chained hydrocarbons are in solid state at room temperature
    - Ex. Eicosane (20 C atoms)
- Molecular mass
  - As # of C ↑, molecular mass ↑
    - Ex. Decane has more mass than pentane

Surviving University: First Year Chemistry

- Density
  - As # of C ↑, density ↑
    - $Density = \frac{Mass}{Volume}$
    - As # of C ↑, molecular mass ↑. Since density is proportional to molecular mass, density also ↑.
- Melting and boiling points
  - Overall, hydrocarbons have very low melting and boiling points
    - London dispersion forces are weak→ not much energy is needed to break intermolecular forces
  - As chain length ↑, melting and boiling points ↑
    - Larger molecules= stronger intermolecular forces
      - Larger molecule has more C atoms→ has ↑ amount of e⁻, ↑ polarizability, and stronger London-dispersion forces
      - More energy is needed to break apart its intermolecular forces
    - Ex. Pentane has a higher boiling point than methane
  - *Cis* has lower melting point than *trans*
    - When stacked on top of each other, *trans* isomers stack closer together than *cis* isomers→ more energy is needed to separate *trans* molecules

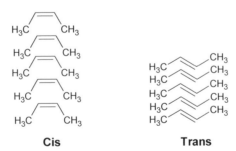

Cis   **Trans**

  - *Cis* has higher boiling point than *trans*
    - *Cis* isomer has dipole-dipole forces and London dispersion forces
    - *Trans* isomer has London dispersion forces
    - More energy is needed to separate molecules in *cis* than *trans* forms

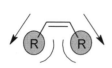
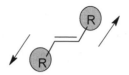

Cis

Trans

There is a net dipole moment

There is no net dipole moment

(forces add together)

(all forces cancel out)

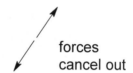

net force

forces cancel out

- Polarity
  - Hydrocarbons are nonpolar molecules
    - There is no dipole moment→ all forces cancel out

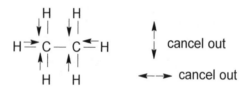

cancel out

cancel out

- Solubility
  - "Like dissolves like"
    - Non-polar substances dissolve in non-polar substances
      - Hydrocarbons are insoluble in water!

Example 1
Which of the following has the highest boiling point? Lowest melting point? Highest molecular mass?

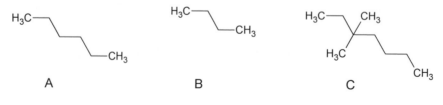

A

B

C

Molecule	# C atoms	Intermolecular forces
A	6	London dispersion
B	4	London dispersion
C	9	London dispersion

- The molecule with the highest boiling point has the highest amount of intermolecular forces. As chain length increases, the strength of London dispersion forces increases.
    - Since molecule C is the longest, it has the highest boiling point.
- The molecule with the lowest melting point has the weakest intermolecular forces. As chain length decreases, the strength of London dispersion forces decreases.
    - Since molecule B is the shortest, it has the lowest melting point.
- The molecule with highest molecular mass has the most amount of C and H atoms→ molecule C.

Example 2
Which of the following has the highest boiling point?

A   B

Molecule	# C atoms	Intermolecular forces
A (trans)	4	London dispersion
B (cis)	4	London dispersion Dipole-dipole

- Both molecules have the same chain length
- When stacked on top of each other, *trans* isomers stack closer together than *cis* isomers→ more energy is needed to separate *trans* molecules
    - This means than molecule A has a higher boiling point than molecule B

Aromatic compounds

- Aromatic compounds have 1 or more benzene rings

Benzene   Ex. Phenalene

Benzene

- Benzene ring consists of 6C atoms
- C atoms are joined by bonds which are neither single nor double→ they have an intermediate length
  - Bond order is 1.5
    - Bond order for single bond is 1
    - Bond order for double bond is 2
- There are 2 resonance structures for benzene→ the actual benzene molecule looks like the resonance hybrid

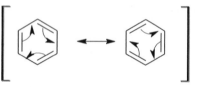

Resonance   Resonance hybrid
structures

- Every C atom in the ring has sp^2 hybridization and has an unhybridized p orbital
  - There are 6 C atoms→ 6 unhybridized p orbitals
  - The ring is planar, p orbitals are perpendicular to the ring
    - p orbitals overlap→ form a continuous e⁻ cloud (continuous p orbital system)
    - 6 π e⁻ are delocalized (spread) throughout the p orbital system
      - Electrons do not belong to specific atoms

Surviving University: First Year Chemistry

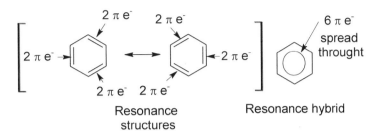

Resonance
structures

Resonance hybrid

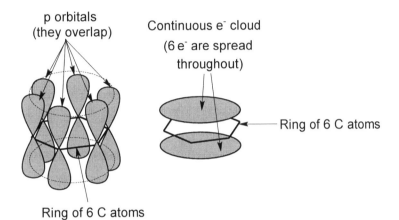

1 lobe of each p orbital is
above the ring, 1 lobe is
below the ring

- Benzene has very low reactivity
  - It is stable and does not undergo addition reactions

Hückel's rule

- Is used to predict whether a molecule is aromatic→ whether it has physical properties of benzene
- Is used for

Monocyclic
molecules

Polycyclic
molecules

Heterocyclic
molecules

(multiple
rings)

(1 or more atoms
in the ring is not C)

- o Is used for **cyclic conjugated compounds** (compounds which have a ring of alternating single and double bonds)
- Count the number of π electrons that ring(s) in a molecule contain(s)

> If the number of π electrons in the ring(s) and free available pairs of a molecule= 4n+2, then the molecule has aromatic properties
>
> n is an integer (n= 0, 1, 2, 3, ...)

n	# e⁻
0	4(0)+2= 2
1	4(1)+2= 6
2	4(2)+2= 10
3	4(3)+2= 14
...	4n+2

- So, if molecule has 2 π e⁻, 6 π e⁻, 10 π e⁻, 14 π e⁻, or etc. , then it is aromatic

> If the number of π electrons does not equal to 4n+2, then the molecule is not aromatic

Aromaticity

- In order for a molecule to be aromatic, it must satisfy the following 4 conditions
    - o The molecule is cyclic
        - The molecule has a ring structure
    - o The molecule is planar
        - All atoms in the molecule lie on one plane
        - Every atom of the ring has sp^2 hybridization
    - o The bonds in a molecule are conjugated
        - Every atom of the ring has π electrons
    - o The molecule satisfies the Hückel's rule
        - The number of π electrons in the molecule is 4n+2
            - Where n is an integer

Example 1
Is the following molecule aromatic?

In order for this molecule to be aromatic, it must satisfy these conditions

Surviving University: First Year Chemistry

☐ The molecule is cyclic
☐ The molecule is planar
☐ The bonds in a molecule are conjugated
☐ The molecule satisfies the Hückel's rule

☑ The molecule is cyclic

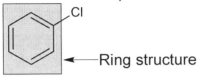

←— Ring structure

☑ The molecule is planar
The benzene ring is planar.

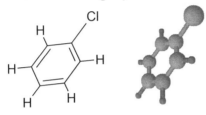

☑ The bonds in a molecule are conjugated
The molecule has alternating single and double bonds→ every C atom has a p orbital.

p orbitals
(they overlap)

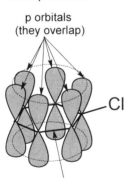

Ring of 6 C atoms

☑ The molecule satisfies the Hückel's rule

$2 \pi e^-$
Cl
$2 \pi e^-$ →

Total: $6 \pi e^-$

$2 \pi e^-$

$6 \pi e^-$ corresponds to n=1→ 4(1)+2= 6 e^-

Since this molecule satisfies the 4 conditions, it is aromatic.

Example 2
Is the following molecule aromatic?

☑ The molecule is cyclic

 ←——Ring structure

☑ The molecule is planar

☑ The bonds in a molecule are conjugated
The molecule has alternating single and double bonds→ every C atom has a p orbital.

p orbitals
(they overlap)

Ring of 4 C atoms

☐ The molecule satisfies the Hückel's rule

$2 \pi e^-$ ← 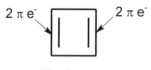 → $2 \pi e^-$

Total: $4 \pi e^-$

$4\pi e^-$ corresponds to n=0.5→ 4(0.5)+2= 4 e^-
However, n cannot be a fraction→ n has to be an integer (0, 1, 2, 3, …)
Since this molecule does not satisfy the Hückel's rule, it is not aromatic.

Surviving University: First Year Chemistry

Derivatives of benzene

- Aromatic compounds can have 1 or more substituents

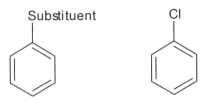

ex. chlorobenzene

- If 2 substituents are present→ *ortho, meta, or para* prefixes are used

Prefix		Drawing
Ortho (o)	▪ First substituent is on C1 ▪ Second substituent is on C2	ex. *ortho-dichlorobenzene*
Meta (m)	▪ First substituent is on C1 ▪ Second substituent is on C3	ex. *meta-dichlorobenzene*
Para (p)	▪ First substituent is on C1 ▪ Second substituent is on C4	ex. *para-dichlorobenzene*

Surviving University: First Year Chemistry

Part 16

Functional Groups

Summary of functional groups

Alcohols

Phenols

Aldehydes and ketones

Tautomerism

Carboxylic acids

Functional groups

- **Organic molecules** are used by all living organisms
- **Functional group** is a part of a molecule where chemical reactions usually occur
    - ○ Functional groups can contain C, H, S, O, Cl, Br, I, N

Summary of functional groups

Note: R stands for the rest of the molecule→ it begins with a C atom
Note: X stands for a halogen (F, Br, Cl, or I)

Name of functional group	Drawing
Alkyl halide	R—X **Haloalkane**- alkane which contains a halogen **Haloalkene**- alkene which contains a halogen **Haloalkyne**- alkyne which contains a halogen
Alcohol	**Primary alcohol**- C atom which is attached to –OH is also attached to 1 C atom H—C(H)(R)—OH **Secondary alcohol**- C atom which is attached to –OH is also attached to 2 C atoms H—C(R)(R)—OH **Tertiary alcohol**- C atom which is attached to –OH is also attached to 3 C atoms R—C(R)(R)—OH
Amine	R—N(R)—R (with lone pair)
Thiol	R—SH
Ether	R—O—R

Surviving University: First Year Chemistry

Phenol	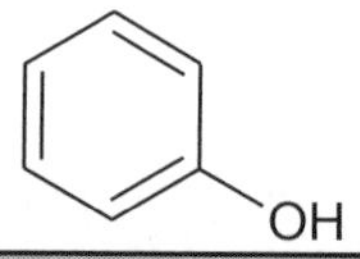
Aldehyde	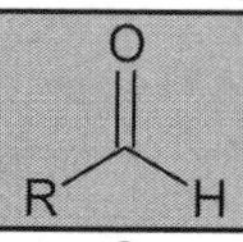
Ketone	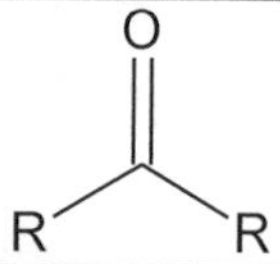
Acid halide	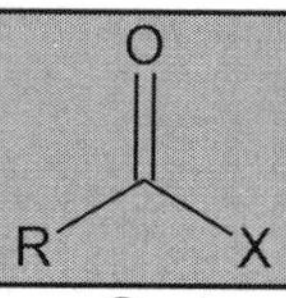
Carboxylic acid	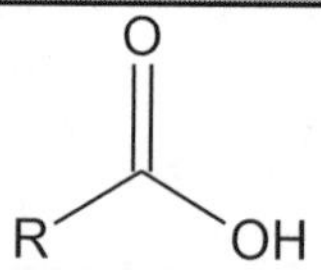
Ester	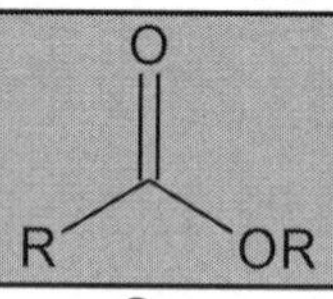
Amide	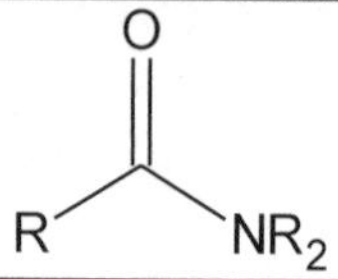
Imine	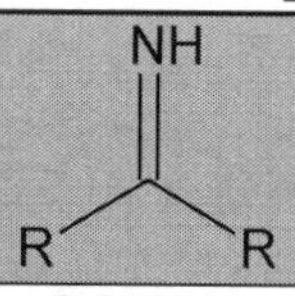
Nitrile	RC≡N

Alcohols

Classification of alcohols

Class	Description	Example
Primary alcohol	C atom which is attached to –OH is also attached to 1 C atom $$\underset{\underset{\displaystyle H}{\mid}}{\overset{\overset{\displaystyle R}{\mid}}{H{-}{\overset{\mid}{}}{-}OH}}$$	$$\underset{\underset{\displaystyle H}{\mid}}{\overset{\overset{\displaystyle CH_3}{\mid}}{H{-}{\overset{\mid}{}}{-}OH}}$$
Secondary alcohol	C atom which is attached to –OH is also attached to 2 C atoms $$\underset{\underset{\displaystyle R}{\mid}}{\overset{\overset{\displaystyle R}{\mid}}{H{-}{\overset{\mid}{}}{-}OH}}$$	$$\underset{\underset{\displaystyle CH_3}{\mid}}{\overset{\overset{\displaystyle CH_3}{\mid}}{H{-}{\overset{\mid}{}}{-}OH}}$$
Tertiary alcohol	C atom which is attached to –OH is also attached to 3 C atoms $$\underset{\underset{\displaystyle R}{\mid}}{\overset{\overset{\displaystyle R}{\mid}}{R{-}{\overset{\mid}{}}{-}OH}}$$	$$\underset{\underset{\displaystyle CH_3}{\mid}}{\overset{\overset{\displaystyle CH_3}{\mid}}{H_3C{-}{\overset{\mid}{}}{-}OH}}$$

Note: R stands for the rest of the molecule→ it begins with a C atom

Physical properties of alcohols

- Intermolecular forces present in alcohols
  - London dispersion forces
    - Temporary attraction between nucleus of 1 molecule and electrons of another molecule
    - This results distortion of e^- cloud of a molecule
  - Dipole-dipole forces
    - O atom is more electronegative than C atom→ e^- are pulled towards O atom→ electrons spend more time around oxygen atom (δ^-) than C atom (δ^+)
      - There is a higher electron density around the O atom

$$\underset{\delta^-}{\overset{\displaystyle \underset{\delta^+}{R}\diagdown\, O\,\diagup H}{}}$$

- Uneven distribution of e⁻ causes O atom to be δ^- and C atom to be δ^+

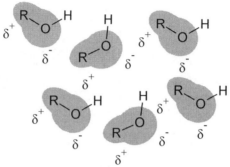

- o Hydrogen bonding
  - H atom which is attached to O of 1 molecule is attracted to O of another molecule

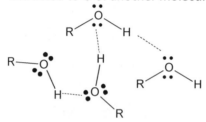

- Solubility
  - o Alcohols are polar substances
    - Alcohols have uneven distribution of e⁻ between C and O atoms
  - o Small alcohols are soluble in polar substances (ex. water)
    - Small alcohols can form strong H bonding, dipole-dipole, and London dispersion forces with polar substances

 Polar end

- H bonding

- Dipole-dipole

- London dispersion

  - o Large alcohols (>6 C atoms) are <u>not</u> soluble in polar substances→ they are soluble in non-polar substances
    - As chain length increases, alcohols have more alkane-like properties→ are less soluble in polar substances

S u r v i v i n g   U n i v e r s i t y :   F i r s t   Y e a r   C h e m i s t r y

- As chain length increases, the strength of H bonds and dipole-dipole forces decreases and the strength of London dispersion forces increases
  - The predominant intermolecular force is London dispersion force

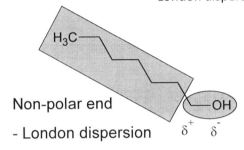

Non-polar end

- London dispersion

Polar end

- H bonding

- Dipole-dipole

- London dispersion

- Melting and boiling points
  - As chain length ↑, melting and boiling points ↑
    - Larger molecules= stronger intermolecular forces
      - Larger molecule has more C atoms→ has ↑ amount of e⁻, ↑ polarizability, and stronger London-dispersion forces
      - More energy is needed to break apart its intermolecular forces
  - Alcohols have higher melting and boiling points than hydrocarbons (alkanes, alkenes, alkynes) with the same number of C atoms
    - Alcohols have stronger intermolecular forces→ more energy is needed to separate molecules

- H bonding

- Dipole-dipole

- London dispersion

Alcohol

H₃C —H - London dispersion

Hydrocarbon

Example 1
Which of the following has a higher boiling point?

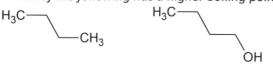

A   B

Molecule	Class	# C atoms	Intermolecular forces
A	Alkane	4	▪ London dispersion forces
B	Alcohol	4	▪ H bonding ▪ Dipole-Dipole forces ▪ London dispersion forces

- Both of these molecules have the same C length
- The molecule with the highest boiling point has the strongest intermolecular forces
    - Alcohol (molecule B) has the strongest intermolecular forces→ it has the highest boiling point

Alcohols in acid-base reactions

- Alcohols are **amphiprotic**
    - They can act as weak acids (donate H^+) or weak bases (accept H^+)

Alcohol acting as a weak acid

$$H_3C—OH \; + \; H_2O \; \rightleftharpoons \; H_3C—O^- \; + \; H_3O^+$$

Acid   Base   Conjugate   Conjugate
                         base   acid

(donates H^+) (accepts H^+)

                       alkoxide   **hydronium**
                         ion   **ion**

Alcohol acting as a weak base

$$H_3C—OH \; + \; H_2O \; \rightleftharpoons \; H_3C—OH_2^+ \; + \; HO^-$$

Base   Acid   Conjugate   Conjugate
                         acid   base

(accepts H^+) (donates H^+)

                       alkyloxonium hydroxide
                           ion   **ion**

Surviving University: First Year Chemistry

Content:

Phenols

- Phenols consist of benzene ring(s) attached to –OH group(s)

Ex. Phenol   p- ethylphenol   *m- chlorophenol*

Phenols in acid-base reactions

- Phenols can act as weak acids (donate H^+)

Acid + H_2O ⇌ Conjugate base + H_3O^+

(donates H^+) (accepts H^+)   phenoxide ion   hydronium ion

- Phenoxide ion has several resonance structures
  - The actual structure of phenoxide is a resonance hybrid (a combination of all of the resonance structures)
    - 1 pair of e^- is delocalized (spread out) throughout the molecule

Aldehydes and Ketones

Reactivity of aldehydes and ketones

- O atom is more electronegative than C atom
  - This results in electrons being pulled towards O atom and away from C atom→ electrons spend more time around oxygen atom (δ^-) than C atom (δ^+)

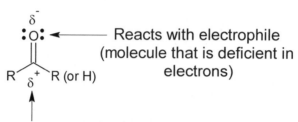

- For more information about nucleophiles and electrophiles, see part 17 of this book

Enol-keto equilibrium (tautomerism)

- There is an equilibrium between 2 **tautomers** (enol form and keto form)
  - Keto form is rapidly converted into enol form and enol form is rapidly converted into keto form

Tautomerization- the process of interconverting of tautomers (from enol form to keto form and vice versa)

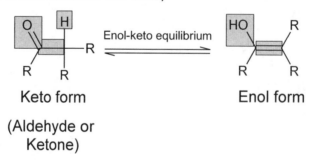

- Tautomerization requires a catalyst (an acid or a base)

Surviving University: First Year Chemistry

Carboxylic Acids

Intermolecular forces present in carboxylic acids

- London dispersion forces
    - Temporary attraction between nucleus of 1 molecule and electrons of another molecule
    - This results distortion of e⁻ cloud of a molecule
- Dipole-dipole forces
    - O atom is more electronegative than C atom→ e⁻ are pulled towards O atom→ electrons spend more time around oxygen atom (δ^-) than C atom (δ^+)
        - There is a higher electron density around the O atom

- Uneven distribution of e⁻ causes O atom to be δ^- and C and H atoms to be δ^+

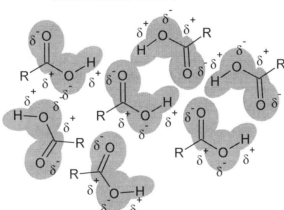

- Hydrogen bonding
    - H atom which is attached to O of 1 molecule is attracted to O of another molecule

o In non-polar solutions, 2 carboxylic acid molecules can form
2 H bonds between each other to form dimers

Solubility of carboxylic acids

- Carboxylic acids are polar substances
   o Carboxylic acids have uneven distribution of e⁻ between C
   and O atoms and between H and O atoms
- Carboxylic acids are soluble in polar substances (ex. water)
   o They can form strong H bonding, dipole-dipole, and London
   dispersion forces with polar substances

Acidity of carboxylic acids

- Carboxylic acids are weak acids and can act as proton (H^+) donors

Carboxylic acid   Carboxylate ion

Surviving University: First Year Chemistry

- Carboxylate ion has several resonance structures

Carboxylate ion   Resonance hybrid

Part 17

Organic Chemistry Reactions

Addition reactions

Elimination reactions

Substitution reactions (SN1, SN2)

Nucleophile

Electrophile

Reactions of benzene

Nucleophilic addition of aldehydes

and ketones

Oxidation reactions

Reduction reactions

Esterification reaction

Hydrolysis reaction

Addition Reactions

- Addition reactions occur in unsaturated compounds (compounds which contain double or triple bonds)
    - Produce saturated compounds (have single bonds)

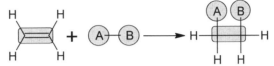

- 2 molecules produce 1 molecule
    - Double bond is replaced with a single bond
    - 1 substituent is added to 1 C atom
    - 2nd substituent is added to another C atom

Examples

A—B	Reaction	Produces
H—H		Alkane
Cl—Cl		Haloalkane
Br—Br		Haloalkane
H—Cl		Haloalkane
H—Br		Haloalkane
H₂O H—OH		Alcohol

Surviving University: First Year Chemistry

- Elimination reactions occur in saturated compounds (compounds which contain single bonds)
  - Produce unsaturated compounds (compounds which contain double or triple bonds)

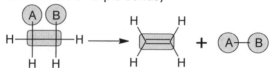

- 1 molecule produces 2 molecule
  - Single bond is replaced with a double bond
  - 2 substituents are removed from a molecule→ join together to form a new molecule

Examples

A—B	Reaction	Produces
H—H		Alkene H$_2$
Cl—Cl		Alkene Cl$_2$
Br—Br		Alkene Br$_2$
H—Cl		Alkene HCl
H—Br		Alkene HBr
H$_2$O H—OH		Alkene H$_2$O

Surviving University: First Year Chemistry

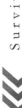

Substitution Reactions

- An atom in a molecule is replaced by another atom/molecule
- **Nucleophile** attacks **electrophile**
  - o Area which is rich in electrons (-ive) of 1 molecule attacks area which is deficient in electrons (+ive) of another molecule

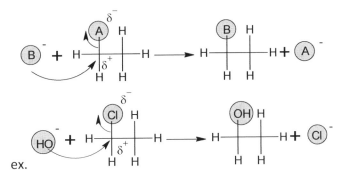

ex.

Nucleophile

- Is a molecule that has unshared pairs of e$^-$ or e$^-$ within π bonds
  - o e$^-$ are found within π bonds in single and double bonds
- Is a Lewis base
  - o Nucleophile donates a pair of electrons to a Lewis acid (electrophile)
- Often has a negative or partial negative (δ$^-$) charge
  - o δ$^-$ is due to the difference in electron density between adjacent atoms
    - Electrons spend more time around δ$^-$ atom
    - Shared electrons are pulled away from δ$^+$ atom towards δ$^-$ atom
- Nucleophile is attracted to positive charge
  - o Nucleo= nucleus (+ive)
  - o Phile= loving

Common nucleophiles
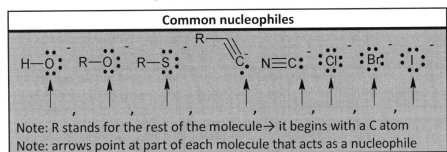
Note: R stands for the rest of the molecule→ it begins with a C atom
Note: arrows point at part of each molecule that acts as a nucleophile

Electrophile

- Is a molecule that is deficient in e⁻
  - Often, an atom does not have a full octet
- Is a Lewis acid
  - Electrophile accepts a pair of electrons from a Lewis base (nucleophile)→ forms a covalent bond
- Often has a positive or partial positive (δ^+) charge
  - δ^+ is due to the difference in electron density between adjacent atoms
    - Electrons spend more time around δ^- atom
    - Shared electrons are pulled away from δ^+ atom towards δ^- atom
- Is attracted to negative charge
  - Electro= electron (-ive)
  - Phile= loving

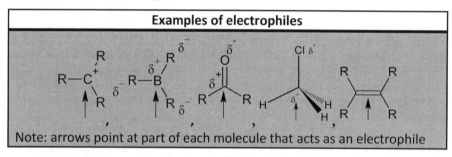

Examples of electrophiles
Note: arrows point at part of each molecule that acts as an electrophile

Interaction between a nucleophile and electrophile

Nucleophile Electrophile

Types of substitution reactions

- There are 2 types of substitution reactions: SN1 and SN2

	SN1	**SN2**
Name	▪ Unimolecular nucleophilic substitution	▪ Bimolecular nucleophilic substitution
# of steps	▪ 2 steps	▪ 1 step
Stereochemistry	▪ There is no inversion of	▪ There is inversion

	configuration	of configuration	
		Reactant	**Product**
		R	S
		S	R

Reaction mechanism of SN1

Reaction mechanism- shows how a reaction occurs at the molecular level

- SN1 occurs in 2 steps
- Step 1: Formation of carbocation

  - **Carbocation** is a carbonium ion ($R-\overset{R}{\underset{R}{C^+}}$)
  - Carbocation has a planar arrangement (all atoms are on the plane of the page)

$$\delta^- \;\; \overset{..}{\underset{..}{:Cl:}} \qquad \rightleftharpoons \qquad R-\overset{R}{\underset{R}{C^+}} \;+\; \overset{..}{\underset{..}{:Cl:}}^-$$

$$R^{\cdots\overset{+}{\underset{\delta}{|}}}R$$

Carbocation

- Step 2: Attack of carbocation by nucleophile
  - Carbocation acts as an electrophile

$$R-\overset{R}{\underset{R}{C^+}} \;+\; \boxed{H-\overset{..}{\underset{..}{O}}{:}^-} \longrightarrow R-\overset{R}{\underset{R}{\overset{|}{\underset{|}{C}}}}-\boxed{\overset{..}{\underset{..}{OH}}}$$

Electrophile   Nucleophile

Example 1
The following reacts via Sn1. Show the reaction mechanism for this reaction.

$$H_3C-\overset{CH_3}{\underset{CH_3}{\overset{|}{\underset{|}{C}}}}-Br \;+\; H_3C-O^- \longrightarrow$$

In order to write down mechanism, it is necessary to know which molecule acts as a nucleophile and which acts as an electrophile.

Electrophile

δ^+ part of the molecule is electron deficient

Nucleophile

δ^- part of the molecule is electron rich

Step 1: Formation of carbocation

Carbocation

Step 2: Attack of carbocation by nucleophile

Electrophile Nucleophile

SN1 reaction of alkenes

- In alkenes, the e^- are found within π bond of double bond
    - The double bond of alkenes acts as an electrophile

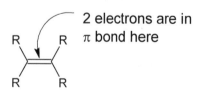

2 electrons are in
π bond here

- The following shows the same molecule

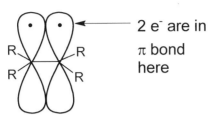

2 e⁻ are in π bond here

- Step 1: formation of carbocation

    - The structure of carbocation which alkene forms is

This is the same as

- Step 2: Attack of carbocation by nucleophile
    - Carbocation acts as an electrophile
    - Since carbocation is planar, nucleophile can attack from the top or from the bottom
        - This can result in a **racemic mixture**
            - 50% of the molecules in the mixture have an R configuration and 50% of the molecules have an S configuration

If nucleophile attacks from the top

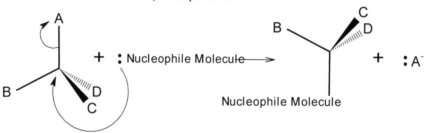

From step 1

Electrophile Nucleophile

If nucleophile attacks from the bottom

From step 1

Electrophile Nucleophile

Reaction mechanism of SN2

- SN2 occurs in 1 step
- This reaction results in inversion of configuration
    - If reactant is R, then product is S
    - If reactant is S, then product is R

R configuration   S configuration

Example 1
The following reacts via Sn1. Show the reaction mechanism for this reaction.

Surviving University: First Year Chemistry

In order to write down mechanism, it is necessary to know which molecule acts as a nucleophile and which acts as an electrophile.

Electrophile

δ^+ part of the molecule is electron deficient

Nucleophile

δ^- part of the molecule is electron rich

Electrophile   Nucleophile

Now, let's assign configurations.

Surviving University: First Year Chemistry

Reactant

Product

S configuration

R configuration

C atom is attached to 4 different substituents→ it is chiral. Since Cl has the highest molecular mass, it has priority of 1. There are 2 C atoms attached to the chiral C. First C in CH_2CH_3 is attached to 2 H atoms and 1 C atom. C in CH_3 is attached to 3 H atoms. Since 2 H atoms and 1 C atom have higher molecular mass than 3 H atoms, CH_2CH_3 has higher priority than CH_3. H has the lowest molecular mass→ it has priority of 4.
There is an inversion of configuration.
Thus,

Electrophile   Nucleophile

R configuration

S configuration

Surviving University: First Year Chemistry

Reactions of benzene

- Benzene is not very reactive
- Benzene commonly reacts via substitution reactions

Electrophilic aromatic substitution

- Hydrogen that is a part of aromatic ring is replaced by an electrophile

- Once electrophile is added to benzene, the molecule becomes more reactive→ other reactions can occur

Examples

E^+	Reaction name	Reaction
Cl^+ Br^+	Halogenation	Note: Cl^+ is from Cl_2 Note: Br^+ is from Br_2
HSO_3	Sulfonation	Note: HSO_3 is from H_2SO_4

Surviving University: First Year Chemistry

NO$_2^+$	Nitration	

Note: NO$_2^+$ is from HNO$_3$

R$^+$	Alkylation	

Note: R$^+$ is from RCl or ROH

Note: H$_3$C——CH$_2^+$ is from H$_3$C——OH

Ex.

O=C$^+$—R	Acylation	

Note: O=C$^+$—R is from O=C(Cl)—R or R—C(=O)—O—C(=O)—R

Surviving University: First Year Chemistry

Nucleophilic Addition of Aldehydes and Ketones

- Double bond between C and O atoms is broken
    - o   H atom is added to O atom
    - o   Nucleophile is added to C atom
- Note: see substitution reactions section of this part of the book for explanation about nucleophiles

Reaction mechanism of nucleophilic addition

- The mechanism depends on pH
    - o   The mechanism is different under basic and acidic conditions
        - ▪   In both cases, the same product is produced
- Nucleophile attacks electrophile at its weak point (at δ^+)
    - o   Oxygen in C=O can be replaced by other atoms (ex. C=Cl)
        - ▪   The more electronegative the atom is→ ↑ δ^+→ more reactive electrophile
- Note: the mechanism below is shown for ketones→ the same mechanism applies for aldehydes

Under acidic conditions

Ketone   Acid

1. Ketone becomes protonated

2. Nucleophile attacks protonated ketone

Under basic conditions

Ketone   Base

1. Nucleophile attacks ketone (nucleophile serves as base)

2. Molecule attacks acid

Surviving University: First Year Chemistry

Oxidation Reactions

- The density of e⁻ around C atom decreases
- Oxidation is the
  - Loss of e⁻
  - Loss of H atom(s)
  - Gain of O atom(s)

Oxidation of alcohols

- 2 H atoms are removed, double bond is formed between C and O atoms

Class of alcohol	Reaction	Produces
Primary	OH — R—C—H, H $\xrightarrow{\text{oxidation}}$ O=C, R H	Aldehyde
Secondary	OH — R—C—R, H $\xrightarrow{\text{oxidation}}$ O=C, R R	Ketone
Tertiary	OH — R—C—R, R $\xrightarrow{\text{oxidation}}$ No reaction Do not undergo oxidation reaction (do not have 2 H atoms to be removed)	-

Oxidation of aldehyde

- O atom is added to the molecule

Molecule	Reaction	Produces
Aldehyde	O=C, R H $\xrightarrow{\text{oxidation}}$ O=C, R OH	Carboxylic acid

Surviving University: First Year Chemistry

Reduction Reactions

- The density of e⁻ around C atom decreases
- Reduction is the
  - Gain of e⁻
  - Gain of H atom(s)
  - Loss of O atom(s)

Reduction of carbonyl group ($\overset{O}{\overset{||}{C}}$)

Molecule	Reaction	Produces
Aldehyde	(reduction)	Primary alcohol
Ketone	(reduction)	Secondary alcohol

Reduction of carbonyl ($\overset{O}{\overset{||}{C}}$) and hydroxide (-OH) groups

Molecule	Reaction	Produces
Carboxylic acid	(reduction)	Primary alcohol
Ester	(reduction)	Secondary alcohol

Surviving University: First Year, Chemistry

Esterification Reaction

- The process of formation of ester from carboxylic acid and alcohol

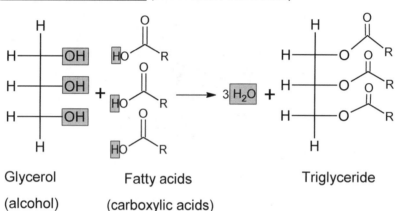

Formation of triglyceride (under acidic conditions)

Glycerol

(alcohol)

Fatty acids

(carboxylic acids)

Triglyceride

Surviving University: First Year Chemistry

Hydrolysis Reaction

- The process of breakdown of ester into carboxylic acid and alcohol

ex.

Breakdown of triglyceride (under basic conditions)

Triglyceride

Glycerol
(alcohol)

Fatty acids
(carboxylic acids)

Part 18

Drawing and Naming Organic Molecules

Drawing organic molecules

Kekulé notation

Lewis notation

Condensed notation

Bond-line notation

Dash-wedged notation

Naming organic molecules

Hydrocarbons

Surviving University: First Year Chemistry

Drawing Organic Molecules

Conventions for drawing

Notation	Example	Details
Kekulé	H–C–C–C–C–H (butane with all H shown), CH₃CH₂CHClCH₃ with Cl lone pairs shown, and an alkene/alcohol structure	<ul><li>All H atoms are shown</li><li>Each line represents 2 bonded e⁻</li><li>Valence electrons which are not bonded are shown</li></ul>
Lewis	Dot structures showing all bonding and non-bonding electrons	<ul><li>All H atoms are shown</li><li>Bonded e⁻ are shown</li><li>Valence electrons which are not bonded are shown</li></ul>
Condensed	$CH_3CH_2CH_2CH_3$ $CH_3CH_2CHClCH_3$ (with Cl shown above)	<ul><li>All H atoms are shown</li><li>Some bonds are shown using lines</li><li>Valence electrons which are not bonded are not shown</li></ul>

Surviving University: First Year Chemistry

	$CH_2{=}CHCCH_3$ (with O double-bonded above the third C)	
Bond-line		■ H atoms bonded to C are not shown ■ H atoms bonded to any atom that is not C are shown ■ Each corner represents a C atom ■ Each end has a C atom ■ Bonded e⁻ are shown using lines ■ No valence electrons are shown
Dash-wedged		■ Shows structure in 3 dimensions ■ All H atoms are shown ■ Each line represents 2 bonded e⁻ ■ Valence electrons which are not bonded are shown

Naming Organic Molecules

Hydrocarbons

- Use these steps to name
  - Alkanes
  - Alkenes
  - Alkynes
  - Cyclic hydrocarbons

Steps for naming
1. Find the longest chain
2. Use prefix for # of carbons in the longest chain

# carbons	Prefix	Drawing for an alkane
1	meth	CH_4
2	eth	H_3C—CH_3
3	prop	H_3C⋀CH_3
4	but	H_3C⋀⋀CH_3
5	pent	H_3C⋀⋀⋀CH_3
6	hex	H_3C⋀⋀⋀⋀CH_3
7	hept	H_3C⋀⋀⋀⋀⋀CH_3
8	oct	H_3C⋀⋀⋀⋀⋀⋀CH_3
9	non	H_3C⋀⋀⋀⋀⋀⋀⋀CH_3
10	dec	H_3C⋀⋀⋀⋀⋀⋀⋀⋀CH_3
20	eicos	H_3C⋀⋀⋀⋀⋀⋀⋀⋀⋀⋀⋀⋀⋀⋀⋀⋀⋀⋀CH_3

3. Number carbons (ex. C_1, C_2, C_3, etc.)→ start at the side with double or triple bonds or functional groups. Substituents need to be on C atoms with lowers numbers.
4. Write functional group names in <u>alphabetical order</u>. Functional groups go before the prefix.

# C	Prefix	Drawing for a functional group
	phenyl	⬡—Attached
1	methyl	H_3C—Attachec
2	ethyl	H_3C⌒Attached
3	propyl	H_3C⌒⌒Attached
3	isopropyl	H_3C / —CH_3 / Attached
4	n-butyl	H_3C⌒⌒⌒Attached
4	sec-butyl	Attachec / H_3C—⌒—CH_3
4	isobutyl	CH_3 / H_3C—⌒ / —Attachec
4	tert-butyl	H_3C —CH_3 / H_3C Attachec
5	pentyl	H_3C⌒⌒⌒⌒Attached
6	hexyl	H_3C⌒⌒⌒⌒⌒Attached
7	heptyl	H_3C⌒⌒⌒⌒⌒⌒Attached
8	octyl	H_3C⌒⌒⌒⌒⌒⌒⌒Attached

| 9 | nonyl | H₃C /\/\/\/\/ Attached |
| 10 | decyl | H₃C /\/\/\/\/\ Attachec |

5. If more than 1 of the same functional group→ use prefixes (di, tri)
6. State position of double and triple bonds using numbers (before functional groups)
7. If more than 1 double/triple bond→ use prefixes (di, tri)

# of bonds/alkyl groups	Prefix	# of bonds/alkyl groups	Prefix
2	Di	7	Hepta
3	Tri	8	Octa
4	Tetra	9	Nona
5	Penta	10	Deca
6	Hexa		

8. If cyclic (carbons arranged in a circle), put cyclo before the name
9. If isomers, put *trans* or *cis* at the beginning

Example 1
Name the following hydrocarbon

Step 1: Find the longest chain

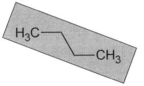

Step 2: Use prefix for # of carbons in the longest chain
4 C atoms→ butane
There are no double/triple bonds or substituents. Thus the name of this hydrocarbon is butane.

Example 2
Name the following hydrocarbon

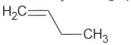

Step 1: Find the longest chain

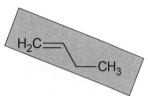

Step 2: Use prefix for # of carbons in the longest chain
4 C atoms→ butane
Step 3: Number carbons (ex. C_1, C_2, C_3, etc.).

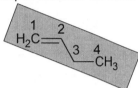
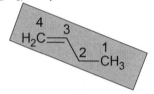

Double bond is at C1   Double bond is at C3

Need to number C atoms so that the C with double bond has the lowest number. Thus, need to start numbering from the left.

There are no substituents. Thus the name of this hydrocarbon is 1-butene.

Example 3
Name the following hydrocarbon
$H_2C{=}CH_2$

Step 1: Find the longest chain

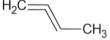

Step 2: Use prefix for # of carbons in the longest chain
2 C atoms, 1 double bond→ ethene.

Note: there is no need to put 1-ethene to indicate the position of the double bond. If you start numbering from the right or from the left, you will still have 1-ethene.

Example 4
Name the following hydrocarbon

$H_2C{=}$ ⟍ —CH_3

Step 1: Find the longest chain

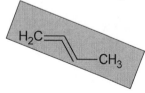

Surviving University: First Year Chemistry

Step 2: Use prefix for # of carbons in the longest chain

4 C atoms→ butane

Step 3: Number carbons (ex. C_1, C_2, C_3, etc.).

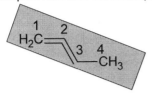

Double bonds are at   Double bonds are at

C1 and C2   C2 and C3

Need to number C atoms so that the C with double bond has the lowest number. Thus, need to start numbering from the left.

There are no substituents→ skip steps 4 and 5.

Step 6 and 7: State position of double bonds using numbers. If more than 1 double/triple bond→ use prefixes (di, tri).

There are 2 double bonds→ di

Thus the name of this hydrocarbon is 1, 2- butadiene.

Example 5

Name the following hydrocarbon

CH_3

H_3C— CH_3

H_3C CH_3

Step 1: Find the longest chain

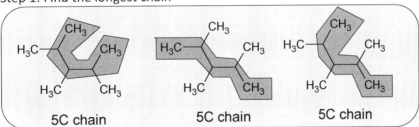

5C chain   5C chain   5C chain

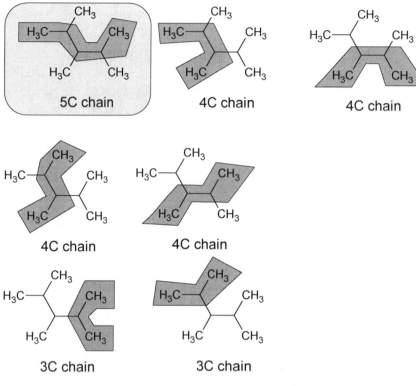

Step 2: Use prefix for # of carbons in the longest chain.
The longest chain is 5C→ pentane
Step 3: Number carbons (ex. C_1, C_2, C_3, etc.)→ substituents need to be on C atoms with lowers numbers.

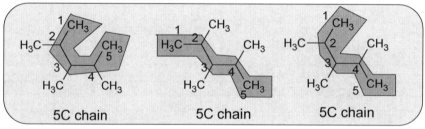

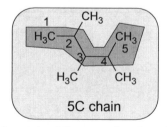

For each of these molecules, numering from right to left gives the same number for C atoms with substituents

In each of these molecules, there are 3 methyl groups attached to C2,

C3, and C4. In each case, the substituent groups are attached to C atoms with the same numbering→ can use any of these longest chains to name the molecule.

Step 4: Write functional group names in <u>alphabetical order</u>. Functional groups go before the prefix. If more than 1 of the same functional group→ use prefixes (di, tri).

There are 3 methyl groups→ trimethyl.

Thus, the name of this hydrocarbon is 2, 3, 4- trimethylpentane.

Part 19

Biomolecules

Carbohydrates

Fischer projections

Proteins and amino acids

Nucleic Acids

Carbohydrates

- Aka sugars
- Contain C, H, O
    - Sometimes contain N or S
    - Have general formula $C_nH_{2n}O_n$ (or $[C(H_2O)_n]$)

Production of carbohydrates

- In plants, carbohydrates are produced by **photosynthesis**
    - Photosynthesis is the process of using sunlight energy to convert $CO_{2(g)}$ into sugars

$$6CO_2 + 6H_2O \rightarrow 6O_2 + C_6H_{12}O_6$$

- In animals, carbohydrates are produced through biochemical reactions

Breakdown of carbohydrates

- Carbohydrates are used to store energy
- Breakdown of carbohydrates releases energy
- Carbohydrates are broken down via **oxidation**
    - This process is also known as burning or combustion
- Breakdown of carbohydrates is exothermic (releases energy). Energy is used for **metabolism**.
    - Metabolism consists of a group of chemical reactions which are needed to maintain organisms' life

General structure

- A chain begins with aldehyde (R⌯H) or ketone (R⌯R)
- Each C (but C_1) is attached to –OH

Drawing carbohydrates: Fischer projections

- In real life, carbohydrates' structure is 3-dimensional
- Fischer projections represent carbohydrates' structure in 2 dimensions
- Drawing Fischer projection

  o Place carbonyl group ($H \overset{O}{\diagup\diagdown} R$) on top
  o Place CH_2OH is at the bottom

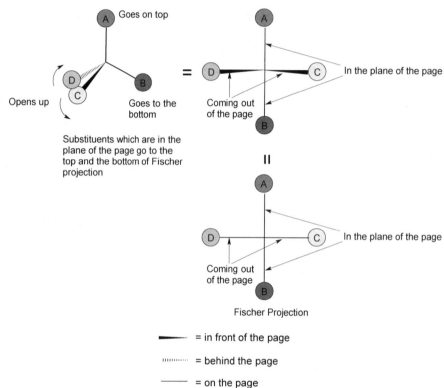

= in front of the page

= behind the page

= on the page

Surviving University: First Year Chemistry

Example 1
Draw Fischer projection for erythrose.

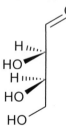

By convention, Fischer projection needs to have carbonyl on top and CH_2OH is at the bottom.

Opens up

Goes on top

Substituents which are in the plane of the page go to the top and the bottom of Fischer projection

Goes to the bottom

In the plane of the page

Coming out of the page

=

In the plane of the page

Coming out of the page

Fischer Projection

Example 2
Draw Fischer projection for the following molecule.

By convention, Fischer projection needs to have carbonyl on top and CH_2OH is at the bottom. The molecule needs to be rotated.

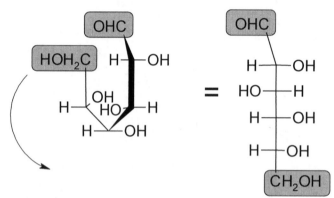

The backbone (C atoms) of the molecule is in the plane of the page. H and –OH groups are coming out of the plane of the page. The molecule now needs to be unfolded.

This is the same as

Fischer projection

Conventions for carbohydrates: D and L forms

- D and L forms are configurations of carbohydrates

S u r v i v i n g   U n i v e r s i t y :   F i r s t   Y e a r   C h e m i s t r y

- **D form** has –OH on the right of C at the stereocenter that is furthest away from C=O
- **L form** has –OH on the left of C at the stereocenter that is furthest away from C=O
    - *Think: L= left*

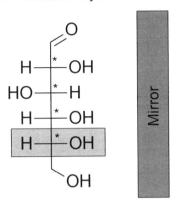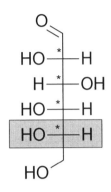

-OH is on the right of C at the stereocenter that is furthest away from C=O

-OH is on the left of C at the stereocenter that is furthest away from C=O

D- glucose

L- glucose

- Note: stereocenter is indicated with *
- Note: this is not the same as R and S forms (part 14)!!!
- The human body recognizes and is able to use the D form of carbohydrates

Chirality of carbohydrates

- From part 14 of this book, a chiral molecule does not have an internal plane of symmetry, is not superimposable onto itself(the molecule is not identical to its mirror image), and has a stereocenter
    - Carbohydrates have stereocenter(s) and are chiral

D- Threose

Ex.

Types of carbohydrates

Monosaccharide- 1 sugar molecule

Disaccharide- 2 sugar molecules bonded together

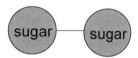

Polysaccharide- many sugar molecules bonded together

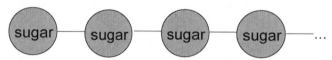

Monosaccharides

- Are simple sugars

Convention
- C1 is at the end of aldehyde/ketone

Aldose- contains an aldehyde (R–C(=O)–H)

Ketose- contains a ketone (R–C(=O)–R)

Name = Aldo/keto + prefix for # of C atoms + ose

# of C atoms in the chain	Prefix
3	Tri
4	Tetra
5	Penta
6	Hexa
7	Hepta

Surviving University: First Year Chemistry

Example 1
What are the following monosaccharides?

A

B

5 C atoms= pentose

Contains = aldose

A

Thus, molecule A is aldopentose.

6 C atoms= hexose

Contains = ketose

B

Thus, molecule B is ketohexose.

Types of monosaccharides

- These are the some common aldoses

# carbons	Name	Drawing
3	D- glyceraldehyde	O⫽C H—OH OH
4	D- erythrose	O⫽C H—OH H—OH OH
5	D- ribose	O⫽C H—OH H—OH H—OH OH
6	D-glucose	O⫽C H—OH HO—H H—OH H—OH OH

6	D- mannose	

6	D- galactose	

These are the some common ketoses

# carbons	Name	Drawing
3	Dihydroxyacetone	
5	D- ribulose	

6	D- fructose	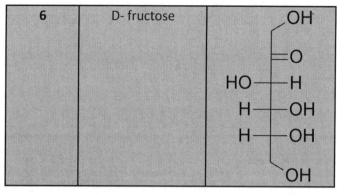

Structure of monosaccharides

- Monosaccharides can exist in linear form or in cyclic form
    - Most monosaccharides are in cyclic form
    - **Furanose**- cyclic form composed of 5C
    - **Pyranose**- cyclic form composed of 6C

Form	D-Glucose	D-Fructose
Linear	 O H——OH HO——H H——OH H——OH OH	 OH O HO——H H——OH H——OH OH
Cyclic	Pyranose form (D- Glucopyranose) α-D-glucopyranose and	Furanose form (D-fructofuranose) α-D-fructofuranose and

Surviving University: First Year Chemistry

CH₂OH structure for β-D-glucopyranose and β-D-fructofuranose (see figures)

β-D-glucopyranose

β-D-fructofuranose

- D-glucopyranose has 2 **anomers**
  - ○ **α anomer** has –OH below the plane at C1 (in aldoses) or C2 (in ketoses)
  - ○ **β anomer** has –OH above the plane at C1 (in aldoses) or C2 (in ketoses)
  - ○ Anomers can be converted between each other via **mutarotation**

α-D-glucopyranose   D- glucose in linear form   β-D-glucopyranose

(same as this)

- Monosaccharides switch from linear form into cyclic form via **intramolecular nucleophilic addition**

  o —OH group attacks aldehyde (R $\overset{O}{\overset{\|}{\underset{}{\frown}}}$ H) group to form a

  hemiacetal ($R\overset{R}{\underset{OH}{-}}OR$ **)**

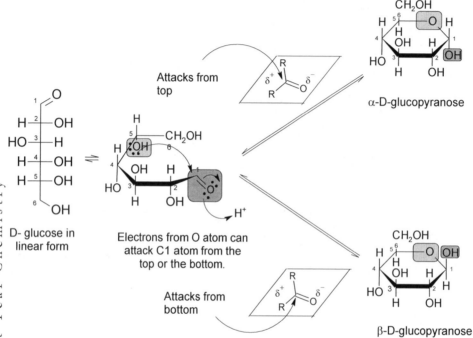

α-D-glucopyranose

D- glucose in linear form

Attacks from top

Electrons from O atom can attack C1 atom from the top or the bottom.

Attacks from bottom

β-D-glucopyranose

Disaccharides

- 2 sugar molecules bonded together via **glycosidic linkage**
- Do not undergo mutarotation

Types of disaccharides
- **Sucrose**= glucose+ fructose (Glu-α-1,2-Fru)
- **Maltose**= glucose+ glucose (Glu-α-1,4-Glu)
- **Lactose**= glucose+ galactose (Gal-β-1,4-Glu)
- **Cellobiose**= glucose+ glucose(Glu-β-1,4-Glu)

Surviving University: First Year Chemistry

Formation of disaccharides

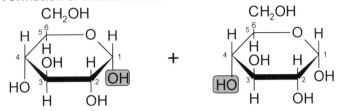

α-D-glucopyranose   α-D-glucopyranose

maltose

Polysaccharides

- Are complex sugars
    - Many sugar molecules bonded together via glycosidic linkage
- Do not undergo mutarotation
- Are polymers
    - **Polymer**- large molecule composed of repeating subunits
- Are **hydrolyzed** (broken down) to form monosaccharides

Types of polysaccharides

- **Cellulose**- is a polymer of β-glucose (Glu-β-1,4-Glu)
    - Forms long straight chains→ chains interact with each other via hydrogen bonds
    - Has a structural role in plants
    - Cannot be digested by humans

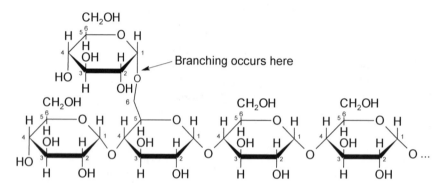

cellulose

- **Starch**- is a polymer of α-glucose
  - ○ Consists of **amylose** (Glu-α-1,4-Glu) and **amylopectin** (Glu-α-1,6-Glu)
  - ○ Is used for energy storage in plants

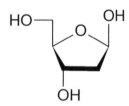

Branching occurs here

Glycogen and starch

- **Glycogen**- is a polymer of α-glucose
  - ○ Has both Glu-α-1,4-Glu and Glu-α-1,6-Glu
  - ○ Is used for energy storage in animals and bacteria
- **2-deoxyribose**- is the sugar component of DNA
  - ○ DNA is a polymer of nucleotides. A nucleotide is composed of a deoxyribose sugar, a nitrogenated base, and a phosphate group.

2-deoxyribose

Surviving University: First Year Chemistry

Proteins

- Are present in all organisms and are needed for proper functioning of cells
- Are polymers of **amino acids**
- **Peptide**- is shorter than protein (<50 amino acids)

Amino acid

- There are many amino acids in nature→ only 20 amino acids are used by cells to make proteins
- Amino acids are composed of
    - C atom
    - H atom
    - Carboxylic acid group
        - This is a weak acid
    - Amino group
    - R group (ex. CH_2 CH_2SCH_3)
        - Each amino acid has its own R group→ amino acids are named based on their R groups

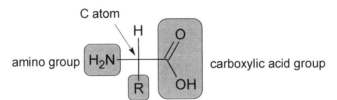

- The structure of amino acid varies according to pH (concentration of H^+ ions in the solution)
    - H atom in amino group and carboxylic acid group can be added or removed
    - Low pH→ NH_3^+, COOH
        - There are many H^+ in the solution
    - High pH→ NH_2, COO^-
        - There are few H^+ in the solution
    - When H^+ is added or removed, the charge of amino acid changes
    - **Zwitterion form**- form of amino acid which is neutral (does not have a charge)
    - **Isoelectric point**- pH at which amino acid is in Zwitterion form

- Each amino acid has its own pH at which H atom can be added/removed *(this is important!)*
  - Ex. At pH=6, some amino acids are +ively charged, some are –ively charged, some are neutral

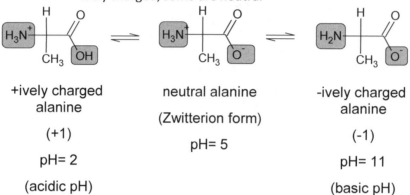

+ively charged alanine

(+1)

pH= 2

(acidic pH)

neutral alanine

(Zwitterion form)

pH= 5

-ively charged alanine

(-1)

pH= 11

(basic pH)

Protein structure

Primary structure- sequence of amino acids in a **polypeptide chain** (short polymer of amino acids)

- Amino acids are connected by **amide bonds** (aka **peptide bonds**)

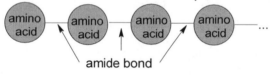

amide bond

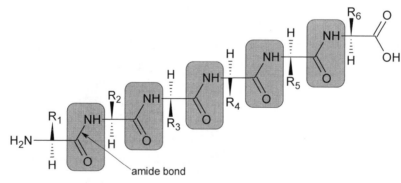

Secondary structure- arrangement of amino acids in a <u>specific region</u> of a polypeptide chain

- Amino acids are held together by **H bonds**
  - H bond is between H atom (attached to N) of 1 amino acid and O atom of another amino acid
- 2 types of secondary structure

S u r v i v i n g   U n i v e r s i t y :   F i r s t   Y e a r   C h e m i s t r y

- o **Alpha helix**
- o **Beta pleated sheet**

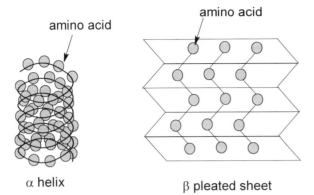

α helix   β pleated sheet

Tertiary structure- folding in an <u>entire</u> polypeptide chain→ forms a 3 dimensional structure

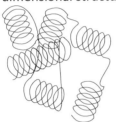

Quaternary structure- 3 dimensional arrangement of <u>several</u> polypeptide chains

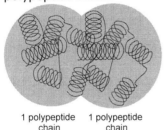

1 polypeptide   1 polypeptide
chain   chain

- ▪ A protein can have 1 chain or several chains→ not all proteins have quaternary structure

Examples of function

- ▪ Structure→ ex. keratin
- ▪ **Enzymes**
  - o Are proteins which act as catalysts for biological reactions (speed up the rate of reactions)
  - o Enzyme names usually end as "ase" (ex. Hydrolase)

Nucleic acids

- Are present in all organisms
- Are used to carry and process genetic information
- 2 major nucleic acids
    - DNA (**deoxyribonucleic acid**)
    - RNA (**ribonucleic acid**)
- Are polymers of **nucleotides**

Nucleoside vs nucleotide vs nucleic acid

Name	Composition
Nucleoside	nitrogenous base / sugar (structure shown)
Nucleotide	nitrogenous base / phosphate group / sugar (structure shown)
Nucleic acid	many nucleotides held together by **phosphodiester bonds**

Surviving University: First Year Chemistry

Sugars

- 2 common sugars
  - Ribose
    - In RNA
  - Deoxyribose
    - In DNA

ribose

deoxyribose

Nitrogenous bases

- Nitrogenous bases can be purines or pyrimidines
- **Purines**- have 2 cycles
  - **Adenine** (A)
  - **Guanine** (G)

Surviving University: First Year Chemistry

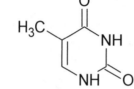

adenine   guanine

- **Pyrimidines**- have 1 cycle
  - ○ **Cytosine** (C)
  - ○ **Thymine** (T)
  - ○ **Uracil** (U)→ found in RNA (instead of thymine)

cytosine   thymine   uracil

DNA

- Consists of 2 strands of nucleotides
- Strands are held together via H bonds between base pairs
  - ○ Base pairs are complementary to each other
    - Adenine on 1 strand pairs up with thymine on another strand
      - A→ T
      - 2 H bonds exist between A and T

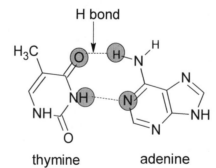

thymine   adenine

Surviving University: First Year Chemistry

- Cytosine on 1 strand pairs up with guanine on another strand
  - C→G
  - 3 H bonds exist between C and G

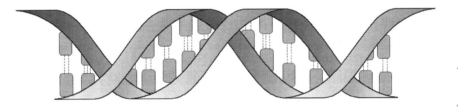

cytosine   guanine

RNA

- Is found in all organisms
- Consists of 1 strand of nucleotides
  - U instead of T
- Has many functions in cells
  - The major function is carried out by mRNA. It carries messages which are translated to form a protein.

Part 20

Investigative Tools

Spectroscopy

Infrared spectroscopy

Mass spectrometry

NMR spectroscopy

Polarimetry

Electrophoresis

Investigative Tools

Summary of investigative tools

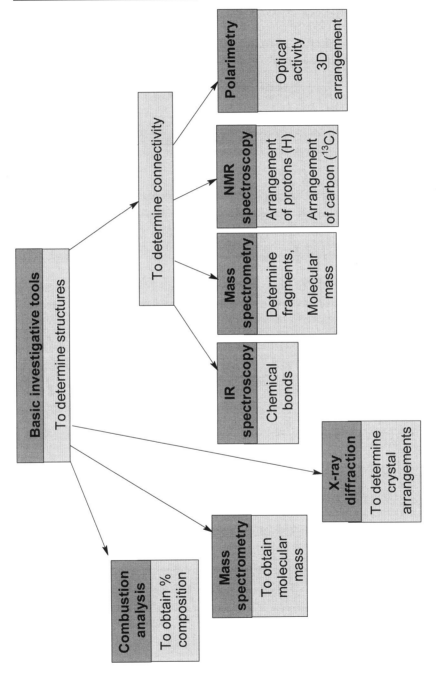

Spectroscopy

- Spectroscopy is a technique which is used to determine structure of a molecule
    - It is based on molecule's ability to absorb electromagnetic radiation

General information about spectroscopy

- Normally, molecules exist in their lowest energy form (called the **ground state**)
- When molecules are exposed to radiation (ex. infrared radiation), they absorb energy and have a higher energy form (called the **excited state**)
    - Different forms of electromagnetic radiation induce different effect on molecules
        - X-rays→ cause molecules to lose e⁻ (become ionized)
        - UV and visible light→ cause e⁻ to move from ground state to higher orbitals
        - Infrared→ causes molecules to vibrate
        - Microwaves→ cause molecules to rotate/tumble
- Molecules then return back to their ground state by releasing the energy that they gained
- The amount of energy released is measured and is used to determine structural features of molecules

3 types of spectroscopy

- Infrared spectroscopy (IR)
- Mass spectrometry (MS)
- Nuclear magnetic resonance spectroscopy (NMR)

Infrared Spectroscopy (IR)

- Is used to determine structure of a molecule

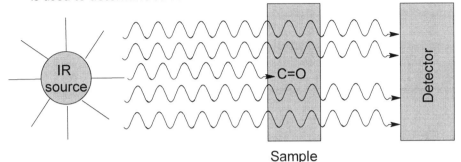

Sample

- A sample is exposed to infrared radiation (λ= 2.5-20μm)
- Energy causes covalent bonds within a molecule to vibrate at distinct frequencies
    - ex. C=O bond vibrates at a different frequency than O-H bond
    - If the frequency of vibration of a bond matches the frequency of infrared radiation, then the bond absorbs radiation
    - The energy is not large enough to break the covalent bonds within the molecule
- The infrared radiation that has not been absorbed is measured by a detector

IR spectra

- Infrared radiation which was absorbed by the sample appears as a peak in the IR spectrum
    - Absorption is the opposite of transmittance
        - 0% transmittance= 100% absorption
- Detected (transmitted) radiation is usually written as a **wavenumber**
    - Wavenumbers in IR spectra are between 400 and 4000cm^{-1}

$$v = \frac{1}{\lambda}$$

Note: v= wavenumber (cm^{-1}), λ= wavelength (cm)

- Since different types of bonds absorb different frequencies of IR, they have different wavenumbers

Surviving University: First Year Chemistry

Molecule	Structure	Bond	Wavenumber
Alkane	$R_3C—CR_3$	C—H	2850-2980 cm^{-1}
Alkene	$R_2C=CR_2$	C=C	1640-1670 cm^{-1}
		$=C^{-H}$	3020-3100 cm^{-1}
Alkyne	$RC\equiv CR$	C$\equiv$C	2100-2260 cm^{-1}
		$\equiv C^{-H}$	3270-3340 cm^{-1}
Aromatic		C—H C—H out of the ring ring vibrations	3000-3100 cm^{-1} 675-900 cm^{-1} 1585-1600, 1400-1500
Alcohol	R—OH	C—O O—H	1000-1260 cm^{-1} 3000-3550 cm^{-1}
Aldehyde	R—CHO	C=O C—H	1700-1740 cm^{-1} 2700-2850 cm^{-1}
Ketone	R—CO—R	C=O	1705-1725 cm^{-1}
Carboxylic acid	R—COOH	C=O O—H	1710-1760 cm^{-1} 2400-3000 cm^{-1}

Example of IR spectrum

2-pentanone

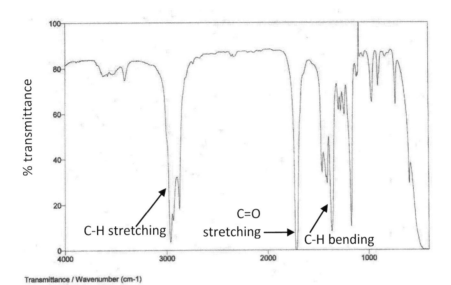

IR spectrum image was prepared by Bernard Shami

Mass Spectrometry

- Is used to
  - o Differentiate between isotopes and determine % abundance
  - o Determine chemical structure and identity of a molecule
  - o Establish molecular mass of a molecule

Mass spectrometer

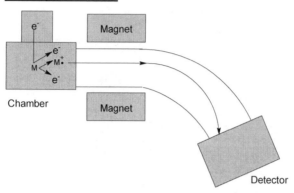

1. Gaseous sample is put into a chamber
2. Sample is bombarded with high energy electrons→ results in production of radical cations called **molecular ions** ($M^{+}_{\bullet}$)
- Covalent bonds can break→ molecule can break apart
  - o Fragments are studied to determine chemical structure
3. Ions travel along a straight path→ magnet causes the path to bend
- Deflection of ions depends on mass/charge ratio
  - o Lighter ions deflect more than heavier ions
4. Molecular ions hit detector→ detector measures amount of ions that it is hit by at different locations

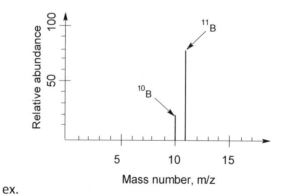

ex.

Surviving University: First Year Chemistry

Carbon (^{13}C) Nuclear Magnetic Resonance (NMR) Spectroscopy

- Is used to
  - Differentiate isomers
  - Determine structure of a molecule
- Is based on number of different chemical environments around C atoms which exist in a molecule
  - e$^-$ density around C atom depends on the chemical environment
  - C atoms in different chemical environments absorb radio waves at different frequencies

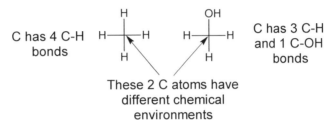

C has 4 C-H bonds

C has 3 C-H and 1 C-OH bonds

These 2 C atoms have different chemical environments

Peaks in ^{13}C NMR spectrum

- **Equivalent C atoms** in a molecule have identical chemical environments
  - These atoms have the same peak in NMR spectrum

$$H_3C-CH_3$$

These 2 C atoms have the same chemical environments (both have 1 C-CH$_3$ and 3 C-H bonds)

- **Nonequivalent C atoms** in a molecule have different chemical environments
  - These atoms have different peaks in NMR spectrum

C has 3 C-H and 1 C-COH bonds

C has 1 C-H, 1 C-CH$_3$, and 1 C=O bonds

These 2 C atoms have different chemical environments

(2 peaks in NMR spectrum)

- The height of a peak depends on the number of H atoms that surround the C atom
  - The height does not correspond to the # of C atoms which have that peak

Example 1
How many peaks is this molecule expected to have in ^{13}C NMR spectrum?

The number of peaks corresponds to the number of chemical environments around C atoms which exist in this molecule

C atom	Surrounded by
1	3 C-H bonds 1 [structure] bond
2	1 C-H bond 1 C-Cl bond 1 [structure] bond 1 [structure] bond
3	2 C-H bonds 1 [structure] bond 1 [structure] bond
4	3 C-H bonds 1 [structure] bond Notice that the distance of Cl atom from the bond is different here than it was for C1

Since there are 4 distinct chemical environments, there will be 4 peaks.

Surviving University: First Year Chemistry

^{13}C NMR spectrum

- Vertical lines represent peaks
  - Position of peaks depends on amount of absorption of radio waves by C atoms in a molecule
- NMR uses absorbance of **TMS** as a reference point
  - TMS is given a value of 0ppm
  - All C atoms in TMS have the same chemical environment

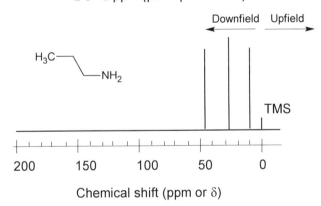

Tetramethylsilane (TMS)

- **Chemical shift** is the difference in absorption of C atom in the molecule of interest and TMS
  - Difference in chemical environments around a C atom in the molecule of interest and TMS results in a chemical shift
  - Chemical shift has δ units
    - 1 δ= 1 ppm (parts per million)

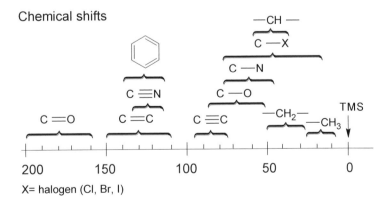

Polarimetry

- Used to determine optical rotation and to differentiate between enantiomers

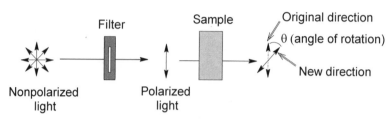

- Nonpolarized light (oscillates in all directions) passes through a filter→ filter limits the oscillations to 1 direction (light is polarized)
- Polarized light passes through a sample containing molecule of interest→ molecule rotates polarized light
- **Polarimeter** is used to measure the angle of rotation
    - += light is rotated clockwise (**dextrorotatory**)
    - -= light is rotated counterclockwise (**levorotatory**)

Specific rotation

- Specific rotation is rotation of polarized light under the following conditions
    - Na lamp (λ= 589.6nm) is used
    - The length of sample (path length) is 1dm (1dm= 10cm)
    - The concentration of sample is 1g/mL

$$[\alpha]_D = \frac{\alpha}{l \times c}$$

Note: $[\alpha]_D$= specific rotation (°), α= observed rotation (°), l= length of sample (dm), c= concentration of sample (g/mL)

Enantiomers

- Enantiomers rotate polarized light by the same angle, but in opposite directions
- The direction of rotation cannot be determined from structure of enantiomer
    - The direction of rotation of light does not depend on the R and S system
- **Racemic mixture** contains equal amounts of + and − enantiomers
    - Each enantiomer rotates plane polarized light by the same amount in the opposite direction→ the resultant optical rotation is 0°

Surviving University: First Year Chemistry

Electrophoresis

- This is a technique which is used to separate amino acids via migration through electric field
    - A mixture of amino acids is placed in an electric field
    - pH is constant
    - Different amino acids have different charge
        - Some amino acids are +ive
        - Some amino acids are −ive
        - Some amino acids are neutral
    - Amino acids migrate based on their charge
        - +ively charged amino acids migrate towards cathode (-ive)
        - -ively charged amino acids migrate towards anode (+ive)
        - Neutral amino acids do not migrate

At pH= 5

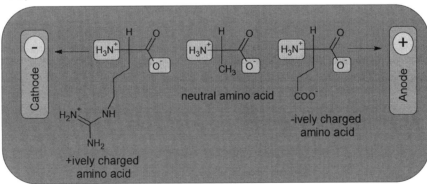

Part 21

Gases

Properties of gases

Gas laws

Avogadro's hypothesis

Stoichiometry of gases

Gas density

Finding molar mass using ideal gas law

Dalton's law of partial pressures

Mole fractions

Kinetic molecular theory

Gas diffusion and effusion

Real gases

Surviving University: First Year Chemistry

Gases

Properties of gases

- Gases can be expanded infinitely
- Gases occupy containers uniformly and completely
- Gases diffuse (spread out) and mix rapidly

Pressure- the amount of force applied to an object over its area

- Pressure is measured with a barometer

$$1 atm = 760 mm\,Hg = 101.325 kPa = 1 bar = 760 torr$$

STP- standard temperature and pressure→ 0°C, 1atm

Example 1
The pressure is 440mm Hg. What is the pressure in atm?

$$Pressure\ atm = 440\ mm\,Hg \times \frac{1 atm}{760 mm\,Hg}$$

$Pressure\ atm = 0.579 atm$
The pressure in atm is 0.579atm.

Gas laws

Boyle's Law: $P_1 V_1 = P_2 V_2$

Charles's Law: $\frac{V_1}{T_1} = \frac{V_2}{T_2}$

General Gas Law: $\frac{P_1 V_1}{T_1} = \frac{P_2 V_2}{T_2}$

Ideal Gas Law: $PV = nRT$

$$R = 0.082057 \frac{L \cdot atm}{K \cdot mol}$$

Note: V_1 = volume in scenario 1 (L); V_2= volume in scenario 2 (L); P_1= pressure in scenario 1 (atm); P_2= pressure in scenario 2 (atm); T_1= temperature in scenario 1 (K); T_2= temperature in scenario 2 (K); P= pressure in the container (atm); V= volume of the container (L), n= number of moles of gas in the container (mol), R= the gas constant $(\frac{L \cdot atm}{K \cdot mol})$; T= temperature inside of the container (K)

When to use which equation?

1 scenario (1 container)	2 scenarios (the original container, then the modified container)
Use $PV = nRT$ Note: P must be in atm, T must be in K, V must be in L	Use $P_1 V_1 = P_2 V_2$, $\frac{V_1}{T_1} = \frac{V_2}{T_2}$, $\frac{P_1 V_1}{T_1} = \frac{P_2 V_2}{T_2}$

Example 1

NO gas occupies 3.5L at 22.0°C. What is the volume that this gas occupies at 37.0°C?

There are 2 scenarios→ so cannot use PV=nRT. The problem deals with volumes and temperatures→ $\frac{V_1}{T_1} = \frac{V_2}{T_2}$.

V_1	3.5L
T_1	22.0°C
V_2	?L
T_2	37.0°C

It is okay that the temperature is in °C (not in Kelvin). Make sure that both T_1 and T_2 have the same units because the units will cancel out.

$$\frac{V_1}{T_1} = \frac{V_2}{T_2}$$
$$V_2 = \frac{V_1 T_2}{T_1}$$
$$V_2 = \frac{3.5L \times 37.0°C}{22.0°C}$$
$$V_2 = 5.9L$$

The volume of NO gas at 37.0°C is 5.9L.

Example 2

3.6L of H_2 gas contained under pressure of 380mm Hg and temperature of 25°C. Find the pressure when the gas is placed in a 5.0L container and cooled to the temperature of 0°C.

There are 2 scenarios→ so cannot use PV=nRT. The problem deals with volumes, temperatures, and pressures→ use $\frac{P_1 V_1}{T_1} = \frac{P_2 V_2}{T_2}$.

V_1	3.6L
T_1	25°C
P_1	380mm Hg
V_2	5.0L
T_2	0°C
P_2	?mm Hg

Need to convert temperatures to Kelvin.

$$T_1 = (25°C + 273.2°C) \times \frac{1K}{1°C} = 298.2K$$
$$T_2 = (0°C + 273.2°C) \times \frac{1K}{1°C} = 273.2K$$

$$P_2 = \frac{P_1 V_1 T_2}{V_2 T_1}$$

$$P_2 = \frac{380mm\,Hg \times 3.6L \times 273.2K}{5.0L \times 298.2K}$$

$$P_2 = 250.7mm\,Hg$$

The final pressure inside of the container was 250.7mm Hg.

Example 3

N_2 gas is put into a 500mL container with a pressure of 67.5mm Hg. Then the gas is transferred into a 125mL flask. What is the new pressure?

There are 2 scenarios→ so cannot use PV=nRT. The problem deals with volumes and pressures→ $P_1 V_1 = P_2 V_2$.

V_1	500mL
P_1	67.5mm Hg
V_2	125mL
P_2	? mm Hg

$$P_1 V_1 = P_2 V_2$$

$$P_2 = \frac{V_1 P_1}{V_2}$$

$$P_2 = \frac{500mL \times 67.5mm\,Hg}{125mL}$$

$$P_2 = 270mm\,Hg$$

The final pressure of nitrogen gas was 270mm Hg.

Example 4

What is the pressure of 1.25g of carbon dioxide (M=44.01g/mol) gas in a 750mL container at a temperature of 22.50°C?

There is 1 scenario→ use PV=nRT.

Steps

1. Convert volume to L, temperature to K
2. Find # moles using $n = \frac{m}{M}$
3. Find pressure using $PV = nRT$

Note: in order to use PV=nRT, you need to have volume in L and temperature in K.

$$Volume\ in\ L = 750mL \times \frac{1L}{1000mL}$$

$$Volume\ in\ L = 0.750L$$

$$Temperature\ in\ K = (22.50°C + 273.15°C) \times \frac{1K}{1°C}$$

$$Temperature\ in\ K = 295.65K$$

P	?atm
V	0.750L
n	?mol
R	0.082057L·atm/K·mol
T	295.65K
m	1.25g
M	44.01g/mol

You need # moles of CO_2. From part 4 of this book,

$$n = \frac{m}{M}$$

$$n_{CO_2} = \frac{1.25g}{44.01g/mol}$$

$$n_{CO_2} = 0.0284mol$$

$$PV = nRT$$

$$P = \frac{nRT}{V}$$

$$P = \frac{0.0284mol \times 0.082057\frac{L \cdot atm}{K \cdot mol} \times 295.65K}{0.750L}$$

$$P = 0.919atm$$

The pressure of carbon dioxide gas was 0.919atm.

Example 4

What mass of N_2 gas (M=28.02g/mol) is needed to fill 27,000L container at 298K and a pressure of 0.98atm?

There is 1 scenario→ use PV=nRT.

Steps

1. Find # moles of N_2 gas needed using $PV = nRT$
2. Find mass of N_2 gas using $n = \frac{m}{M}$

P	0.98atm
V	27,000L
n	?mol
R	0.082057L·atm/K·mol
T	298K
m	?g
M	28.02g/mol

$$PV = nRT$$

$$n_{N_2} = \frac{PV}{RT}$$

Surviving University: First Year Chemistry

$$n_{N_2} = \frac{0.98atm \times 27{,}000L}{0.082057\frac{L \cdot atm}{K \cdot mol} \times 298K}$$

$n_{N_2} = 1.1 \times 10^3 mol$

$m_{N_2} = M \times n$

$m_{N_2} = 28.02\,g/mol \times 1.1 \times 10^3 mol$

$m_{N_2} = 3.0 \times 10^3 g$

The mass of nitrogen gas needed was 3.0x10³g.

Avogadro's hypothesis

- 2 gases that have the same temperature, pressure, and volumes have the same amount of molecules
- Volume of a gas is proportional to the # moles of a gas

Example 1
How much oxygen (in L) is needed to completely react with 5.2L of C₂H₆ gas to produce carbon dioxide and water?
Note: This problem is very similar to the problems in stoichiometry section (part 4)→ volume is used for ratio instead of the # of moles. First, you need to write down the equation. Do not forget that oxygen is a diatomic molecule (comes in pairs→ O_2). Make sure that you balance the equation!

	2 C₂H₆₍g₎	+7 O₂₍g₎	→ 4CO₂₍g₎	+ 6H₂O₍l₎
V	5.2L	?L		
Ratio	2	7	4	6

$$V_{O_2} = 5.2L\ C_2H_6 \times \frac{7mol\ O_2}{2mol\ C_2H_6}$$

$V_{O_2} = 18L$

18L of oxygen are needed to completely react with 5.2L of C₂H₆ gas.

Stoichiometry of gases

Example 1
What mass of NaN₃₍g₎ is needed to produce 75.0L of N₂₍g₎ when the temperature is 25°C and the pressure is 1.3atm?
2NaN₃₍s₎→ 2Na₍s₎+ 3N₂₍g₎
Steps
1. Use $PV = nRT$ to find the # moles of N_2
2. Use a ratio to convert the # moles of N_2 to the # moles of NaN₃
3. Use $n = \frac{m}{M}$ to find the mass of NaN₃

Note: in order to use $PV = nRT$, you need to have temperature in K.

$$Temperature\ in\ K = (25°C + 273.2°C) \times \frac{1K}{1°C}$$

$Temperature\ in\ K = 298.2K$

First, you need to write down the equation. Do not forget that nitrogen is a diatomic molecule (comes in pairs→ N_2). Make sure that you balance the equation!

	2 NaN$_{3(s)}$	→ 2Na$_{(s)}$	+ 3N$_{2(g)}$
m	?g		
M			
n	?mol		?mol
V			75.0L
T			298.2K
P			1.3atm
Ratio	2	2	3

$$n = \frac{PV}{RT}$$

$$n_{N_2} = \frac{1.3atm \times 75.0L}{0.082057\frac{L \cdot atm}{K \cdot mol} \times 298.2K}$$

$n_{N_2} = 4.0mol$

$$n_{NaN_3} = 4.0mol\ N_2 \times \frac{2mol\ NaN_3}{3mol\ N_2}$$

$n_{NaN_3} = 2.7mol$

$M_{NaN_3} = 3(14.01g/mol) + 22.99g/mol$

$M_{NaN_3} = 65.02g/mol$

$m_{NaN_3} = M \times n$

$m_{NaN_3} = 65.02\ g/mol \times 2.7mol$

$m_{NaN_3} = 176g$

The mass of NaN$_3$ needed was 176g.

Example 2

0.11g of H_2O_2 is placed into a 2.50L container with the temperature of 25°C. What are the pressures of water and oxygen gases in the container?

$2H_2O_{2(l)}$→ $2H_2O_{(g)}+O_{2(g)}$

Steps

1.   Use $n = \frac{m}{M}$ to find the # moles of H_2O_2
2.   Use $PV = nRT$ to find the pressure of H_2O_2

Surviving University: First Year Chemistry

3. Use a ratio to convert the pressure of H_2O_2 into pressures of H_2O and O_2

Note: in order to use $PV = nRT$, you need to have temperature in K.

$Temperature\ in\ K = (25°C + 273.2°C) \times \dfrac{1K}{1°C}$

$Temperature\ in\ K = 298.2K$

	2 H$_2$O$_{2(l)}$	**→ 2H$_2$O$_{(g)}$**	**+ O$_{2(g)}$**
m	0.11g		
M			
n	?mol		
V	2.50L		
T	298.2K		
P	?atm	?atm	?atm
Ratio	2	2	1

$M_{H_2O_2} = 2(1.01g/mol) + 2(16.00g/mol)$

$M_{H_2O_2} = 34.02g/mol$

$n = \dfrac{m}{M}$

$n_{H_2O_2} = \dfrac{0.11g}{34.02g/mol}$

$n_{H_2O_2} = 0.0032mol$

$PV = nRT$

$P_{H_2O_2} = \dfrac{nRT}{V}$

$P_{H_2O_2} = \dfrac{0.0032mol \times 0.082057\frac{L\cdot atm}{K\cdot mol} \times 298.2K}{2.50L}$

$P_{H_2O_2} = 0.032atm$

$P_{H_2O} = 0.032atm\ H_2O_2 \times \dfrac{2mol\ H_2O}{2mol\ H_2O_2}$

$P_{H_2O} = 0.032atm$

$P_{O_2} = 0.032atm\ H_2O_2 \times \dfrac{1mol\ O_2}{2mol\ H_2O_2}$

$P_{O_2} = 0.016atm$

The pressure of water vapour was 0.032atm and the pressure of oxygen gas was 0.016atm.

Gas density

In order to solve problems that involve density on midterms/exams, you must to be able to rearrange $PV = nRT$ to include density.
From part 1 of this book,
$Density = \frac{Mass}{Volume}$ or $\rho = \frac{m}{V}$ (where ρ= density, m= mass, V= volume)
In order to incorporate $\rho = \frac{m}{V}$ into $PV = nRT$, look what is in common in these 2 equations. Both equations have a volume. Rearrange density equation for volume.
$$V = \frac{m}{\rho}$$
Now sub $V = \frac{m}{\rho}$ into $PV = nRT$ (replace V with $\frac{m}{\rho}$ in $PV = nRT$).
$$\frac{Pm}{\rho} = nRT$$
If the problem asks you to find the molar mass, sub $n = \frac{m}{M}$ (replace n with $\frac{m}{M}$ in $PV = nRT$).
$$\frac{Pm}{\rho} = \frac{mRT}{M}$$
Since m appears on both sides of the equation, it can be cancelled out.
$$\frac{P}{\rho} = \frac{RT}{M}$$
You can now use this equation to solve a gas density problem.
Note: $\frac{P}{\rho} = \frac{RT}{M}$ will most likely not be given to you on midterms/exams. So you need to be able to manipulate $PV = nRT$ to derive $\frac{P}{\rho} = \frac{RT}{M}$.

Example 1
Organofluorine compound has a density of 0.355g/L at the temperature of 17°C and the pressure of 189mm Hg. Find the molar mass of this compound.
$$\frac{P}{\rho} = \frac{RT}{M}$$
Note: you need to convert the temperature to K and pressure to atm in order to use $\frac{P}{\rho} = \frac{RT}{M}$.
$$Temperature\ in\ K = (17°C + 273.2°C) \times \frac{1K}{1°C}$$
$$Temperature\ in\ K = 290.2K$$
$$Pressure\ in\ atm = 189mm\,Hg \times \frac{1atm}{760mm\,Hg}$$
$$Pressure\ in\ atm = 0.249atm$$

P	0.249atm
ρ	0.355g/L
R	0.082057L•atm/K•mol
T	290.2K
M	?g/mol

$$\frac{P}{\rho} = \frac{RT}{M}$$

Rearrange for M by cross-multiplying.

$$PM = \rho RT$$

$$M = \frac{\rho RT}{P}$$

$$M = \frac{0.355 \ g/L \times 0.082057 \frac{L \cdot atm}{K \cdot mol} \times 290.2K}{0.249atm}$$

$$M = 33.99g/mol$$

The molar mass of organofluorine is 33.99g/mol.

Finding the molar mass using ideal gas law

In order to solve for the molar mass, you must be able to rearrange $PV = nRT$ to include molar mass.

$$PV = nRT$$

Sub in $n = \frac{m}{M}$ (replace n with $\frac{m}{M}$ in $PV = nRT$).

$$PV = \frac{mRT}{M}$$

Cross multiply

$$PVM = mRT$$

$$M = \frac{mRT}{PV}$$

Note: $M = \frac{mRT}{PV}$ will most likely not be given to you on midterms/exams.

So you need to be able to manipulate $PV = nRT$ to derive $M = \frac{mRT}{PV}$.

Example 1
1.007g of gas is put into a 0.452L container at 296.2K. The gas exerts pressure of 0.941atm. Find its molar mass.

P	0.941atm
m	1.007g
R	0.082057L•atm/K•mol
T	296.2K
M	?g/mol

V	0.452L

$$M = \frac{mRT}{PV}$$

$$M = \frac{1.007g \times 0.082057\frac{L \cdot atm}{K \cdot mol} \times 296.2K}{0.941atm \times 0.452L}$$

$$M = 57.54g/mol$$

The molar mass of the gas is 57.54g/mol.

Dalton's law of partial pressures

- This law is used for a container that has more than 1 type of gas
- Pressure is created when molecules collide with each other and with the walls of the container
- **Pressure is created by gases only! (not by liquids or solids!!)**

Partial pressure- the pressure created by 1 type of gas in a container

- Partial pressure measures how much each type of gas collides with the walls of container and other molecules
- The total pressure is the sum of partial pressures of each type of gas

$$P_T = P_A + P_B + \cdots$$

Note: P_T = total pressure created by all gases (atm), P_A= pressure created by gas A (atm), P_B= pressure created by gas B (atm)

Example 1
a) A container contains $H_2O_{(l)}$, $H_2O_{(g)}$, and $O_{2(g)}$. Which of these molecules create the pressure present in the container?
b) The pressure of water vapour is 0.032atm. The pressure of oxygen gas is 0.016atm. What is the total pressure in the container?

a) A container contains $H_2O_{(l)}$, $H_2O_{(g)}$, and $O_{2(g)}$. Which of these molecules create the pressure present in the container?
$2H_2O_{(l)} \rightarrow 2H_2O_{(g)} + O_{2(g)}$
The pressure is created by molecules that are in a gas state→ water vapour and oxygen gas.

b) The pressure of water vapour is 0.032atm. The pressure of oxygen gas is 0.016atm. What is the total pressure in the container?

	2 $H_2O_{(l)}$	→ 2$H_2O_{(g)}$	+ $O_{2(g)}$
P	-----------	0.032atm	0.016atm

$$P_T = P_{H_2O} + P_{O_2}$$
$$P_T = 0.032atm + 0.016atm$$

Surviving University: First Year Chemistry

$P_T = 0.048 atm$
The total pressure in the container is 0.048atm.

Mole fractions

- Mole fractions are used for containers which contain more than 1 type of a gas
- The total # of moles in a container is the sum of the # moles of each type of a gas

Mole fraction (X)- the # of moles of 1 type of gas divided by the total # of moles of gas in a container

- Mole fraction does not have units

$$X = \frac{n_A}{n_T}$$
Where $n_T = n_A + n_B + \cdots$

Note: n_A= # moles of gas A (mol), n_B= # moles of gas B (mol), n_T= total # moles of gas in container (mol), X= mole fraction

$$P_T V_T = n_T RT \text{ where}$$
$$P_1 = X_1 P_T$$
$$P_2 = X_2 P_T$$

Note: P_T= the total pressure present in a container (atm), V_T= the total volume of a container (L), n_T= the total # moles of gas in a container (mol), T= the temperature in a container (K), R=0.082057L•atm/K•mol, P_1= the pressure exerted by gas 1 (atm), P_2= the pressure exerted by gas 2 (atm), X_1= the mole fraction of gas 1, X_2= the mole fraction of gas 2

Example 1
Nitrogen gas is placed into a 0.500L container and the pressure is measured to be 0.921atm. Oxygen gas is placed into a 0.400L container and the pressure is measured to be 1.25atm. There is a barrier between the 2 containers. This barrier is then removed and the gases are mixed together. Find the partial pressures of each gas and the total pressure in the container.

Let P_1 be the pressure of nitrogen gas (atm), V_1 be the volume of nitrogen gas (L), P_2 be the pressure of oxygen gas (atm), V_2 be the volume of oxygen gas (L), P_t be the total pressure created by both gases (atm).

Steps
1. Find P_t
2. Find X_1 using $X_1 = \frac{n_1}{n_T}$
3. Find P_1 using $P_1 = X_1 P_T$

4. Find P_2 using $P_T = P_1 + P_2$

Since the barrier was removed, the total volume of container is

$V_T = V_1 + V_2$

$V_T = 0.500L + 0.400L$

$V_T = 0.900L$

	Nitrogen	Oxygen	Total
V	0.500L	0.400L	0.900L
P	0.921atm	1.25atm	?atm
Partial pressures	?atm	?atm	---------

You need to find the total pressure. You know $P_T = \frac{n_T RT}{V_T}$, but you do not know the temperature. So you need to remove temperature from the equation.

You know $P_T V_T = n_T RT$ ①

For gas 1: $P_1 V_1 = n_1 RT$ ②

For gas 2: $P_2 V_2 = n_2 RT$ ③

$n_T = n_1 + n_1$ ④

Rearrange ② and ③ for n and sub these 2 equations into ④.

From ②: $\frac{P_1 V_1}{RT} = n_1$

From ③: $\frac{P_2 V_2}{RT} = n_2$

From ④:

$n_T = n_1 + n_2$

$n_T = \frac{P_1 V_1}{RT} + \frac{P_2 V_2}{RT}$

Note: 1/RT is common on the right side of the equation→ factor out 1/RT.

$n_T = \frac{1}{RT}(P_1 V_1 + P_2 V_2)$

Now sub in n_T into ①

$P_T V_T = \frac{1}{RT}(P_1 V_1 + P_2 V_2)RT$

$P_T = \frac{\frac{1}{RT}(P_1 V_1 + P_2 V_2)RT}{V_T}$

RT cancel out→ you have cancelled out the temperature (which you did not know).

$P_T = \frac{P_1 V_1 + P_2 V_2}{V_T}$

Surviving University: First Year Chemistry

$$P_T = \frac{[(0.921 atm)(0.500L) + (1.25 atm)(0.400L)]}{0.900L}$$

$P_T = 1.068 atm$

Now you need to find the partial pressures of each gas.

$P_1 = X_1 P_T$

You need to find the mole fraction of nitrogen gas.

$X_1 = \frac{n_1}{n_T}$ ⑤

Where $\frac{P_1 V_1}{RT} = n_1$ ⑥, $n_T = \frac{1}{RT}(P_1 V_1 + P_2 V_2)$ ⑦

Sub ⑥ and ⑦ into ⑤.

$$X_1 = \frac{\frac{1}{RT}(P_1 V_1)}{\frac{1}{RT}(P_1 V_1 + P_2 V_2)}$$

1/RT cancel out.

$$X_1 = \frac{P_1 V_1}{(P_1 V_1 + P_2 V_2)}$$

$$X_1 = \frac{0.500L \times 0.921 atm}{[(0.921 atm)(0.500L) + (1.25 atm)(0.400L)]}$$

$X_1 = 0.48$

The mole fraction of nitrogen gas is 0.48.

Now you need to find the partial pressure of nitrogen gas.

$P_1 = X_1 P_T$

$P_1 = 0.48 \times 1.068 atm$

$P_1 = 0.51 atm$

The partial pressure of nitrogen gas is 0.51atm.

Now you need to find the partial pressure of oxygen gas.

$P_T = P_{N_2} + P_{O_2}$

$P_{O_2} = P_T - P_{N_2}$

$P_{O_2} = 1.068 atm - 0.51 atm$

$P_{O_2} = 0.56 atm$

The total pressure in container was 1.068atm. The partial pressure of oxygen gas was 0.56atm. The partial pressure of nitrogen gas was 0.51atm.

Kinetic molecular theory

Assumptions
- Gas molecules are in constant motion
  - Molecules move in different directions
- Pressure is due to collisions of gas molecules among themselves and the walls of container
- There are no attractive/repulsive forces between molecules

- All collisions are elastic (energy is conserved)
- Gas molecules have no volume
- Kinetic energy varies with temperature
    - ↑ temperature, ↑ kinetic energy
    - When the temperature is the same, all gases have the same kinetic energy

$$K = \frac{1}{2}mv^2$$

$$\sqrt{\bar{u}^2} = \sqrt{\frac{3RT}{M}}$$

Note: M must be in kg/mol, T must be in K

Where $R = 8.3145 \frac{J}{K \cdot mol}$

Note: K= kinetic energy of molecules (J), m=mass of molecules (kg), v= speed of molecules (m/s), ū= mean square speed (rms) (average speed of molecules) (m/s), T= temperature (K), M= molar mass (kg/mol)

Note: the value of R is different (from what was used in PV=nRT) since the units are J/K•mol (not L•atm/K•mol)

- As the mass of molecules ↑, the speed of molecules ↓

Example 1

Find the rms speed of nitrogen molecules at the temperature of 298K.

Note: you need to have molar mass in kg/mol.

$M_{N_2} = 2(14.01g/mol)$

$M_{N_2} = 28.02g/mol$

$M\_(N\_2) = 28.02g/mol \times (1kg)/(1000g)$

$M_{N_2} = 0.02802kg/mol$

ū	?m/s
R	$8.3145 \frac{J}{K \cdot mol}$
T	298K
M	0.02802kg/mol

$$\sqrt{\bar{u}^2} = \sqrt{\frac{3RT}{M}}$$

$$\bar{u} = \sqrt{\frac{3RT}{M}}$$

$$\bar{u} = \sqrt{\frac{3 \times 8.3145 \frac{J}{K \cdot mol} \times 298K}{0.02802 kg/mol}}$$

$\bar{u} = 515 m/s$

The rms speed of nitrogen molecules was 515m/s.

Gas diffusion and effusion

Diffusion- the movement of gases from high concentration (of gas molecules) to low concentration (of gas molecules)

- The rate of diffusion ↑ as the mass of molecules ↓
  - Lighter gases diffuse faster than heavier gases

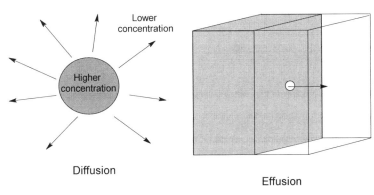

Diffusion

Effusion

Effusion- the movement of gas molecules from a container through a small hole into an empty container

Graham's law of effusion

- Rate of effusion is proportional to the temperature and inversely proportional to M (the molar mass of a gas)

$$\frac{Rate\ for\ A}{Rate\ for\ B} = \sqrt{\frac{M_B}{M_A}}$$

Note: Rate for A= rate of effusion for gas A; rate for B= rate of effusion for gas B; M_A= molar mass of gas A (g/mol); M_B= molar mass of gas B (g/mol)

Example 1
Gas A effuses through an opening 3 times slower than helium gas. Find the molar mass of gas A.
If helium has a rate of 3, then gas A will have a rate of 1 (gas A is slower than He).

	Gas A	He
Rate	1	3
M	?g/mol	4.003g/mol

$$\frac{Rate\ for\ He}{Rate\ for\ A} = \sqrt{\frac{M_A}{M_{He}}}$$

$$\frac{3}{1} = \sqrt{\frac{M_A}{4.003\ g/mol}}$$

$$3^2 = \frac{M_A}{4.003\ g/mol}$$

$$M_A = 3^2 \times 4.003 g/mol$$

$$M_A = 36 g/mol$$

The molar mass of unknown gas is 36g/mol.

Example 2

B_5H_9 effuses from 1 container into another at a rate of $4.5x10^{-6}$mol/h. Under the same conditions, gas A effuses at a rate of $5.2x10^{-6}$mol/h. What is the molar mass of gas A?

	B$_5$H$_9$	Gas A
Rate	4.5x10^{-6}mol/h	5.2x10^{-6}mol/h
M	?g/mol	?g/mol

$$M_{B_5H_9} = 5(10.81g/mol) + 9(1.01g/mol) = 63.14g/mol$$

$$\frac{Rate\ for\ B_5H_9}{Rate\ for\ gas\ A} = \sqrt{\frac{M_A}{M_{B_5H_9}}}$$

$$\frac{4.5 \times 10^{-6}mol/h}{5.2 \times 10^{-6}mol/h} = \sqrt{\frac{M_A}{63.14g/mol}}$$

$$0.865 = \sqrt{\frac{M_A}{63.14g/mol}}$$

$$0.865^2 = \frac{M_A}{63.14g/mol}$$

$$0.749 = \frac{M_A}{63.14g/mol}$$

$$M_A = 47.3g/mol$$

The molar mass of gas A is 47.3g/mol.

Surviving University: First Year Chemistry

Real gases

- Real gas molecules have volume and experience intermolecular forces
- When pressure is applied to a gas, it condenses into a liquid
- Real gases have a **critical point** (31.04°C)→ at this temperature no matter how much pressure is applied, liquid will not be formed→ instead **supercritical fluid** is formed (a new phase)

Part 22

Chemical Kinetics

Reaction rates

Rate equation

Integrated rate laws

Reaction orders

Half-life

Collision theory

Factors which affect reaction rate

Arrhenius equation

Chemical Kinetics

Chemical kinetics- deals with rates of chemical reactions
Reaction mechanism- shows steps how reactants form products

Reaction rates

- Different reactions occur at different speeds→ the speed of a reaction is influenced by certain factors

$$Rate\ of\ a\ reaction = \frac{change\ in\ concentration}{change\ in\ time} = \frac{d[conc]}{dt}$$
$$= \frac{[C]_f - [C]_i}{t_f - t_i}$$

Note: $[C]_f$= final concentration (M), $[C]_i$= initial concentration (M), t_f= final time (s or min or h), t_i= initial time (s or min or h)
Average reaction rate- the rate of change in concentration over a period of time
Instantaneous reaction rate- the rate of change in concentration at a specific instant

Rate of disappearance of reactants= Rate of appearance of products

If $aA + bB \rightarrow cC + dD$

$$-\frac{1}{a}\frac{d[A]}{dt} = -\frac{1}{b}\frac{d[B]}{dt} = \frac{1}{c}\frac{d[C]}{dt} = \frac{1}{d}\frac{d[D]}{dt}$$

Note: lower case letters represent stoichiometric coefficients, upper case letters represent molecules, brackets represent concentrations (M)
Note: negative signs mean that reactants are disappearing; positive signs mean that products are appearing

Example 1
The rate of disappearance of hydrogen gas is 4.5×10^{-4} mol/L·min. What is the rate of disappearance of nitrogen gas?
$$N_{2(g)} + 3H_{2(g)} \rightarrow 2NH_{3(g)}$$
$$-\frac{1}{1}\frac{d[N_2]}{dt} = -\frac{1}{3}\frac{d[H_2]}{dt}$$
$$\frac{d[N_2]}{dt} = \frac{1}{3}\frac{d[H_2]}{dt}$$
$$\frac{d[N_2]}{dt} = \frac{1}{3} \times 4.5 \times 10^{-4} mol/L \cdot min$$
$$\frac{d[N_2]}{dt} = 0.00015 mol/L \cdot min$$
The rate of disappearance of nitrogen gas is 0.00015mol/L·min.

Surviving University: First Year Chemistry

Rate equation

Rate constant (k)- relates rate and concentration at a specific temperature

- The rate constant is independent of concentration→ it varies with temperature

---

If $aA + bB \rightarrow xX$

$$Rate = k[A]^m[B]^n$$

Note: only concentrations of reactants go into the rate equation

$$Overall\ reaction\ order = m + n$$

Note: lower case letters represent stoichiometric coefficients and upper case letters represent molecules

Note: m and n are not stoichiometric coefficients→ they are determined experimentally

Note: k= rate constant, [A]= the concentration of reactant A (M), [B]= concentration of reactant B (M), m= reaction order for reactant A, n= reaction order for reactant B

Example 1
The following reaction is third order for NO and first order for Br₂.
$2NO_{(g)} + Br_{2(g)} \rightarrow 2NOBr_{(g)}$
a) Write the rate equation.
b) How does the rate of this reaction change if the concentration of NO is doubled?
c) How does the rate of this reaction change if the concentration of Br₂ is halved?

a) Write the rate equation.
You know $Rate = k[A]^m[B]^n$. Only reactants go into the rate equation.
$Rate = k[NO]^m[Br_2]^n$
Since the reaction is third order for NO, m=3; and first order for Br₂, n=1.
$Rate = k[NO]^3[Br_2]^1$

b) How does the rate of this reaction change if the concentration of NO is doubled?
If the initial concentration of NO was 1M, then the doubled concentration would be 2M.
Sub 2M for [NO] into $Rate = k[NO]^3[Br_2]^1$
$Rate = k[2]^3[Br_2]^1$
$Rate = k[8][Br_2]^1$
The rate will increase by a factor of 8.

Surviving University: First Year Chemistry

c) *How does the rate of this reaction change if the concentration of Br_2 is halved?*

If the initial concentration of Br_2 was 1M, then the halved concentration would be 1/2M.

Sub 1/2M for [Br_2] into $Rate = k[NO]^3[Br_2]^1$

$$Rate = k[NO]^3[\frac{1}{2}]^1$$

The rate will decrease by a factor of 2.

Example 2

The following table is for the reaction of X and Y at the temperature of 360K.

X+Y→Z

Note: [X]= concentration of reactant X (M), [Y]= concentration of reactant Y

Trial	[X] (M)	[Y] (M)	Rate of disappearance of X (M/s)
1	0.10	0.50	0.053
2	0.20	0.30	0.127
3	0.40	0.60	1.02
4	0.20	0.60	0.254
5	0.40	0.30	0.509

a) What is the order for X and Y?
b) Write the rate expression for this reaction.
c) What is the overall order of the reaction?
d) Find the rate constant at 360K.
e) Find rate of disappearance of reactants if the concentration of X is 0.30M/s and the concentration of Y is 0.40M.

a) What is the order for X and Y?
Use the following equation

$$\frac{Rate_2}{Rate_1} = \frac{k[X_2]^m[Y_2]^n}{k[X_1]^m[Y_1]^n}$$

Note: $Rate_2$= rate in trial 2 (M/s), $Rate_1$= rate in trial 1 (M/s), k= rate constant, [X_2]= concentration of 1st reactant in trial 2 (M), [X_1]= concentration of 1st reactant in trial 1 (M), [Y_2]= concentration of 2nd reactant in trial 2 (M), [Y_1]= concentration of 2nd reactant in trial 1 (M), m= order for X, n= order for Y

To find the order for Y, use 2 trials in which X is constant→ trials 2 and 4.

$$\frac{0.254M/s}{0.127M/s} = \frac{k\cancel{[0.20M]^m}[0.60M]^n}{k\cancel{[0.20M]^m}[0.30M]^n}$$

$2 = 2^n$

$n = 1$

Y is first order.

To find order for X, use 2 trials in which Y is constant→ trials 2 and 5.

$$\frac{0.509M/s}{0.127M/s} = \frac{k[0.40M]^m\cancel{[0.30M]^n}}{k[0.20M]^m\cancel{[0.30M]^n}}$$

$4 = 2^m$

$m = 2$

X is second order.

b) Write the rate expression for this reaction.
$Rate = k[Y]^1[X]^2$

c) What is the overall order of the reaction?

$Overall\ reaction\ order = m + n$

$Overall\ reaction\ order = 1 + 2$

$Overall\ reaction\ order = 3$

The overall order of the reaction is 3.

d) Find the rate constant at 360K.
Use data from any of the trials→ you need to find k.

$$k = \frac{Rate}{[Y]^1[X]^2}$$

Using trial 1

$$k = \frac{0.053M/s}{[0.50M]^1[0.10M]^2}$$

$k = 10.6$

The rate constant at 360K is 10.6.

e) Find rate of disappearance of reactants if the concentration of X is 0.30M/s and the concentration of Y is 0.40M.
$Rate = k[Y]^1[X]^2$
$-Rate = 10.6[0.40M]^1[0.30M]^2$
$-Rate = 0.3816M/s$
$Rate = -0.3816M/s$
Rate has a negative sign since reactants are disappearing.
The rate of disappearance of reactants was 0.3816M/s.

Surviving University: First Year Chemistry

Integrated rate laws

Order	Integrated rate equation	Graph	Slope	Units of k
0	$[R]_0 - [R]_t = kt$	$[R]_t$ vs t $[R]_t = -kt + [R]_0$ $[R]_t$ y slope x t	-k	mol/L·time
1	$\ln \left(\dfrac{[R]_t}{[R]_0} \right) = -kt$	ln[R]$_t$ vs t $\ln[R]_t = -kt + \ln[R]_0$ ln[R]$_t$ y slope x t	-k	time^{-1}
2	$\dfrac{1}{[R]_0} - \dfrac{1}{[R]_t} = kt$	1/[R]$_t$ vs t $1/[R]_t = +kt + 1/[R]_0$ 1/[R]$_t$ y slope x t	k	L/mol·time

Note: $[R]_o$= initial concentration (M), $[R]_t$= concentration at time t (M), k= rate constant, t= time (s or min or h), $\dfrac{[R]_0}{[R]_t}$= fraction remaining after time t

Example 1
Decomposition of sucrose is a first order reaction. The rate constant is 0.21hr^{-1}. Find the time it takes for sucrose to decompose from 0.010M to 0.0010M.
First order→ $\ln \left(\dfrac{[R]_t}{[R]_0} \right) = -kt$

[R]$_o$	0.010M
[R]$_t$	0.0010M
k	0.21hr^{-1}
t	?hr

$$\ln\left(\frac{[R]_t}{[R]_0}\right) = -kt$$

$$t = \frac{\ln\left(\frac{[R]_t}{[R]_0}\right)}{-k}$$

$$t = \frac{\ln\left(\frac{0.0010\ M}{0.010\ M}\right)}{-0.21\ hr^{-1}}$$

$$t = 11\ hr$$

The time it took for sucrose to decompose from 0.010M to 0.0010M was 11 hours.

Half-life

Half-life- the time it takes for concentration to decrease to ½ of its value (ex. it takes 32 min for concentration of azomethane to decrease from 5M to 2.5M→ half-life is 32min)

$$t_{1/2} = \frac{\ln 2}{k}$$

Note: $t_{1/2}$= half-life (s or min or h or days), k= rate constant (s^{-1} or min^{-1} or h^{-1} or days^{-1})

Example 1
Half-life of a reaction is 4000s. Find the rate constant for the reaction.

t$_{1/2}$	4000s
k	?s^{-1}

$$t_{1/2} = \frac{\ln 2}{k}$$

$$k = \frac{\ln 2}{t_{1/2}}$$

$$k = \frac{\ln 2}{4000s}$$

$$k = 0.000173\ s^{-1}$$

The rate constant of the reaction was 0.000173s^{-1}.

Surviving University: First Year Chemistry

Example 2
The half-life of radon-222 is 3.8 days. If initially there are 4.0×10^{13} atoms/L of radon, what is the concentration of radon-222 after 30 days? This is a first order reaction.
Steps

1. Find the rate constant using $t_{1/2} = \dfrac{\ln 2}{k}$

2. Find the concentration after 30 days using $\ln \left(\dfrac{[R]_t}{[R]_0}\right) = -kt$

$[Rn]_o$	4.0×10^{13} atoms/L
$[Rn]_t$	? atoms/L
k	? days^{-1}
t	30 days
$t_{1/2}$	3.8 days

$$t_{1/2} = \frac{\ln 2}{k}$$

$$k = \frac{\ln 2}{t_{1/2}}$$

$$k = \frac{\ln 2}{3.8 days}$$

$$k = 0.18 days^{-1}$$

$$\ln \left(\frac{[Rn]_0}{[Rn]_t}\right) = -kt$$

$$\frac{[Rn]_t}{[Rn]_0} = e^{-kt}$$

$$[Rn]_t = [Rn]_0 \times e^{-kt}$$

$$[Rn]_t = (4.0 \times 10^{13} atoms/L) \times e^{-(0.18 days^{-1})(30 days)}$$

$$[Rn]_t = 1.8 \times 10^{11} atoms/L$$

The concentration of radon-222 after 30 days was 1.8×10^{11} atoms/L.

Collision Theory

In order for reactants to form products, the following conditions must be met:

- Molecules must collide with each other
- Molecules must collide with enough energy to break bonds and form new bonds
- Molecules must collide specific at angles (correct orientation in space) that enable the formation of products

Types of collisions

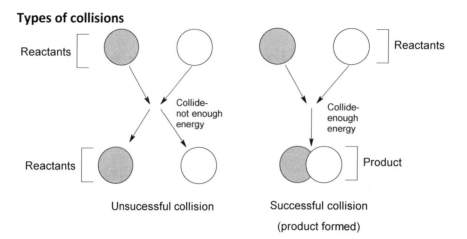

Unsuccessful collision

Successful collision
(product formed)

Factors which affect reaction rate

1. Concentration
2. Temperature
3. Surface area
4. Catalyst

Concentration

 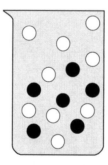

Low concentration   High concentration

- As the concentration ↑, the reaction rate ↑
  - ○ ↑ concentration means that there are more molecules per unit volume
    - ■ Higher amount of molecules in the same amount of space means that there is a higher chance of a successful collision
      - • There are more successful collisions and more products are produced

Temperature

- as the temperature ↑, the reaction rate ↑

Surviving University: First Year Chemistry

- o ↑ temperature means that energy is added to the system
  - Energy is added in the form of heat
- o This energy is transferred into kinetic energy of molecules→ velocity of molecules ↑
  - More molecules have enough energy to produce a successful collision
    - There are more successful collisions and more products are produced

Surface area

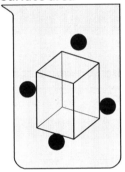 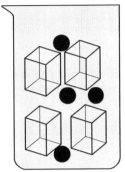

Small surface area   Large surface area

- as the surface area ↑, the reaction rate ↑
  - o ↑ surface area means there are more molecules to collide with
  - o ↑ amount of molecules can create a successful collision
    - There are more successful collisions and more products are produced

Catalyst

Activation energy- the minimum amount of energy required for reactants to form products

- If reactants do not have the minimum amount of energy to form products, products are not formed

Catalyst- a substance that increases the rate of the reaction by lowering the activation energy

- A catalyst is not consumed in a chemical reaction
- Catalyst ↑ reaction rate
  - o Since catalyst lowers the activation energy, more molecules possess enough energy to form products
  - o ↑ amount of molecules can create a successful collision
    - There are more successful collisions and more products are produced

Arrhenius equation

- The rate constant (k) changes as temperature changes

$$k = Ae^{\frac{-E_a}{RT}}$$
$$\text{where } R = 8.3145 \times 10^{-3} \frac{KJ}{K \cdot mol}$$
T must be in K

Note: k= rate constant (s^{-1} or min^{-1} or h^{-1}), A= frequency of collisions, E_a= activation energy (kJ), T= temperature (K)

$$\ln\left(\frac{k_1}{k_2}\right) = -\frac{E_a}{R}\left(\frac{1}{T_2} - \frac{1}{T_1}\right)$$
$$\text{Note: } \ln\left(\frac{k_1}{k_2}\right) = lnk_1 - lnk_2$$
$$\text{where } R = 8.3145 \times 10^{-3} \frac{KJ}{K \cdot mol}$$
T must be in K

Note: k_1= rate constant at temperature 1 (s^{-1} or min^{-1} or h^{-1}), k_2= rate constant at temperature 2 (s^{-1} or min^{-1} or h^{-1}), E_a= activation energy (kJ), T_1= temperature 1 (K), T_2= temperature 2 (K)

Example 1
Find the activation energy if k is $3.46x10^{-5}s^{-1}$ at 298K and $1.5x10^{-3}s^{-1}$ at 328K.

E_a	?kJ/mol
k_1	$3.46x10^{-5}s^{-1}$
k_2	$1.5x10^{-3}s^{-1}$
T_1	298K
T_2	328K
R	$8.3145x10^{-3}$kJ/K•mol

$$\ln\left(\frac{k_1}{k_2}\right) = -\frac{E_a}{R}\left(\frac{1}{T_2} - \frac{1}{T_1}\right)$$

$$E_a = \frac{\ln\left(\frac{k_1}{k_2}\right)}{\left(\frac{1}{T_2} - \frac{1}{T_1}\right)} \times (-R)$$

$$E_a = \frac{\ln\left(\frac{3.46 \times 10^{-5}s^{-1}}{1.5 \times 10^{-3}s^{-1}}\right)}{\left(\frac{1}{328K} - \frac{1}{298K}\right)} \times \left(-8.3145 \times 10^{-3} \frac{KJ}{K \cdot mol}\right)$$

$$E_a = -102KJ/mol$$
The activation energy is -102kJ/mol.

Surviving University: First Year Chemistry

Part 23

Chemical Equilibrium

Equilibrium and reaction constants

Equilibrium constant expression

Reaction quotient

ICE table

Equilibrium problems

Manipulating equilibrium constant expression

Le Chatelier's principle

Chemical Equilibrium

- All chemical reactions are reversible→ reactants form products (**forward reaction**) and products form reactants (**reverse reaction**)
- Reversible reaction is indicated by ⇌
- Forward and reverse reactions occur until equilibrium is reached

Equilibrium- when the rate of a forward reaction is equal to the rate of a reverse reaction

- If the concentration of products is greater than the concentration of reactants at equilibrium, then reaction is product favoured
- If the concentration of reactants is greater than the concentration of products at equilibrium→ reaction is reactant favoured

Equilibrium and reaction constants

Equilibrium constant (K)- indicates whether the reaction is reactant or product favoured at equilibrium; depends on temperature

Reaction quotient (Q)- indicates whether the reaction is reactant or product favoured at any point during the reaction

	K
Product favoured	>1
Reactant favoured	<1

Equilibrium constant expression

- The equilibrium constant (K) is used in both aqueous and gaseous solutions

If $aA + bB \rightleftharpoons cC + dD$

$$K_c = \frac{[products]}{[reactants]} = \frac{[C]^c[D]^d}{[A]^a[B]^b}$$

Solids and liquids <u>never</u> appear in the equilibrium expression!

$$K_p = \frac{[products]}{[reactants]} = \frac{P_C^c P_D^d}{P_A^a P_B^b}$$

Note: the lower case letters represent stoichiometric coefficients and the upper case letters represent names of molecules

Note: K_c= equilibrium constant for an aqueous solution (no units), K_p= equilibrium constant for a gaseous solution (no units), []= concentration (M), P= pressure (atm)

Surviving University: First Year Chemistry

Example 1

Write the equilibrium constant expression for the following reaction. Use concentrations.

$Fe_{(s)} + 5CO_{(g)} \rightleftharpoons Fe(CO)_{5(g)}$

Solids do not appear in the equilibrium expression. Use stoichiometric coefficients.

$$K_c = \frac{[products]}{[reactants]} = \frac{[Fe(CO)_5]^1}{[CO]^5}$$

Example 2

Write the equilibrium constant expression for the following. Use concentrations.

$PCl_{3(l)} + Cl_{2(g)} \rightleftharpoons PCl_{5(s)}$

Liquids and solids do not appear in the equilibrium expression. Use stoichiometric coefficients.

$$K_c = \frac{[products]}{[reactants]} = \frac{1}{[Cl_2]^1}$$

Reaction quotient

- Reaction quotient is used in both aqueous and gaseous solutions

If $aA + bB \rightleftharpoons cC + dD$

$$Q_c = \frac{[products]}{[reactants]} = \frac{[C]^c[D]^d}{[A]^a[B]^b}$$

Solids and liquids <u>never</u> appear in the reaction quotient expression!

$$Q_p = \frac{[products]}{[reactants]} = \frac{P_C^c P_D^d}{P_A^a P_B^b}$$

Note: the lower case letters represent stoichiometric coefficients and the upper case letters represent names of molecules

Note: Q_c = reaction quotient for an aqueous solution (no units), Q_p = reaction quotient for a gaseous solution (no units), []= concentration (M), P= pressure (atm)

System	
Must shift to the left to reach equilibrium	Q>K
Is at equilibrium	Q=K
Must shift to the right to reach equilibrium	Q<K

Example 1

For the following reaction, the equilibrium constant (K) is 170 at the temperature of 298K. After a certain period of time, the concentration of NO_2 is 0.010M and the concentration of N_2O_4 is 0.020M. Is the reaction at equilibrium? What is the direction in which the reaction has to shift to reach equilibrium?

$2NO_{2(g)} \rightleftharpoons N_2O_{4(g)}$

Q	?
[N₂O₄]	0.010M
[NO₂]	0.020M
K	170

$$Q_c = \frac{[products]}{[reactants]} = \frac{[N_2O_4]^1}{[NO_2]^2}$$

$$Q_c = \frac{[0.010M]^1}{[0.020M]^2}$$

$$Q_c = 25$$

Since Q<K (25<170), the reaction is not at equilibrium. The reaction must produce more products (shift to the right) in order to reach equilibrium.

ICE table

- When reactants are put into a flask, products are produced
- ICE table summarizes concentrations/pressures of reactants and products at the beginning of the reaction and at equilibrium
- ICE table has the following general form
  - Change in concentration symbolizes the increase or decrease in concentration of reactant/product as the system reaches equilibrium

Equation:	
I= initial concentration (M)	
C= change in concentration	
E= concentration at equilibrium (M)	

Surviving University: First Year Chemistry

Types of equilibrium problems

1. Solve for x using simple algebra→ the equation will be linear or cubic→ the highest degree will not be x^2
2. Solve for x using the quadratic equation→ the highest degree will bt x^2
3. Solve for x by taking a square root of both sides→ both the numerator and the denominator of equation will be squared $(^2)$

Problem type 1→ simple algebra

Example 1
2.00mol of NOCl were placed into a 1.00L flask. At equilibrium, 0.66M of NO was present. Find the equilibrium constant.
$2NOCl_{(g)} \rightleftharpoons 2NO_{(g)} + Cl_{2(g)}$
Steps
1. Use $C = \frac{n}{V}$ to find the initial concentration of NOCl
2. Make an ICE table
3. Solve for x
4. Find concentrations of all species at equilibrium
5. Make an equilibrium expression using $K_c = \frac{[products]}{[reactants]}$
6. Sub in concentrations of all species at equilibrium to find K

First you need to find the initial concentration of NOCl.

$$C = \frac{n}{V}$$

$$C_{NOCl} = \frac{2.00mol}{1.00L}$$

$$C_{NOCl} = 2.00M$$

2.00M of NOCl were placed into the flask→ NO and Cl_2 were originally not present in the flask (so their concentrations were 0M).

	$2NOCl_{(g)}$	$\rightleftharpoons 2NO_{(g)}$	$+Cl_{2\,(g)}$
I	2.00M	0M	0M
C			
E			

You do not know the change in concentration→ use x to represent the change in concentration.
Since the concentration of reactant is higher than the concentration of products, the system will shift to the right in order to produce more products.

In order to show that NOCl will be lost, put a negative sign in front of x for NOCl. In order to show that NO and Cl_2 will be gained, put a positive sign in front of x for NO and Cl_2.

Put the stoichiometric coefficient in front of x for each of the species.

	$2NOCl_{(g)}$	$\rightleftharpoons 2NO_{(g)}$	$+Cl_{2(g)}$
I	2.00M	0M	0M
C	-2x	+2x	+x
E			

The equilibrium concentration is the initial concentration plus the change in concentration

You know that [NO] at equilibrium was 0.66M.

	$2NOCl_{(g)}$	$\rightleftharpoons 2NO_{(g)}$	$+Cl_{2(g)}$
I	2.00M	0M	0M
C	-2x	+2x	+x
E	2.00+(-2x)	0+2x= 0.66M	0+x

Now solve for x.

$0 + 2x = 0.66M$

$x = 0.66M \div 2$

$x = 0.33M$

Use x=0.33M to find [NOCl] and [Cl_2] at equilibrium.

$[NOCl]_{eq} = 2.00 - 2x = 2.00M - 2(0.33M) = 1.34M$

$[Cl_2]_{eq} = x = 0.33M$

$K_c = \dfrac{[products]}{[reactants]} = \dfrac{[Cl_2]^1[NO]^2}{[NOCl]^2}$

$K_c = \dfrac{[0.33M]^1[0.66M]^2}{[1.34M]^2}$

$K_c = 0.080M$

The equilibrium constant is 0.080M.

Problem type 2→ the quadratic equation

Example 1

0.50M of N_2O_4 are placed into a flask. The equilibrium constant is 0.0059. Find the equilibrium concentrations of each of the species.

$N_2O_{4(g)} \rightleftharpoons 2NO_{2(g)}$

Surviving University: First Year Chemistry

See problem type 1 for detailed description of how to solve equilibrium problems

Steps
1. Make an ICE table
2. Make an equilibrium expression using $K_c = \frac{[products]}{[reactants]}$
3. Solve for x
4. Find concentrations of all species at equilibrium

Since N_2O_4 was placed into an empty flask, the original concentration of NO_2 was 0M.

The initial concentration of N_2O_4 is bigger than the initial concentration of NO_2. The concentration of N_2O_4 will decrease and the concentration of NO_2 will increase.

	$N_2O_{4\,(g)} \rightleftharpoons$	$2NO_{2(g)}$
I	0.50M	0M
C	-x	+2x
E	0.50-x	0+2x

$$K_c = \frac{[products]}{[reactants]} = \frac{[NO_2]^2}{[N_2O_4]^1}$$

$$K_c = 0.0059 = \frac{(2x)^2}{0.50 - x}$$

$$0.0059(0.50 - x) = 4x^2$$

$$0.0029 - 0.0059x = 4x^2$$

$$-4x^2 - 0.0059x + 0.0029 = 0$$

Use the quadratic formula to solve for x.

$$x = \frac{-b \pm \sqrt{b^2 - 4ac}}{2a}$$

$$x = \frac{0.0059 \pm \sqrt{(-0.0059)^2 - 4(-4)(0.0029)}}{2(-4)}$$

$$x = 0.026M \text{ or} -0.028M$$

Since concentration cannot be a negative value, -0.028M is inadmissible.

$[N_2O_4]_{eq} = 0.50 - x = 0.50M - 0.026M = 0.47M$

$[NO_2]_{eq} = 2x = 2(0.026M) = 0.052M$

The equilibrium concentration of N_2O_4 was 0.47M and the equilibrium concentration of NO_2 was 0.052M.

Problem type 3→ taking a square root of both sides

Example 1
1.00M of H_2 and I_2 are placed into a flask. The equilibrium constant is 55.3. Find the equilibrium concentrations of all species.
$H_{2(g)}+ I_{2(g)} \rightleftharpoons 2HI_{(g)}$
See problem type 1 for detailed description of how to solve equilibrium problems
Steps
1. Make an ICE table
2. Make an equilibrium expression using $K_c = \frac{[products]}{[reactants]}$
3. Solve for x
4. Find concentrations of all species at equilibrium

Since there are more reactants than products, the concentration of reactants will decrease and the concentration of products will increase.

	$H_{2(g)}+$	$I_{2(g)}$	$\rightleftharpoons 2HI_{(g)}$
I	1.00M	1.00M	0M
C	-x	-x	+2x
E	1.00-x	1.00-x	0+2x

$$K_c = \frac{[products]}{[reactants]} = \frac{[HI]^2}{[I_2]^1[H_2]^1}$$

$$K_c = 55.3 = \frac{(2x)^2}{(1.00 - x)^2}$$

In order to solve for x, take a square root of both sides

$$\sqrt{55.3} = \sqrt{\frac{(2x)^2}{(1.00 - x)^2}}$$

$$\sqrt{55.3} = \frac{2x}{1.00 - x}$$

$\sqrt{55.3}\,(1.00 - x) = 2x$ Expand

$\sqrt{55.3} - \sqrt{55.3}\,x - 2x = 0$

$-\sqrt{55.3}\,x - 2x = -\sqrt{55.3}$ Multiply both sides by (-1)

$\sqrt{55.3}\,x + 2x = \sqrt{55.3}$ Factor out x

$x(\sqrt{55.3} + 2) = \sqrt{55.3}$

$$x = \frac{\sqrt{55.3}}{(\sqrt{55.3} + 2)}$$

$x = 0.79M$

$[H_2]_{eq} = 1.00 - x = 1.00M - 0.79M = 0.21M$
$[I_2]_{eq} = 1.00 - x = 1.00M - 0.79M = 0.21M$
$[HI]_{eq} = 2x = 2(0.79M) = 1.58M$

The equilibrium concentration of H_2 and I_2 was 0.21M. The equilibrium concentration of HI was 1.58M.

Manipulating equilibrium constant expression

1. Changing direction of the reaction (from forward to backward)

$$K_{new} = \frac{1}{K_{old}}$$

Note: K_{new}= equilibrium constant for the new reaction, K_{old}= equilibrium constant for the original reaction

Example 1

$S_{(s)}+O_{2(g)} \rightleftharpoons SO_{2(g)}$ $K = \frac{[SO_2]}{[O_2]}$

$SO_{2(g)} \rightleftharpoons S_{(s)}+O_{2(g)}$ $K = \frac{[O_2]}{[SO_2]}$

2. Adding equations

$$K_{net} = K_1 \times K_2$$

Note: K_{net}= equilibrium constant for the overall reaction, K_1= equilibrium constant for reaction 1, K_2= equilibrium constant for reaction 2

Example 1
Find K_{net}.

Net:	$S_{(s)}+ 3/2O_{2(g)} \rightleftharpoons SO_{2(g)}$	K_{net}= ?
	1. $S_{(s)}+ O_{2(g)} \rightleftharpoons SO_{2(g)}$	$K_1 = \dfrac{[SO_2]^1}{[O_2]}$
	2. $SO_{2(g)} + \frac{1}{2} O_{2(g)} \rightleftharpoons SO_{3(g)}$	$K_2 = \dfrac{[SO_3]^1}{[O_2]^{\frac{1}{2}}[SO_2]}$

$K_{net} = K_1 \times K_2$

$K_{net} = \dfrac{[SO_2]^1}{[O_2]} \times \dfrac{[SO_3]^1}{[O_2]^{\frac{1}{2}}[SO_2]^1}$

$K_{net} = \dfrac{[SO_3]^1}{[O_2]^{\frac{3}{2}}}$

3. Changing coefficients (multiplying a reaction by a number)

$$K_{new} = (K_{old})^n$$

Surviving University: First Year Chemistry

Note: n= # that the reaction is multiplied by, K_{new}= equilibrium constant for the new reaction, K_{old}= equilibrium constant for the original reaction

Example 1
Find K_{new}.

$S_{(s)} + O_{2(g)} \rightleftharpoons SO_{2(g)}$	$K_{old} = \dfrac{[SO_2]^1}{[O_2]}$
$2S_{(s)} + 2O_{2(g)} \rightleftharpoons 2SO_{2(g)}$	$K_{new} = ?$

$$K_{new} = (K_{old})^n$$
$$K_{new} = (\frac{[SO_2]^1}{[O_2]})^2$$

$$K_{new} = \frac{[SO_2]^2}{[O_2]^2}$$

Le Chatelier's Principle

- Equilibrium can be moved by changing temperature, concentrations, volumes, and/or pressure
- When equilibrium is disturbed, the system adjusts itself in order to oppose the change

1. Change in temperature

Reaction	Change		Equilibrium	K
Endothermic	Temperature	↑	Shifts towards products	↑
($\Delta H° > 0$)	Temperature	↓	Shifts towards reactants	↓
Exothermic	Temperature	↑	Shifts towards reactants	↓
($\Delta H° < 0$)	Temperature	↓	Shifts towards products	↑

Note: if the equilibrium shifts towards products, then the concentration of products increases; if the equilibrium shifts towards reactants, then the concentration of reactants increases

2. Catalyst
- Reaction comes to equilibrium faster
- K and concentrations at equilibrium do not change

3. Adding reactant/taking away product
- K does not change
- Equilibrium shifts to the right to produce more products→ the concentration of products increases

Surviving University: First Year Chemistry

4. **Adding product/taking away reactant**
- K does not change
- Equilibrium shifts to the left to produce more reactants→ the concentration of reactants increases

5. **Increasing pressure by decreasing volume**
- The system moves to the side with the least # of molecules

Example 1
0.500mol of $COCl_2$ are placed into a 2.0L flask. When the system reaches equilibrium, 2mol of CO are added to the flask. The temperature remains constant. K_c is 5.2.
$CO_{(g)} + Cl_{2(g)} \rightleftharpoons COCl_{2(g)}$
a) How is equilibrium affected by adding more CO to the flask?
b) Find $[COCl_2]$, $[CO]$, and $[Cl_2]$ at equilibrium.

a) How is equilibrium affected by adding more CO to the flask?
Adding more reactant causes equilibrium to shift to the right to produce more products. The concentration of reactants will decrease and the concentration of products will increase.

b) Find $[COCl_2]$, $[CO]$, and $[Cl_2]$ at equilibrium.
This problem has 2 parts.
Part 1: the system when 0.500mol of $COCl_2$ were placed into 2.0L flask→ find the equilibrium concentrations of each species.
Part 2: disturbing equilibrium: 2mol of CO were added to the flask→ find the new equilibrium concentrations of each species.
Steps: Part 1
1. Use $C = \frac{n}{V}$ to find the initial concentration of $COCl_2$
2. Make an ICE table
3. Make equilibrium expression→ sub in K= 5.2
4. Solve for x
5. Find concentrations of all species at equilibrium
Steps: Part 2
6. Use $C = \frac{n}{V}$ to find the initial concentration of $COCl_2$
7. Find the new initial concentration of $COCl_2$ in the flask
8. Make an ICE table
9. Make an equilibrium expression→ sub in K= 5.2
10. Solve for x
11. Find the concentrations of all species at the new equilibrium

Part 1
Need to find the initial concentration of $COCl_2$

$$C = \frac{n}{V}$$

$$C_{COCl_2} = \frac{0.500 mol}{2.0L}$$

$$C_{COCl_2} = 0.25M$$

Since there are only products at the beginning of the reaction, the reaction will shift to the left to produce reactants.

	$CO_{(g)}$+	$Cl_{2(g)} \rightleftharpoons$	$COCl_{2(g)}$
I	0M	0M	0.25M
C	+x	+x	-x
E	x	x	0.25-x

$$K_c = \frac{[products]}{[reactants]} = \frac{[COCl_2]^1}{[CO]^1[Cl_2]^1}$$

$$K_c = 5.2 = \frac{(0.25 - x)}{x^2}$$

$$5.2x^2 = 0.25 - x$$

$$5.2x^2 + x - 0.25 = 0$$

Use the quadratic formula to solve for x.

$$x = \frac{-b \pm \sqrt{b^2 - 4ac}}{2a}$$

$$x = \frac{-1 \pm \sqrt{1^2 - 4(5.2)(-0.25)}}{2(5.2)}$$

$$x = 0.143M \text{ or} - 0.336M$$

Concentration cannot be a negative value, -0.336 is inadmissible.

$$[CO]_{eq_1} = x = 0.143M$$

$$[Cl_2]_{eq_1} = x = 0.143M$$

$$[COCl_2]_{eq_1} = 0.25M - x = 0.25M - 0.143M = 0.107M$$

Part 2

Now consider this part as a new problem→ you have 0.0143M of CO, 0.0143M of Cl_2, and 0.107M of $COCl_2$. You then add 2.00mol of CO to a 2.0L flask. You need to find new concentrations at a new equilibrium. Need to find the new initial concentration of $COCl_2$.

$$C = \frac{n}{V}$$

$$C_{COCl_2} = \frac{2.00 mol}{2.0L}$$

$$C_{COCl_2} = 1.0M$$

Surviving University: First Year Chemistry

Since there are more reactants at the beginning of the reaction, the reaction will shift to the right to produce products.

	$CO_{(g)}+$	$Cl_{2(g)} \rightleftharpoons$	$COCl_{2(g)}$
I	0.143M+1.0M =1.143M	0.143M	0.107M
C	-x	-x	+x
E	1.143-x	0.143-x	0.107+x

$$K_c = \frac{[products]}{[reactants]} = \frac{[COCl_2]^1}{[CO]^1[Cl_2]^1}$$
$$K_c = 5.2 = \frac{(0.107 + x)}{(0.143 - x)(1.143 - x)}$$
$$5.2 = \frac{(0.107 + x)}{0.163 - 1.286x + x^2}$$
$$5.2 \times (0.163 - 1.286x + x^2) = 0.107 + x$$
$$0.848 - 6.69x + 5.2x^2 = 0.107 + x$$
$$5.2x^2 - 7.69x + 0.741 = 0$$

Use the quadratic formula to solve for x.
$$x = \frac{-b \pm \sqrt{b^2 - 4ac}}{2a}$$
$$x = \frac{7.69 \pm \sqrt{(-7.69)^2 - 4(5.2)(0.741)}}{2(5.2)}$$
$$x = 0.104M \text{ or } 1.375M$$

Since a concentration cannot be a negative value, 1.375M is inadmissible (since $[CO] = 1.143M - 1.375M = -0.232M$).
$[CO]_{eq2} = 1.143 - x = 1.143M - 0.104M = 1.039M$
$[Cl_2]_{eq2} = 0.143 - x = 0.143M - 0.104M = 0.039M$
$[COCl_2]_{eq2} = 0.107 + x = 0.107M + 0.104M = 0.211M$

The equilibrium concentrations after the addition of 2.00mol of CO were [CO]=1.039M, [Cl₂]=0.039M, [COCl₂]=0.211M.

Le Chatelier's Principle problem involving Kₚ

Example 1
K_p for the following reaction at 298K is 0.16. 1.00atm of N_2O_3 are placed inside a 1.00L flask. The reaction is endothermic.
$N_2O_{3(g)} \rightleftharpoons NO_{(g)} + NO_{2(g)}$
a) Find the partial pressures of all gases at equilibrium.

b) How will the system respond to
- The addition of more $N_2O_{3(g)}$?
- Removal of some NO?
- Decrease in temperature?
- Decrease in volume by increasing pressure?

c) The volume of the flask is compressed to 0.50L. Find new equilibrium pressures of all species.

a) Find the partial pressures of all gases at equilibrium.
Steps
1. Make an ICE table
2. Make an equilibrium expression→ sub in K= 0.16
3. Solve for x
4. Find pressures of all species at equilibrium

Since there are only reactants at the beginning of the reaction, the reaction will shift to the right to produce products.

	$N_2O_{3(g)} \rightleftharpoons$	$NO_{(g)}$ +	$NO_{2(g)}$
I	1.00atm	0atm	0atm
C	-x	+x	+x
E	1.00-x	x	x

$$K_p = \frac{P_{products}}{P_{reactants}} = \frac{P_{NO_2} P_{NO}}{P_{N_2O_3}}$$

$$K_p = 0.16 = \frac{x^2}{1-x}$$

$$0.16(1-x) = x^2$$

$$0.16 - 0.16x = x^2$$

$$-x^2 - 0.16x + 0.16 = 0 \qquad \text{Multiply by (-1)}$$

$$x^2 + 0.16x - 0.16 = 0$$

Use the quadratic formula to solve for x.

$$x = \frac{-b \pm \sqrt{b^2 - 4ac}}{2a}$$

$$x = \frac{-0.16 \pm \sqrt{(0.16)^2 - 4(1)(-0.16)}}{2(1)}$$

$$x = 0.33atm \text{ or } -0.49atm$$

Pressure cannot be a negative value, -0.49atm is inadmissible

$$P_{NO} = x = 0.33atm$$

$$P_{NO_2} = x = 0.33atm$$

$$P_{N_2O_3} = 1 - x = 1atm - 0.33atm = 0.67atm$$

Surviving University: First Year Chemistry

The equilibrium pressure of NO and NO_2 was 0.33atm. The equilibrium pressure of N_2O_3 was 0.67atm.

b) How will the system respond to
- *The addition of more $N_2O_{3(g)}$?*

Adding reactant will cause the system to move right to produce more products.
- *Removal of some NO?*

Removal of product will cause the system to move to the right to produce more products.
- *Decrease in temperature?*

The reaction is endothermic→ energy in the form of heat is needed for reaction to occur. If heat is removed, the reaction will move to the left (there is not enough energy to produce products).
- *Decrease in volume by increasing pressure?*

The equilibrium will move to the side with least # of molecules. There is 1 molecule on the left and 2 molecules on the right. The equilibrium will move to the left.

c) The volume of the flask is compressed to 0.50L. Find new equilibrium pressures of all species.

Steps
1. Find the change in pressure of the system using $P_1V_1 = P_2V_2$
2. Multiply the pressure of each specie at equilibrium by a factor from step 1
3. Make an ICE table
4. Make an equilibrium expression→ sub in K= 0.16
5. Solve for x
6. Find pressures of all species at equilibrium

Since the volume of the system changed, the pressure of the system changed. Let's assume that the overall initial pressure of the system was 1atm.

V_1	1.00L
P_1	1.00atm
V_2	0.50L
P_2	?atm

$$P_1V_1 = P_2V_2$$
$$P_2 = \frac{V_1P_1}{V_2}$$

$$P_2 = \frac{1.00L \times 1.00atm}{0.50L}$$

$$P_2 = 2.0atm$$

The pressure increased by a factor of 2 (from 1.00atm to 2.0atm). This means that the pressure of all species increased by a factor of 2.

Since pressure increased, the equilibrium shifted to the side with the least # of molecules. There is 1 molecule on the left side and 2 molecules on the right side. The system shifted to the left to produce more reactants.

	$N_2O_{3(g)} \rightleftharpoons$	$NO_{(g)} +$	$NO_{2(g)}$
I	2(0.67atm) = 1.34atm	2(0.33atm) = 0.66atm	2(0.33atm) = 0.66atm
C	+x	-x	-x
E	1.34+x	0.66-x	0.66-x

Note: K_p value does not change since the equilibrium constant depends on temperature. It does not pressure or volume.

$$K_p = \frac{P_{products}}{P_{reactants}} = \frac{P_{NO_2}P_{NO}}{P_{N_2O_3}}$$

$$K_p = 0.16 = \frac{(0.66 - x)(0.66 - x)}{1.34 + x}$$

$$0.16(1.34 + x) = x^2 - 1.32x + 0.436$$

$$0.2144 + 0.16x = x^2 - 1.32x + 0.436$$

$$x^2 - 1.48x + 0.22 = 0$$

Use the quadratic formula to solve for x.

$$x = \frac{-b \pm \sqrt{b^2 - 4ac}}{2a}$$

$$x = \frac{1.48 \pm \sqrt{(-1.48)^2 - 4(1)(0.22)}}{2(1)}$$

$$x = 0.17atm \text{ or } 1.31atm$$

Since pressure cannot be a negative value, 1.31atm is inadmissible (since $P_{NO} = 0.66atm - 1.31atm = -0.65atm$).

$$P_{NO} = 1.34 + x = 1.34atm + 0.17atm = 1.51atm$$

$$P_{NO_2} = 0.66 - x = 0.66atm - 0.17atm = 0.49atm$$

$$P_{N_2O_3} = 0.66 - x = 0.66atm - 0.17atm = 0.49atm$$

The new equilibrium pressure of NO and NO_2 was 0.49atm. The new equilibrium pressure of N_2O_3 was 1.51atm.

Part 24

Acids and Bases

Autoionization of water

pH and pOH

Equilibrium constants for acids and bases

Direction of an acid-base reaction

Acid-base reactions

Calculations with acids and bases

Polyprotic acids and bases

Lewis concept of acids and bases

Acid-base properties of salts

Surviving University: First Year Chemistry

Acids and Bases

Please review part 3 for the introduction about acids and bases

Autoionization of water

$2H_2O_{(l)} \rightleftharpoons H_3O^+_{(aq)} + OH^-_{(aq)}$

- Water molecules produce H_3O^+ and OH^- ions, which are then converted into H_2O molecules
- Autoionization of water is a product favoured reaction
    - In 1 billion of water molecules, 2 molecules are converted into its ions (this is a very small amount!)
- Water conducts a small amount of electricity
    - H_3O^+ and OH^- ions conduct electricity

$$K_w = [H_3O^+][OH^-] = 1.0 \times 10^{-14} \quad at\ 298K$$

Note: K_w= autoionization constant for water

$$Neutral\ solution:\ [H_3O^+] = [OH^-] = 1.0 \times 10^{-7}M\ at\ 298K$$
$$Acidic\ solution:\ [H_3O^+] > [OH^-]$$
$$[H_3O^+] > 1.0 \times 10^{-7}M\ at\ 298K$$
$$[OH^-] < 1.0 \times 10^{-7}M\ at\ 298K$$
$$Basic\ solution:\ [H_3O^+] < [OH^-]$$
$$[H_3O^+] < 1.0 \times 10^{-7}M\ at\ 298K$$
$$[OH^-] > 1.0 \times 10^{-7}M\ at\ 298K$$

Example 1
0.0010mol of NaOH are added to 1.0L of pure water. What are the concentrations of H_3O^+ and OH^- ions at 298K?
$2H_2O_{(l)} \rightleftharpoons H_3O^+_{(aq)} + OH^-_{(aq)}$
Since NaOH is a strong base→ it will completely dissociate into its ions.
$NaOH_{(aq)} \rightarrow Na^+_{(aq)} + OH^-_{(aq)}$
Steps
1. Find the # moles of OH^- using a ratio
2. Find the initial concentration of OH^-
3. Make an ICE table
4. Make an equilibrium expression→ sub in $K_w = 1.0 \times 10^{-14}$
5. Solve for x
6. Find the concentration of all species at equilibrium

$$n_{OH^-} = 0.0010mol \times \frac{1mol\ OH^-}{1mol\ NaOH}$$

$$n_{OH^-} = 0.0010mol$$

So 0.0010mol OH^- were added to water.

Surviving University: First Year Chemistry

$$C = \frac{n}{V}$$
$$C_{OH^-} = \frac{0.0010 mol}{1.0 L}$$
$$C_{OH^-} = 0.0010M$$

Adding NaOH to water increases the concentration of OH⁻ ions→ so you will start off with 0.0010M of OH⁻.

Since autoionization of water is a product favoured reaction, concentrations of H_3O^+ and OH⁻ will increase.

$2H_2O_{(l)} \rightleftharpoons$	$H_3O^+_{(aq)}+$	$OH^-_{(aq)}$
I	-----	0M	0M+0.0010M= 0.0010M
C	-----	+x	+x
E	-----	x	0.0010+x

$$K_w = [H_3O^+][OH^-] = 1.0 \times 10^{-14}$$
$$1.0 \times 10^{-14} = [x][0.0010 + x]$$

Since autoionization of water produces very small amounts of H_3O^+ and OH⁻ ions, assume that (0.0010+x)≈0.0010 (see simple approximation method in this part of the book)

$$1.0 \times 10^{-14} = [x][0.0010]$$
$$x = 1.0 \times 10^{-11}M$$
$$[H_3O^+] = x = 1.0 \times 10^{-11}M$$
$$[OH^-] = 0.0010M + x = 0.0010M + 1.0 \times 10^{-11}M = 0.0010M$$

The concentration of hydronium ion at equilibrium was 1.0x10⁻¹¹M and the concentration of hydroxide ion at equilibrium was 0.0010M.

pH and pOH

$$pH = -log[H_3O^+] \text{ and } [H_3O^+] = 10^{-pH}$$
$$pOH = -log[OH^-] \text{ and } [OH^-] = 10^{-pOH}$$
$$pKw = 14 = pH + pOH$$

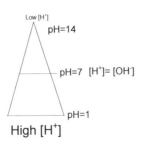
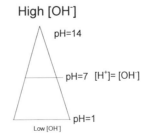

Example 1
pH of a solution is 12. Find concentration of OH⁻.
Hydroxide ion is related to pOH.
$$14 = pH + pOH$$
$$14 = 12 + pOH$$
$$pOH = 14 - 12 = 2$$
$$[OH^-] = 10^{-pOH}$$
$$[OH^-] = 10^{-2}$$
$$[OH^-] = 0.01M$$
The concentration of hydroxide ion was 0.01M.

Equilibrium constants for acids and bases

If $aA + bB \rightleftharpoons cC + dD$

$$K_a = \frac{[products]}{[reactants]} = \frac{[C]^c[D]^d}{[A]^a[B]^b}$$

$$K_b = \frac{[products]}{[reactants]} = \frac{[C]^c[D]^d}{[A]^a[B]^b}$$
$$pKa = -logKa \text{ and } Ka = 10^{-pKa}$$
$$pKb = -logKb \text{ and } Kb = 10^{-pKb}$$
$$pKa + pKb = 14$$
$$Kw = Ka \times Kb = 1.0 \times 10^{-7} \text{ at } 298K$$

Note: Ka= acid equilibrium constant, Kb= base equilibrium constant
Note: all Ka and Kb values can be found at the back of your chemistry textbook

- $Ka \, \alpha \frac{1}{Kb} \rightarrow$ Ka value is inversely proportional to Kb value
  - As pH ↓, [H₃O⁺] ↑, and [OH⁻] ↓

> If Ka<1, then the substance is a weak acid
> If Kb<1, then the substance is a weak base
> As acid strength ↑, conjugate base strength ↓
> If pKa is low, then the substance is a strong acid
> If pKb is low, then the substance is a strong base

Example 1
Ka value is 6.76x10⁻⁴. Find Kb and pKb values.
$$pKa + pKb = 14$$
Steps
1. Find pKa using $pKa = -logKa$
2. Find pKb using $pKa + pKb = 14$
3. Find Kb using $pKb = -logKb$

Surviving University: First Year Chemistry

$pKa = -logKa$
$pKa = -\log(6.76 \times 10^{-4})$
$pKa = 3.17$
$pKa + pKb = 14$
$3.17 + pKb = 14$
$pKb = 14 - 3.17$
$pKb = 10.83$
$Kb = 10^{-pKb}$
$Kb = 10^{-10.83}$
$Kb = 1.48 \times 10^{-11}$
Kb is 20.83 and pKb is 1.48×10^{-11}.

Direction of an acid-base reaction

- All acid-base reactions have the following general form

$Acid + Base \rightleftharpoons Conjugate\ base\ of\ the\ acid + Conjugate\ acid\ of\ base$

See part 3 of this book for an explanation of these terms.

- Equilibrium is to the side with the weaker acid and base

As Ka ↑, acid strength ↑
As Kb ↑, base strength ↑

- Strong acid (K>>1)
- Weak acid (K<<1)

Example 1
What is the direction of equilibrium in the following reaction?
$HCl_{(aq)} + H_2O_{(l)} \rightleftharpoons H_3O^+_{(aq)} + Cl^-_{(aq)}$ $Ka = 7.2 \times 10^{-4}$

acid   base   conjugate   conjugate
                    acid   base

		Ka	Kb
HCl	acid	very large	
H₂O	base		1.0×10^{-14}
H₃O⁺	conjugate acid	1.0	
Cl⁻	conjugate base		very small

Note: Ka and Kb values can be found at the back of your chemistry textbook

Since Ka of HCl was larger than that of H_3O^+, HCl is a stronger acid than H_3O^+. Since Kb of water was larger than that of Cl^-, H_2O is a stronger base than Cl^-.

$$HCl_{(aq)} + H_2O_{(l)} \rightleftharpoons H_3O^+_{(aq)} + Cl^-_{(aq)}$$

stronger   stronger   weaker   weaker
acid   base   conjugate conjugate
                      acid   base

The equilibrium will lie to the side that has a weaker acid-base pair→ it will lie to the right.

Acid-base reactions

Reaction	pH
Strong acid + strong base → $H_2O_{(l)}$	7
Weak acid + strong base → basic	>7
Strong acid + weak base → acidic	<7
Weak acid + weak base → depends on Ka and Kb *If Kb > Ka, then basic* *if Kb < Ka, then acidic* *Cation is the conjugated acid, anion is the conjugated base*	<7 or >7

Calculations with acids and bases

Problem types	Method types
1. Find pH from Ka 2. Find Ka from pH 3. Find % protonated	1. Simple approximation method 2. Successive approximations method

Note: If you forget any of these methods, you can still use the quadratic formula to solve for x→ these methods are just shortcuts to save you time

% protonated

- % of all base molecules that have gained a proton (H^+)

$$\% \; protonated = \frac{[conjugate \; acid]}{[base]} \times 100\%$$

Simple approximation method

$$K_a = \frac{x^2}{[\# - x]^1}$$

If $100 \times K_a < C_0$,
then assume that $1.00 - x \approx 1.00$
and $K_a = \frac{x^2}{[\#]}$

Note: Co= initial concentration of acid (M), Ka= acid equilibrium constant

Surviving University: First Year Chemistry

Successive approximation method

$$K_a = \frac{x^2}{[\# - x]^1}$$

If $100 \times K_a > C_0$, then

1. Assume x= 0 in denominator
2. Solve for x in numerator
3. Plug x from step 2 into the original equation into denominator, solve for x in the numerator
4. Repeat steps 2-3 until the value of x stops changing

Note: Co= initial concentration of acid. Ka= acid equilibrium constant

Problem type 1: Find pH from Ka

Example 1
1.00M of acetic acid is added to water. Find the equilibrium concentrations of HOAc, H_3O^+, Aco⁻. Find pH of the solution. Ka=1.8x10⁻⁵.

$HOAc_{(aq)} + H_2O_{(l)} \rightleftharpoons H_3O^+_{(aq)} + Aco^-_{(aq)}$

Note: HOAc stands for acetic acid (CH_3CO_2H), Aco⁻ stands for acetate ion ($CH_3CO_2^-$)

Steps

1. Make an ICE table
2. Make an equilibrium expression→ sub in $K_a = 1.8 \times 10^{-5}$
3. Solve for x
4. Find the concentrations of all species at equilibrium
5. Find pH using $pH = -log[H_3O^+]$

Since the concentration of reactants is higher than the concentration of products, the equilibrium shifts to produce more products.

	HOAc$_{(aq)}$+	H$_2$O$_{(l)}$	⇌ H$_3$O$^+$$_{(aq)}$+	Aco$^-$$_{(aq)}$
I	1.00M	--------	0M	0M
C	-x	--------	+x	+x
E	1.00-x	--------	x	x

$$K_a = \frac{[products]}{[reactants]} = \frac{[Aco^-]^1[H_3O^+]^1}{[HOAc]^1}$$

$$K_a = 1.8 \times 10^{-5} = \frac{[x]^1[x]^1}{[1.00 - x]^1}$$

$$1.8 \times 10^{-5} = \frac{x^2}{[1.00 - x]^1}$$

Check if $100 \times K_a < C_0$
$100 \times K_a = 100 \times (1.8 \times 10^{-5}) = 1.8 \times 10^{-3} < 1.00M$
Assume that $1.00 - x \approx 1.00$

$1.8 \times 10^{-5} = \dfrac{x^2}{[1.00]^1}$
$1.8 \times 10^{-5} = x^2$
$x = 4.2 \times 10^{-3}M$
$[Aco^-] = x = 4.2 \times 10^{-3}M$
$[H_3O^+] = x = 4.2 \times 10^{-3}M$
$[HOAc] = 1.00M - x = 1.00M - 4.2 \times 10^{-3}M = 0.9958M$
$pH = -log[H_3O^+]$
$pH = -log[4.2 \times 10^{-3}]$
$pH = 2.38$

The equilibrium concentration of HOAc was 0.9958M and the concentration of OAc⁻ and H_3O^+ was 4.2×10^{-3}M. The pH of the solution was 2.38.

Example 2

0.0010M of formic acid (HCO₂H) was added to water. What is the pH of the solution at equilibrium? Ka=1.8x10⁻⁴.

$HCO_2H_{(aq)} + H_2O_{(l)} \rightleftharpoons HCO_2^-{}_{(aq)} + H_3O^+{}_{(aq)}$

Steps

1. Make an ICE table
2. Make an equilibrium expression→ sub in $K_a = 1.8 \times 10^{-4}$
3. Solve for x
4. Find concentration of hydronium ion at equilibrium
5. Find pH using $pH = -log[H_3O^+]$

Since the concentration of reactants is higher than products, the equilibrium shifts to produce more products.

	$HCO_2H_{(aq)}+$	$H_2O_{(l)}$	$\rightleftharpoons HCO_2^-{}_{(aq)}+$	$H_3O^+{}_{(aq)}$
I	0.0010M	--------	0M	0M
C	-x	--------	+x	+x
E	0.0010-x	--------	x	x

$K_a = \dfrac{[products]}{[reactants]} = \dfrac{[HCO_2^-]^1[H_3O^+]^1}{[HCO_2H]^1}$

$K_a = 1.8 \times 10^{-4} = \dfrac{[x]^1[x]^1}{[0.0010 - x]^1}$

Surviving University: First Year Chemistry

$$1.8 \times 10^{-4} = \frac{x^2}{[0.0010 - x]^1}$$

Check if $100 \times K_a < C_0$

$$100 \times K_a = 100 \times (1.8 \times 10^{-4}) = 1.8 \times 10^{-2} > 0.0010M$$

Cannot assume that $0.0010 - x \approx 0.0010$

So use successive approximation method.

Assume that x in denominator= 0

$$1.8 \times 10^{-4} = \frac{x^2}{[0.0010 - 0]^1}$$

$$1.8 \times 10^{-4} = \frac{x^2}{0.0010}$$

$$\sqrt{(1.8 \times 10^{-4}) \times 0.0010} = x$$

$$x = 4.24 \times 10^{-4}$$

Sub $x = 4.24 \times 10^{-4}$ into the denominator of $1.8 \times 10^{-4} = \frac{x^2}{[0.0010-x]^1}$

$$1.8 \times 10^{-4} = \frac{x^2}{[0.0010 - 4.24 \times 10^{-4}]^1}$$

$$\sqrt{(1.8 \times 10^{-4}) \times [0.0010 - 4.24 \times 10^{-4}]^1} = x$$

$$x = 3.2 \times 10^{-4}$$

Sub $x = 3.2 \times 10^{-4}$ into the denominator of $1.8 \times 10^{-4} = \frac{x^2}{[0.0010-x]^1}$

$$1.8 \times 10^{-4} = \frac{x^2}{[0.0010 - 3.2 \times 10^{-4}]^1}$$

$$\sqrt{(1.8 \times 10^{-4}) \times [0.0010 - 3.2 \times 10^{-4}]^1} = x$$

$$x = 3.5 \times 10^{-4}$$

Sub $x = 3.5 \times 10^{-4}$ into the denominator of $1.8 \times 10^{-4} = \frac{x^2}{[0.0010-x]^1}$

$$1.8 \times 10^{-4} = \frac{x^2}{[0.0010 - 3.5 \times 10^{-4}]^1}$$

$$\sqrt{(1.8 \times 10^{-4}) \times [0.0010 - 3.5 \times 10^{-4}]^1} = x$$

$$x = 3.4 \times 10^{-4}$$

Sub $x = 3.4 \times 10^{-4}$ into the denominator of $1.8 \times 10^{-4} = \frac{x^2}{[0.0010-x]^1}$

$$1.8 \times 10^{-4} = \frac{x^2}{[0.0010 - 3.4 \times 10^{-4}]^1}$$

$$\sqrt{(1.8 \times 10^{-4}) \times [0.0010 - 3.4 \times 10^{-4}]^1} = x$$

$$x = 3.4 \times 10^{-4}$$

Since the value of x stopped changing, then $x = 3.4 \times 10^{-4}$M

$$[H_3O^+] = x = 3.4 \times 10^{-4}M$$

$$pH = -log[H_3O^+]$$

$$pH = -log[3.4 \times 10^{-4}]$$

Surviving University: First Year Chemistry

$pH = 3.47$
The pH of the solution was 3.47.

Problem type 2: Find Ka from pH

Example 1
When 0.10M of lactic acid was added to water, the pH at equilibrium was 2.43. Find the equilibrium constant.
$CH_3CHOHCO_2H_{(aq)} + H_2O_{(l)} \rightleftharpoons H_3O^+_{(aq)} + CH_3CHOHCO_2^-_{(aq)}$
Steps
1. Find [H₃O⁺] using $pH = -log[H_3O^+]$
2. Make an ICE table
3. Find concentrations of all species at equilibrium using [H₃O⁺]
4. Make an equilibrium expression
5. Solve for Ka

$[H_3O^+] = 10^{-pH}$
$[H_3O^+] = 10^{-2.43}$
$[H_3O^+] = 3.7 \times 10^{-3}M$

Since the original concentration of reactants is higher than products→ the equilibrium shifts towards products.

	CH₃CHOHCO₂H₍ₐ૧₎ +	H₂O₍ₗ₎	⇌ CH₃CHOHCO₂⁻₍ₐ૧₎ +	H₃O⁺₍ₐ૧₎
I	0.10M	--------	0M	0M
C	-x	--------	+x	+x
E	0.10-x	--------	x= 3.7x10⁻³M	x

$[H_3O^+] = [CH_3CHOHCO_2^-] = x = 3.7 \times 10^{-3}M$
$[CH_3CHOHCO_2^-] = 0.10M - x = 0.10M - 3.7 \times 10^{-3}M = 0.0963M$
$K_a = \dfrac{[products]}{[reactants]} = \dfrac{[CH_3CHOHCO_2^-]^1[H_3O^+]^1}{[CH_3CHOHCO_2H]^1}$
$K_a = \dfrac{(3.7 \times 10^{-3}M)(3.7 \times 10^{-3}M)}{0.0963M}$
$K_a = 1.4 \times 10^{-4}$

The equilibrium constant for the reaction was 1.4x10⁻⁴.

Type 3: % protonated

Example 1
If the concentration of NH₄⁺ at equilibrium is 4.2x10⁻⁴M and the concentration of NH₃ at equilibrium is 0.01M, find % of NH₃ protonated.
$NH_{3(aq)} + H_2O_{(l)} \rightleftharpoons NH_4^+_{(aq)} + OH^-_{(aq)}$

$$\% \, protonated = \frac{[conjugate \, acid]}{[base]} \times 100\%$$

[conjugate acid]= $[NH_4^+]$= 4.2x10^{-4}M

[base]= $[NH_3]$= 0.01M

$$\% \, protonated = \frac{[NH_4^+]}{[NH_3]} \times 100\%$$

$$\% \, protonated = \frac{4.2 \times 10^{-4}M}{0.01M} \times 100\%$$

$$\% \, protonated = 4.2\%$$

The percentage of NH_4^+ protonated was 4.2%.

Polyprotic acids/bases

- Can donate/accept more than 1 proton
- Lose protons in steps

pH of the solution at equilibrium is determined by 1st ionization of acid

Example 1

H_2SO_3 can donate 2 hydrogen ions according to the following equations.

① $H_2SO_3 {}_{(aq)}$+ $H_2O_{(l)} \rightleftharpoons HSO_3^- {}_{(aq)}$+ $H_3O^+ {}_{(aq)}$ Ka_1= 1.2x10^{-2}

② $HSO_3^- {}_{(aq)}$+ $H_2O_{(l)} \rightleftharpoons SO_3^{2-} {}_{(aq)}$+ $H_3O^+ {}_{(aq)}$ Ka_1= 6.2x10^{-8}

a) 0.45M of H_2SO_3 is added to water. Find pH of the solution at equilibrium.

b) What is the equilibrium concentration of SO_3^{2-}?

a) 0.45M of H_2SO_3 is added to water. Find pH of the solution at equilibrium.

Since pH of the solution is determined by 1st ionization of acid, use ①.

Steps

1. Make an ICE table
2. Make an equilibrium expression→ sub in $K_a = 1.2 \times 10^{-2}$
3. Solve for x
4. Find the concentration of hydronium ion at equilibrium
5. Find pH using $pH = -log[H_3O^+]$

Since the concentration of reactants is higher than products→ the equilibrium shifts to produce more products.

	$H_2SO_{3(aq)}$+	$H_2O_{(l)}$	$\rightleftharpoons HSO_3^- {}_{(aq)}$+	$H_3O^+ {}_{(aq)}$
I	0.45M	--------	0M	0M
C	-x	--------	+x	+x

E	0.45-x	--------	x	x

$$K_a = \frac{[products]}{[reactants]} = \frac{[HSO_3^-]^1[H_3O^+]^1}{[H_2SO_3]^1}$$

$$K_a = 1.2 \times 10^{-2} = \frac{[x]^1[x]^1}{[0.45 - x]^1}$$

$$1.2 \times 10^{-2} = \frac{x^2}{[0.45 - x]^1}$$

Check if $100 \times K_a < C_0$

$$100 \times K_a = 100 \times (1.2 \times 10^{-2}) = 1.2 > 0.45M$$

Cannot assume that $0.45 - x \approx 0.45$.

So use successive approximation method.

Assume that x in denominator= 0.

$$1.2 \times 10^{-2} = \frac{x^2}{[0.45 - 0]^1}$$

$$1.2 \times 10^{-2} = \frac{x^2}{[0.45]^1}$$

$$\sqrt{(1.2 \times 10^{-2}) \times 0.45} = x$$

$$x = 0.07348$$

Sub $x = 0.07348$ into the denominator of $1.2 \times 10^{-2} = \frac{x^2}{[0.45-x]^1}$

$$1.2 \times 10^{-2} = \frac{x^2}{[0.45 - 0.07348]}$$

$$\sqrt{(1.2 \times 10^{-2}) \times (0.45 - 0.07348)} = x$$

$$x = 0.06722$$

Sub $x = 0.06722$ into the denominator of $1.2 \times 10^{-2} = \frac{x^2}{[0.45-x]^1}$

$$1.2 \times 10^{-2} = \frac{x^2}{[0.45 - 0.06722]}$$

$$\sqrt{(1.2 \times 10^{-2}) \times (0.45 - 0.06722)} = x$$

$$x = 0.0677$$

Sub $x = 0.0677$ into the denominator of $1.2 \times 10^{-2} = \frac{x^2}{[0.45-x]^1}$

$$1.2 \times 10^{-2} = \frac{x^2}{[0.45 - 0.0677]}$$

$$\sqrt{(1.2 \times 10^{-2}) \times (0.45 - 0.0677)} = x$$

$$x = 0.0677$$

Since the value of x stopped changing, then $x = 0.0677M$

$[HSO_3^-] = x = 0.0677M$

$[H_3O^+] = x = 0.0677M$

$$pH = -log[H_3O^+]$$
$$pH = -log[0.0677]$$
$$pH = 1.17$$

The pH of the solution was 1.17.

b) What is the equilibrium concentration of SO_3^{2-}?

Since the problem is about SO_3^{2-} ion, use equation ②.

② $HSO_3^-{}_{(aq)} + H_2O_{(l)} \rightleftharpoons SO_3^{2-}{}_{(aq)} + H_3O^+{}_{(aq)}$ $Ka_1 = 6.2 \times 10^{-8}$

Steps

1. Make an ICE table
2. Make an equilibrium expression→ sub in Kb= 6.2×10^{-8}
3. Solve for x
4. Find $[SO_3^{2-}]$ using x

You know from part a that $[HSO_3^-]$ is 0.0677M and $[H_3O^+]$ is 0.0677M. Use these concentrations as the original concentrations for this part of the problem. The 2nd ionization reaction is product favoured.

	$HSO_3^-{}_{(aq)}+$	$H_2O_{(l)}$	$\rightleftharpoons SO_3^{2-}{}_{(aq)}+$	$H_3O^+{}_{(aq)}$
I	0.0677M	-------	0M	0.0677M
C	-x	-------	+x	+x
E	0.0677-x	-------	x	0.0677+x

$$K_a = \frac{[products]}{[reactants]} = \frac{[SO_3^{2-}]^1[H_3O^+]^1}{[HSO_3^-]^1}$$

$$K_a = 6.2 \times 10^{-8} = \frac{[x]^1[x+0.0677]^1}{[0.0677-x]^1}$$

Check if $100 \times K_a < C_0$

$$100 \times K_a = 100 \times (6.2 \times 10^{-8}) = 6.2 \times 10^{-6} < 0.0677M$$

Assume that $0.0677 - x \approx 0.0677$ and $0.0677 + x \approx 0.0677$

$$K_a = 6.2 \times 10^{-8} = \frac{[x]^1[0.0677]^1}{[0.0677]^1}$$

$$6.2 \times 10^{-8} = x$$

$$[SO_3^{2-}] = x = 6.2 \times 10^{-8}M$$

The equilibrium concentration of SO_3^{2-} was 6.2×10^{-8}M.

Lewis concept of acids and bases

Lewis acid- a specie that accepts a pair of electrons from a Lewis base

- The greater the electronegativity difference, the stronger the acid

Lewis base- a specie that donates a pair of electrons to a Lewis acid

Acid-base adduct- a specie that is formed by joining of a Lewis acid and a Lewis base via a **coordinate covalent bond**

Coordinate
covalent
bond

A + :B ⟶ B→A

acid   base   adduct

ex. $H^+_{(aq)} + H_2O_{(l)} \rightarrow H_3O^+_{(aq)}$

Cationic Lewis Acids

- Metals ions+ water→ hydrated cations (called **complex ions** or **coordination complexes**)

ex. $Fe^{2+}_{(aq)} + 6H_2O_{(l)} \rightarrow [Fe(H_2O)_6]^{2+}_{(aq)}$

- When complex ions (containing Fe^{3+}, Cu^{2+}, Al^{3+}, Pb^{2+}) are added to water, they increase acidity of the solution

ex. $[Cu(H_2O)_4]^{2+}_{(aq)} + H_2O_{(l)} \rightleftharpoons [Cu(H_2O)_3(OH)]^+_{(aq)} + H_3O^+_{(aq)}$

- Some metal hydroxides are **amphiprotic** (behave as acids in some situations, behave as bases in other situations)

Acid-base properties of salts

- When a salt (an ionic compound) is placed into an aqueous solution, it dissociates into its ions
  - Ex. $NaCl_{(s)} \rightarrow Na^+_{(aq)} + Cl^-_{(aq)}$
- When the following cations and anions are added to an aqueous solution, they make the solution neutral, acidic, or basic

	Neutral	Acidic	Basic
Cations	Li^+, Na^+, Ca^{2+}, K^+, Ba^{2+} (are spectator ions)	NH_4^+, transition metals, hydrated compounds (ex. $[Cu(H_2O)_4]^{2+}$)	ex. $[Al(H_2O)_5(OH)]^{2+}$
Anions	Cl^-, Br^-, I^-, NO_3^-, ClO_4^- (are spectator ions)	HSO_4^-, $H_2PO_4^-$, HSO_3^-	$CH_3CO_2^-$, HCO_2^-, CO_3^{2-}, S^{2-}, F^-, CN^-, PO_4^{3-}, HCO_3^-, HS^-, NO_2^-, SO_4^{2-}, HPO_4^{2-}, SO_3^{2-}, ClO^-

Surviving University: First Year Chemistry

Example 1
When the following ionic compounds are placed into an aqueous solution, will the solution become acidic, basic, or neutral?
a) NaCl
b) NH₄Cl
c) NH₄F

a) NaCl
$NaCl_{(s)} \rightarrow Na^+_{(aq)} + Cl^-_{(aq)}$
The solution will be neutral since both ions are spectator ions.

b) NH₄Cl
$NH_4Cl_{(s)} \rightarrow NH_4^+_{(aq)} + Cl^-_{(aq)}$
The solution will be acidic since NH_4^+ is acidic and Cl^- is neutral.

c) NH₄F
$NH_4F_{(s)} \rightarrow NH_4^+_{(aq)} + F^-_{(aq)}$
NH_4^+ is acidic and F^- is basic. Compare Ka and Kb values of each to see which value is bigger.
Ka= 5.71×10^{-10} and Kb= 1.48×10^{-11}
Since Ka>Kb, the solution will be acidic.

Example 2
0.10M of Na₂CO₃ is added to water. Find the pH of the solution. Kb for CO_3^{2-} is 2.1×10^{-4}.
$Na_2CO_{3(s)} \rightarrow 2Na^+_{(aq)} + CO_3^{2-}_{(aq)}$
Since both ions are in water,
$CO_3^{2-}_{(aq)} + H_2O_{(l)} \rightleftharpoons HCO_3^-_{(aq)} + OH^-_{(aq)}$ ①
The solution will be basic due to hydroxide ion.
$Na^+_{(aq)} + H_2O_{(l)} \rightleftharpoons Na^+_{(aq)} + H_2O_{(l)}$ ②
The solution will be neutral→ Na^+ is a spectator ion.
Since CO_3^{2-} will make the solution basic, the pH will be determined by equation ①.
Steps
1. Make an ICE table
2. Make an equilibrium expression→ sub in $K_b = 2.1 \times 10^{-4}$
3. Solve for x
4. Find the concentrations of hydroxide ion at equilibrium
5. Find pOH using $pOH = -log[OH^-]$
6. Find pH using $pOH + pH = 14$
Since the concentration of reactants is higher than products→ the equilibrium shifts to produce more products.

	$CO_3^{2-}{}_{(aq)}+$	$H_2O_{(l)}$	$\rightleftharpoons HCO_3^-{}_{(aq)}+$	$OH^-{}_{(aq)}$
I	0.10M	---------	0M	0M
C	-x	---------	+x	+x
E	0.10-x	---------	x	x

$$K_b = \frac{[products]}{[reactants]} = \frac{[HCO_2^-]^1[OH^-]^1}{[CO_2^{2-}]^1}$$

$$K_a = 2.1 \times 10^{-4} = \frac{[x]^1[x]^1}{[0.10-x]^1}$$

$$2.1 \times 10^{-4} = \frac{x^2}{[0.10-x]^1}$$

Check if $100 \times K_b < C_0$

$$100 \times K_b = 100 \times (2.1 \times 10^{-4}) = 2.1 \times 10^{-2} < 0.10\ M$$

Assume that $0.10 - x \approx 0.10$

$$2.1 \times 10^{-4} = \frac{x^2}{[0.10]^1}$$

$0.000021 = x^2$

$x = 0.0046M$

$[OH^-] = x = 0.0046M$

$pOH = -log[OH^-]$

$pOH = -log[0.0046]$

$pOH = 2.34$

$pOH + pH = 14$

$pH = 14 - pOH$

$pH = 14 - 2.34$

$pH = 11.66$

The solution has a pH of 11.66.

Part 25

Buffers

Common ion effect

Buffers

Finding pH of a buffer system

Preparing a buffer solution

Buffers

Common ion effect

- Is the same as Le Chatelier's principle
- Adding more acid ↓ pH
- Adding more base ↑ pH

Adding reactant/taking away product
- K does not change
- Equilibrium shifts to the left to produce more products→ concentration of products increases

Adding product/taking away reactant
- K does not change
- Equilibrium shifts to the left to produce more reactants→ concentration of reactants increases

Example 1

The pH of 0.25M of $CH_3CO_2H_{(aq)}$ solution is 2.67. 0.10M of $NaCH_3CO_{2(aq)}$ is added to the solution. What is the new pH of the solution? Ka= 1.8x10⁻⁵.

When $NaCH_3CO_2$ is added to the solution, it will dissociate into its ions (Na^+ and $CH_3CO_2^-$). Na^+ is a spectator ion.

$NaCH_3CO_{2\ (aq)} \rightarrow Na^+_{(aq)} + CH_3CO_2^-{}_{(aq)}$

$CH_3CO_2H_{(aq)} + H_2O_{(l)} \rightleftharpoons H_3O^+_{(aq)} + CH_3CO_2^-{}_{(aq)}$

Adding more base ($CH_3CO_2^-$) to the solution will make the solution more basic→ pH will ↑

Steps

1. Make an ICE table
2. Make equilibrium expression→ sub in $K_a = 1.8 \times 10^{-5}$
3. Solve for x
4. Find the concentration of hydronium ion at equilibrium
5. Find pH using $pH = -log[H_3O^+]$

Since the concentration of reactants is higher than the concentration of products→ the equilibrium will shift to produce more products.

	$CH_3CO_2H_{(aq)}$ +	$H_2O_{(l)}$	$\rightleftharpoons H_3O^+_{(aq)}$+	$CH_3CO_2^-{}_{(aq)}$
I	0.25M		0	0.10M
C	-x	--------	+x	+x
E	0.25-x	--------	x	0.10+x

$$K_a = \frac{[products]}{[reactants]} = \frac{[CH_3CO_2^-]^1[H_3O^+]^1}{[CH_3CO_2H]^1}$$

$$K_a = 1.8 \times 10^{-5} = \frac{[0.10 + x]^1[x]^1}{[0.25 - x]^1}$$

Check if $100 \times K_a < C_0$

$100 \times K_a = 100 \times (1.8 \times 10^{-5}) = 1.8 \times 10^{-3} < 0.25M$ and

$1.8 \times 10^{-3} < 0.10M$

Assume that $0.25 - x \approx 0.25$ and $0.10 + x \approx 0.10$

$$1.8 \times 10^{-5} = \frac{0.10x}{[0.25]^1}$$

$$\frac{(1.8 \times 10^{-5})(0.25)}{0.10} = x^2$$

$x = 4.5 \times 10^{-5}M$

$[H_3O^+] = x = 4.5 \times 10^{-5}M$

$pH = -log[H_3O^+]$

$pH = -log[4.5 \times 10^{-5}M]$

$pH = 4.35$

The solution has a pH of 4.35.

Buffers

- Resist changes in pH
- Contain a weak acid and its conjugate base or a weak base and its conjugate acid
- In order to have a buffer solution
    - A solution must have 2 substances
        1. An acid that can consume all of the OH⁻ added to the solution to produce H_2O
        2. A base that can consume all of the H_3O^+ added to the solution to produce H_2O
    - An acid and a base in the solution cannot interact with each other
- Diluting (adding more water) to a buffer solution does not change its pH
- To prepare a buffer solution
    - Choose an acid that has pH≈ pKa or $[H_3O^+]$≈Ka
    - The concentrations of acid and its conjugate base are not important

Common buffers

Weak acid	Conjugate base	Ka	pKa
$C_6H_4(CO_2H)_2$	$C_6H_4(CO_2H)(CO_2)^-$	1.3×10^{-3}	2.89
CH_3CO_2H	$CH_3CO_2^-$	1.8×10^{-5}	4.74
$H_2PO_4^-$	HPO_4^{2-}	6.2×10^{-8}	7.21
HPO_4^{2-}	PO_4^{3-}	3.6×10^{-13}	12.44

Buffer equations

$$HA_{(aq)} + H_2O_{(l)} \rightleftharpoons H_3O^+_{(aq)} + A^-_{(aq)}$$

acid   base   conjugate   conjugate
                     acid   base

Note: HA is an acid (ex. HCl)→ A⁻ is any anion (ex. Cl⁻)

$$B_{(aq)} + H_2O_{(l)} \rightleftharpoons BH_{(aq)} + OH^-_{(aq)}$$

base   acid   conjugate   conjugate
                    acid   base

$$[H_3O^+] = \frac{[acid]}{[conjugate\ base]} \times Ka$$

$$[OH^-] = \frac{[base]}{[conjugate\ acid]} \times Kb$$

Henderson-Hasselbalch equation:

$$pH = pKa + \log \frac{[conjugate\ base]}{[acid]}$$

Note: Ka= acid equilibrium constant, Kb= base equilibrium constant

Finding pH of a buffer system

Example 1

What is the pH of acetic acid/sodium acetate buffer where $[CH_3CO_2H]$ is 0.700M and $[CH_3CO_2^-]$ is 0.600M? Ka=1.8x10⁻⁵.

When sodium acetate is added to water, it dissociates into its ions.

$CH_3CO_2Na_{(s)} \rightarrow Na^+_{(aq)} + CH_3CO_2^-_{(aq)}$

Na^+ is a spectator ion→ it does not participate in the buffer system.

Acetic acid is a weak acid, so the buffer has a general equation of

$HA_{(aq)} + H_2O_{(l)} \rightleftharpoons H_3O^+_{(aq)} + A^-_{(aq)}$

$CH_3CO_2H_{(aq)} + H_2O_{(l)} \rightleftharpoons H_3O^+_{(aq)} + CH_3CO_2^-_{(aq)}$

pH is measured from the concentration of hydronium ion.

Steps

1. Make an ICE table
2. Make an equilibrium expression→ sub in $K_a = 1.8 \times 10^{-5}$

Surviving University: First Year Chemistry

3. Solve for x
4. Find the concentration of hydronium ion at equilibrium
5. Find pH using $pH = -log[H_3O^+]$

Since the concentration of reactants is higher than products→ the equilibrium shifts to produce more products.

	CH$_3$CO$_2$H$_{(aq)}$+	H$_2$O$_{(l)}$	⇌ H$_3$O$^+_{(aq)}$+	CH$_3$CO$_2^-_{(aq)}$
I	0.700M		0	0.600M
C	-x	--------	+x	+x
E	0.700-x	--------	x	0.600+x

$$K_a = \frac{[products]}{[reactants]} = \frac{[CH_3CO_2^-]^1[H_3O^+]^1}{[CH_3CO_2H]^1}$$

$$K_a = 1.8 \times 10^{-5} = \frac{[0.600 + x]^1[x]^1}{[0.700 - x]^1}$$

Check if $100 \times K_a < C_0$

$100 \times K_a = 100 \times (1.8 \times 10^{-5}) = 1.8 \times 10^{-3} < 0.700M$ and $1.8 \times 10^{-3} < 0.600M$

Assume that $0.700 - x \approx 0.700$ and $0.600 + x \approx 0.600$.

$$1.8 \times 10^{-5} = \frac{0.600x}{[0.700]^1}$$

$$\frac{(1.8 \times 10^{-5})(0.700)}{0.600} = x$$

$x = 2.1 \times 10^{-5}M$

$[H_3O^+] = x = 2.1 \times 10^{-5}M$

$pH = -log[H_3O^+]$

$pH = -log[2.1 \times 10^{-5}M]$

$pH = 4.68$

The solution has a pH of 4.68.

Example 2

2.00g of C$_6$H$_5$CO$_2$H and 2.00g of C$_6$H$_5$CO$_2$Na are dissolved in water in order to make 1.00L solution. What is the pH of this solution? Ka=6.3x10^{-5}.

When sodium benzoate is added to water, it dissociates into its ions
C$_6$H$_5$CO$_2$Na$_{(s)}$→ Na$^+_{(aq)}$+ C$_6$H$_5$CO$_2^-_{(aq)}$

Na$^+$ is a spectator ion→ it does not participate in the buffer system.
Benzoic acid is a weak acid, so the buffer has a general equation of
HA$_{(aq)}$+H$_2$O$_{(l)}$ ⇌ H$_3$O$^+_{(aq)}$+A$^-_{(aq)}$
C$_6$H$_5$CO$_2$H$_{(aq)}$+ H$_2$O$_{(l)}$ ⇌ H$_3$O$^+_{(aq)}$+ C$_6$H$_5$CO$_2^-_{(aq)}$

pH will be measured from the concentration of hydronium ion.
Instead of making an ICE table (like in example 1), you can use the
Henderson-Hasselbalch equation→ ICE table also works, but Henderson-
Hasselbalch equation takes less time (this is a shortcut).
Steps

1. Find the # moles of $C_6H_5CO_2H$ and $C_6H_5CO_2^-$ using $n = \frac{m}{M}$
2. Find the original concentrations of $C_6H_5CO_2H$ and $C_6H_5CO_2^-$ using $C = \frac{n}{V}$
3. Find pKa using $pKa = -logKa$
4. Find pH using $pH = pKa + log\frac{[conjugate\ base]}{[acid]}$

$n_{C_6H_5CO_2H}$	?mol
$m_{C_6H_5CO_2H}$	2.00g
$M_{C_6H_5CO_2H}$	? g/mol
$C_{C_6H_5CO_2H}$	?M
$n_{C_6H_5CO_2^-}$	?mol
$m_{NaC_6H_5CO_2}$	2.00g
$M_{NaC_6H_5CO_2}$	?g/mol
$C_{C_6H_5CO_2^-}$	?M
V	1.00L

$$M_{C_6H_5CO_2H} = 6(12.01g/mol) + 5(1.01g/mol) + 12.01g/mol \\ + 2(16.00g/mol) + 1.01g/mol$$

$$M_{C_6H_5CO_2H} = 122.1g/mol$$

$$n_{C_6H_5CO_2H} = \frac{m}{M}$$

$$n_{C_6H_5CO_2H} = \frac{2.00g}{122.1g/mol}$$

$$n_{C_6H_5CO_2H} = 0.0164mol$$

$$C_{C_6H_5CO_2H} = \frac{n}{V}$$

$$C_{C_6H_5CO_2H} = \frac{0.0164mol}{1.00L}$$

$$C_{C_6H_5CO_2H} = 0.0164M$$

$$M_{NaC_6H_5CO_2} = 6(12.01g/mol) + 5(1.01g/mol) + 12.01g/mol \\ + 2(16.00g/mol) + 22.99g/mol$$

$$M_{NaC_6H_5CO_2} = 144.1g/mol$$

$$n_{NaC_6H_5CO_2} = \frac{m}{M}$$

$$n_{NaC_6H_5CO_2} = \frac{2.00g}{144.1g/mol}$$

$$n_{C_6H_5CO_2H} = 0.0139mol$$

$$C_{NaC_6H_5CO_2} = \frac{n}{V}$$

$$C_{NaC_6H_5CO_2} = \frac{0.0139mol}{1.00L}$$

$$C_{NaC_6H_5CO_2} = 0.0139M$$

$$pKa = -logKa$$

$$pKa = -\log(1.8 \times 10^{-5})$$

$$pKa = 4.74$$

$$pH = pKa + log\frac{[conjugate\ base]}{[acid]}$$

$$pH = 4.74 + log\frac{[0.0139M]}{[0.0164M]}$$

$$pH = 4.67$$

The pH of the solution was 4.67.

Example 3   ** This is an excellent midterm/exam question!**
a) Find pH when 0.001L of 1.00M of HCl is added to 1.00L of water.
$HCl_{(aq)} + H_2O_{(l)} \rightleftharpoons H_3O^+_{(aq)} + Cl^-_{(aq)}$
This problem has 2 scenarios. The 1st scenario is when HCl is in a 0.001L solution. The 2nd scenario is when HCl is in a 1.001L solution (with water).
Steps
1. Find the concentration of HCl in the solution with water using
   $C_1V_1 = C_2V_2$
2. Find the concentration of H_3O^+ using a ratio
3. Find pH using $pH = -log[H_3O^+]$

$C_1V_1 = C_2V_2$
$C_1 = 1.00M$
$V_1 = 0.001L$
$C_2 = ?M$
$V_2 = 1.001L$
Since 0.001L of HCl is added to 1.00L of water, then the total final volume becomes 1.001L.

$$C_2 = \frac{C_1V_1}{V_2}$$

$$C_2 = \frac{(1.00M)(0.001L)}{1.001L}$$

$$C_2 = 0.001M$$

	HCl$_{(aq)}$+	H$_2$O$_{(l)}$ ⇌	H$_3$O$^+$$_{(aq)}$+	Cl$^-$$_{(aq)}$
C	0.001M	--------		
Ratio	1	1	1	1

$[H_3O^+] = 0.001M\ HCl \times \dfrac{1mol\ H_3O^+}{1mol\ HCl}$

$[H_3O^+] = 0.001M$

$pH = -log[H_3O^+]$

$pH = -log[0.001]$

$pH = 3.00$

The pH of solution was 3.00.

b) Find pH when 0.001L of 1.00M of HCl is added to acetic acid/sodium acetate buffer with [CH$_3$CO$_2$H]= 0.700M and [CH$_3$CO$_2^-$]= 0.600M. Ka=1.8x10^{-5}.

First, HCl is added to water.

HCl$_{(aq)}$+ H$_2$O$_{(l)}$ ⇌ H$_3$O$^+$$_{(aq)}$+ Cl$^-$$_{(aq)}$

You know from part a that pH is 3.00 and [H$_3$O$^+$] is 0.001M when 0.001L of 1.00M HCl is added to water.

The equation for the buffer is

H$_2$O$_{(l)}$+ CH$_3$CO$_2$H$_{(aq)}$ ⇌ H$_3$O$^+$$_{(aq)}$+ CH$_3CO_2^-$ $_{(aq)}$

H$_3$O$^+$ with contribute to the change in pH of the buffer solution.

This problem will have 2 steps.

Stage 1: the reaction

- The purpose of the buffer is to consume all H$_3$O$^+$ added
    - After the reaction, the [H$_3$O$^+$] will be 0M

Stage 2: equilibrium

- Once all H$_3$O$^+$ is used up, the reaction will come to an equilibrium→ treat it as a regular equilibrium buffer problem

Stage 1

Steps

1. Make a before reaction/change/after reaction table

The concentration of hydronium ion at the beginning of the reaction comes from addition of HCl→ [H$_3$O$^+$] is 0.001M.

	CH$_3$CO$_2$H$_{(aq)}$+	H$_2$O$_{(l)}$	⇌ H$_3$O$^+$$_{(aq)}$+	CH$_3$CO$_2^-$ $_{(aq)}$
Before rxn	0.700M	--------	0.001M← all will be consumed	0.600M
Change	+0.001M	--------	-0.001M	-0.001M

Surviving University: First Year Chemistry

After rxn	0.701M	--------	0M	0.599M

Stage 2

Steps
1. Make an ICE table
2. Make the equilibrium expression→ sub in $K_a = 1.8 \times 10^{-5}$
3. Solve for x
4. Find concentrations of hydronium ion at equilibrium
5. Find pH using $pH = -log[H_3O^+]$

Since the concentration of reactants is higher than products→ the equilibrium shifts to produce more products.

	$CH_3CO_2H_{(aq)}$+	$H_2O_{(l)}$	$\rightleftharpoons H_3O^+_{(aq)}$+	$CH_3CO_2^-_{(aq)}$
I	0.701M	--------	0M	0.599M
C	-x	--------	+x	+x
E	0.701-x	--------	x	0.599+x

$$K_a = \frac{[products]}{[reactants]} = \frac{[CH_3CO_2^-]^1[H_3O^+]^1}{[CH_3CO_2H]^1}$$

$$K_a = 1.8 \times 10^{-5} = \frac{[0.599 + x]^1[x]^1}{[0.701 - x]^1}$$

Check if $100 \times K_a < C_0$

$100 \times K_a = 100 \times (1.8 \times 10^{-5}) = 1.8 \times 10^{-3} < 0.701M$ and $1.8 \times 10^{-3} < 0.599M$

Assume that $0.701 - x \approx 0.701$ and $0.599 + x \approx 0.599$.

$$1.8 \times 10^{-5} = \frac{0.599x}{[0.701]^1}$$

$$\frac{(1.8 \times 10^{-5})(0.701)}{0.599} = x$$

$x = 2.1 \times 10^{-5}M$

$[H_3O^+] = x = 2.1 \times 10^{-5}M$

$pH = -log[H_3O^+]$

$pH = -log[2.1 \times 10^{-5}]$

$pH = 4.68$

The solution has a pH of 4.68.

OR (this is an alternative method)

Stage 2

Steps

1. Find pKa using $pKa = -logKa$
2. Find pH using $pH = pKa + log \dfrac{[conjugate\ base]}{[acid]}$

$pKa = -logKa$

$pKa = -log\,(1.8 \times 10^{-5})$

$pKa = 4.74$

$pH = pKa + log\dfrac{[conjugate\ base]}{[acid]}$

$pH = 4.74 + log\dfrac{[0.599M]}{[0.701M]}$

$pH = 4.68$

The solution has a pH of 4.68.

Preparing a buffer solution

Example 1

You need to prepare a buffer solution that has pH of 4.30 or [H₃O⁺] of 5.0x10⁻⁵M.

a) From the following buffer systems, which buffer system should you choose?

HSO_4^-/SO_4^{2-} Ka= 1.2x10⁻²

HOAc/Aco⁻   Ka= 1.8x10⁻⁵

HCN/CN⁻   Ka= 4.0x10⁻¹⁰

b) Find the concentrations of weak acid and its conjugate base needed to prepare the solution.

a) From the following buffer systems, which buffer system should you choose?

You need to choose a buffer system that has its Ka closest to the pH. Choose HOAc/Aco⁻ system since both Ka and [H₃O⁺] are 1.8x10⁻⁵M→ the value is closest to 5.0x10⁻⁵M.

b) Find the concentrations of weak acid and its conjugate base needed to prepare the solution.

$HOAc_{(aq)} + H_2O_{(l)} \rightleftharpoons H_3O^+_{(aq)} + Aco^-_{(aq)}$

$pH = pKa + log\dfrac{[conjugate\ base]}{[acid]}$

Steps

1. Find pKa using $pKa = -logKa$

Surviving University: First Year Chemistry

2. Find $\frac{[conjugate\ base]}{[acid]}$ using $pH = pKa + log\frac{[conjugate\ base]}{[acid]}$

3. Divide [conjugate base] by [acid] to find the concentrations of HOAc/Aco⁻ needed

$pKa = -logKa$

$pKa = -\log(1.8 \times 10^{-5})$

$pKa = 4.74$

$pH = pKa + log\frac{[conjugate\ base]}{[acid]}$

$pH = 4.30 = 4.74 + log\frac{[conjugate\ base]}{[acid]}$

$4.30 - 4.74 = log\frac{[conjugate\ base]}{[acid]}$

$-0.44 = log\frac{[conjugate\ base]}{[acid]}$

$10^{-0.44} = \frac{[conjugate\ base]}{[acid]}$

$0.36 = \frac{[conjugate\ base]}{[acid]}$

This is the same as

$\frac{0.36}{1} = \frac{[Aco^-]}{[HOAc]}$

And the same as

$\frac{1}{0.36} = \frac{[HOAc]}{[Aco^-]}$

$\frac{2.8M}{1\ M} = \frac{[HOAc]}{[Aco^-]}$

You will need 2.8M of HOAc and 1M of Aco⁻.

Part 26

Titrations

Titration

Titrating a strong acid with a strong base

Titrating a weak acid with a strong base

Titration calculations

Titrations

Titration

- Titration is a technique used to determine concentration of an acid or a base
- A base is added to an acid containing phenolphthalein (an indicator) until solution changes to pink colour (then the concentration of base= concentration of acid)

Titrant- a specie that is being added during a titration (in the diagram below, titrant is NaOH)

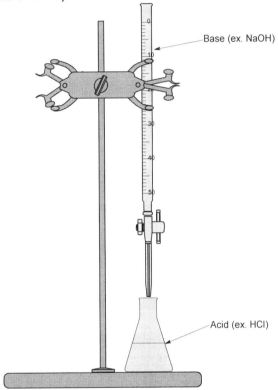

Base (ex. NaOH)

Acid (ex. HCl)

Halfway point

$$[H_3O^+] = Ka \qquad pH = pKa$$

Equivalence point: [acid]= [base]

	pH at the equivalence point
Strong acid+ strong base	7
Weak acid+ strong base	>7
Strong acid+ weak base	<7

Titrating a strong acid with a strong base

ex. $HCl_{(aq)} + NaOH_{(aq)} \rightarrow NaCl_{(aq)} + H_2O_{(l)}$

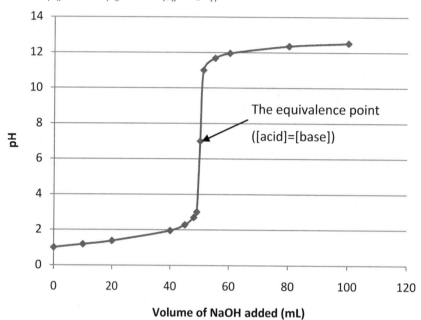

- At the beginning of a titration, there is a slow rise in pH
  - OH^- is being consumed, but solution is being diluted
    - There is the same # H_3O^+ ions, but the volume is increasing
- At the equivalence point, all of the H^+ ions of acid have reacted with the OH^- ions added
  - [acid]=[base]
  - pH rises quickly since there are no more H_3O^+ ions left in the solution to lower the pH
  - pH of the solution is 7 $\rightarrow$ neutral
- At the end of a titration, there is a slow rise in pH
  - There are no more H_3O^+ ions left
  - More OH^- ions are added $\rightarrow$ they have nothing to react with, but the volume is increasing

Titrating a weak acid with a strong base

ex. $CH_3CO_2H_{(aq)} + NaOH_{(aq)} \rightarrow CH_3CO_2Na_{(aq)} + H_2O_{(l)}$

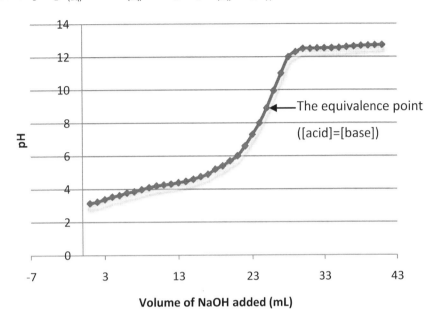

- The explanation to these observations is the same as the explanation for a titration of a strong acid with a strong base
  - pH at the beginning of a titration is higher (than that for a strong acid with a strong base) since there are fewer H⁺ ions originally present in the solution

Titration calculations

$$[H_3O^+] = \frac{[acid\ remaining]}{[conjugate\ base\ produced]} \times Ka$$

$$pH = pKa + log\frac{[conjugate\ base\ produced]}{[acid\ remaining]}$$

$$pH = -log[H_3O^+]$$

Example 1
0.1000L of 0.100M CH_3CO_2H is titrated with 0.100M of NaOH.
Kb=5.6x10⁻¹⁰. Find pH when
a) 0.090L of NaOH have been added
b) at the equivalence point
c) 0.110L of NaOH have been added

a) 0.090L of NaOH have been added

Steps

1. Find the # moles of CH_3CO_2H and NaOH using $C = \frac{n}{V}$
2. Make before reaction/change/after reaction table
3. Find $[H_3O^+]$ using $[H_3O^+] = \frac{mol\ acid\ remaining}{mol\ conjugate\ base\ produced} \times Ka$
4. Find pH using $pH = -log[H_3O^+]$

$n_{CH_3CO_2H}$	?mol
$C_{CH_3CO_2H}$	0.100M
$V_{CH_3CO_2H}$	0.1000L
n_{NaOH}	?mol
C_{NaOH}	0.100M
V_{NaOH}	0.090L

$n = C \times V$
$n_{CH_3CO_2H} = (0.100M)(0.1000L)$
$n_{CH_3CO_2H} = 0.0100mol$
$n = C \times V$
$n_{NaOH} = (0.100M)(0.090L)$
$n_{NaOH} = 0.00900mol$

$n_{OH^-} = 0.00900mol\ NaOH \times \dfrac{1mol\ OH^-}{1mol\ NaOH}$

$n_{OH^-} = 0.00900mol$

Since 0.0090mol< 0.100mol, all of the OH⁻ ions will be fully consumed (OH⁻ is the limiting reagent)→ all of OH⁻ ions will react with acetic acid.

	$CH_3CO_2H_{(aq)}$+	$OH^-_{(aq)}$	$\rightleftharpoons H_2O_{(l)}$	+$CH_3CO_2^-_{(aq)}$
Before rxn	0.0100mol	0.00900mol← all will be consumed	--------	0M
Change	-0.0090mol	-0.0090mol	--------	+0.0090mol
After rxn	0.0010mol	0 mol	--------	0.0090mol

$[H_3O^+] = \dfrac{mol\ acid\ remaining}{mol\ conjugate\ base\ produced} \times Ka$

$[H_3O^+] = \dfrac{0.0010mol}{0.0090mol} \times (1.8 \times 10^{-5})$

$[H_3O^+] = 2.0 \times 10^{-6}M$

Surviving University: First Year Chemistry

$pH = -log[H_3O^+]$
$pH = -log[2.0 \times 10^{-6}]$
$pH = 5.70$
The pH of solution after 0.090L of NaOH has been added is 5.70.

b) at equivalence point
Note: this part has 2 steps
Stage 1: the reaction
- At the equivalence point, all of the acid reacted with all of the base added. The amount of acid= amount of base
- Since 0.0100mol of acid was originally in the solution, then 0.0100mol of base must have been added
- So all of the acid and all of the base will be converted into $CH_3CO_2^-$ and H_2O

Stage 2: the equilibrium
- Once all acid and base are used up, the reaction will come to equilibrium→ treat it as a regular equilibrium problem

Stage 1
Steps
1. Make a before reaction/change/after reaction table

	$CH_3CO_2H_{(aq)}+$	$OH^-_{(aq)}$	$\rightleftharpoons H_2O_{(l)}$	$+CH_3CO_2^-_{(aq)}$
Before rxn	0.0100mol	0.0100mol	-------	0M
Change	-0.0100mol	-0.0100mol	--------	+ 0.0100mol
After rxn	0mol	0mol	--------	0.0100mol

Stage 2
Steps
1. Find the concentration of $CH_3CO_2^-$ using $C = \frac{n}{V}$
2. Make an ICE table
3. Make an equilibrium expression→ sub in $K_b = 5.6 \times 10^{-10}$
4. Solve for x
5. Find the concentration of hydroxide ion at equilibrium
6. Find pOH using $pOH = -log[OH^-]$
7. Find pH using $pOH + pH = 14$

$C_{CH_3CO_2^-}$	?M
$n_{CH_3CO_2^-}$	0.0100mol
V	0.100L+0.100L=0.200L

There were 2 solutions (0.100L each) added to make 1 solution of 0.200L.

$$C_{CH_3CO_2^-} = \frac{n}{V}$$

$$C_{CH_3CO_2^-} = \frac{0.0100mol}{0.200L}$$

$$C_{CH_3CO_2^-} = 0.0500M$$

Since the concentration of reactants is higher than products→ the equilibrium shifts to produce more products.

	$H_2O_{(l)}$	$+CH_3CO_2^-{}_{(aq)}$	$\rightleftharpoons CH_3CO_2H_{(aq)}+$	$OH^-{}_{(aq)}$
I	--------	0.0500M	0M	0M
C	--------	-x	+x	+x
E	--------	0.0500-x	x	x

$$K_b = \frac{[products]}{[reactants]} = \frac{[OH^-]^1[CH_3CO_2H]^1}{[CH_3CO_2^-]^1}$$

$$K_b = 5.6 \times 10^{-10} = \frac{x^2}{[0.0500-x]^1}$$

Check if $100 \times K_b < C_0$

$100 \times K_b = 100 \times (5.6 \times 10^{-10}) = 5.6 \times 10^{-8} < 0.00500M$

Assume that $0.0500 - x \approx 0.0500$

$$5.6 \times 10^{-10} = \frac{x^2}{0.0500}$$

$$\sqrt{0.0500 \times (5.6 \times 10^{-10})} = x$$

$$x = 5.29 \times 10^{-6}M$$

$$[OH^-] = x = 5.29 \times 10^{-6}M$$

$$pOH = -log[OH^-]$$

$$pOH = -log[5.29 \times 10^{-6}]$$

$$pOH = 5.28$$

$$pOH + pH = 14$$

$$pH = 14 - pOH$$

$$pH = 14 - 5.28$$

$$pH = 8.72$$

The pH of the solution at the equivalence point is 8.72.

c) 0.110L of NaOH have been added

Steps

1. Make a before reaction/change/after reaction table
2. Find the # moles OH⁻ remaining
3. Find the concentration of OH⁻ using $C = \frac{n}{V}$
4. Find pOH using $pOH = -log[OH^-]$
5. Find pH using $pOH + pH = 14$

Since 0.0110mol> 0.0100mol, CH_3CO_2H will be fully consumed (it is the limiting reagent).

	$CH_3CO_2H_{(aq)}+$	$OH^-_{(aq)}$	$\rightleftharpoons H_2O_{(l)}$	$+CH_3CO_2^-_{(aq)}$
Before rxn	0.0100mol← all will be consumed	0.0110mol	--------	0M
Change	-0.0100mol	-0.010mol	--------	+0.0100mol
After rxn	0mol	0.0010mol	--------	0.0100mol

C_{OH^-}	?M
n_{OH^-}	0.0100mol
V	0.100L+0.110L=0.210L

There were 2 solutions (0.100L each) added to make 1 solution of 0.200L.

$$C_{OH^-} = \frac{n}{V}$$
$$C_{OH^-} = \frac{0.0010mol}{0.210L}$$
$$C_{OH^-} = 4.8 \times 10^{-3}M$$
$$pOH = -log[OH^-]$$
$$pOH = -log[4.8 \times 10^{-3}]$$
$$pOH = 2.32$$
$$pOH + pH = 14$$
$$pH = 14 - pOH$$
$$pH = 14 - 2.32$$
$$pH = 11.68$$

The pH of the solution at the equivalence point is 11.68.

Part 27

Solubility

Solubility of salts

Reaction quotient expression

Precipitation reactions

The common ion effect

Complex ions

Solubility

Please review part 3 for solubility guidelines
Solubility- # moles of a substance present per 1 litre of a solution
Solubility product constant (K_{sp})- equilibrium constant for ionic compounds

If $aA + bB \rightleftharpoons cC + dD$

$$K_{sp} = \frac{[products]}{[reactants]} = \frac{[C]^c[D]^d}{[A]^a[B]^b}$$

Solids and liquids never appear in the Ksp expression!

Note: Ksp= solubility product constant, lower case letters represent stoichiometric coefficients, upper case letters represent molecules, brackets represent concentrations (M)

Solubility of salts

- During a precipitation reaction, an insoluble compound is formed

ex. $Pb(NO_3)_{2(aq)} + 2KI_{(aq)} \rightleftharpoons PbI_{2(s)} + 2KNO_{3(aq)}$

- When an insoluble compound is placed into an aqueous solution, most of it remains in the solid form and some of it dissociates into its ions

ex. $PbI_{2(s)} \rightleftharpoons Pb^{2+}_{(aq)} + 2I^-_{(aq)}$

Example 1
Find Ksp when $AgCl_{(s)}$ is dissolved in water. At equilibrium, the concentration of silver ions is $1.67 \times 10^{-5} M$.
An ionic compound dissociates into its ions when it is placed into water.
$AgCl_{(s)} \rightleftharpoons Ag^+_{(aq)} + Cl^-_{(aq)}$

	$AgCl_{(s)} \rightleftharpoons$	$Ag^+_{(aq)} +$	$Cl^-_{(aq)}$
C	-----	$1.67 \times 10^{-5} M$	? M
Ratio	1	1	1

$$C_{Cl^-} = 1.67 \times 10^{-5} M\ Ag^+ \times \frac{1mol\ Cl^-}{1mol\ Ag^+}$$

$$C_{Cl^-} = 1.67 \times 10^{-5} M\ Cl^-$$

$$K_{sp} = \frac{[products]}{[reactants]}$$

$$K_{sp} = \frac{[Cl^-]^1[Ag^+]^1}{1}$$

Surviving University: First Year Chemistry

$$K_{sp} = \frac{[1.67 \times 10^{-5}M]^1[1.67 \times 10^{-5}M]^1}{1}$$

$$K_{sp} = 2.79 \times 10^{-10}$$

Ksp of the solution is 2.79×10^{-10}.

Reaction quotient expression

If $aA + bB \rightleftharpoons cC + dD$

$$Q = \frac{[products]}{[reactants]} = \frac{[C]^c[D]^d}{[A]^a[B]^b}$$

Solids and liquids never appear in the reaction quotient expression!

Note: Q= reaction quotient, lower case letters represent stoichiometric coefficients, upper case letters represent molecules, brackets represent concentrations (M)

	Solution
Q=Ksp	Saturated
Q<Ksp	Not saturated
Q>Ksp	Precipitate forms

Precipitation reactions

Non-saturated solution- a solution in which more solute can dissolve
Saturated solution- a solution in which the maximum amount of solute has been dissolved→ if you add any more of the solute, precipitate will form

Example 1
$PbI_{2(s)}$ dissolves in water. The solubility of the solution is 0.00130M. Find Ksp.
When PbI_2 dissolves in water, it dissociates into its ions.
$PbI_{2(s)} \rightleftharpoons Pb^{2+}_{(aq)} + 2I^-_{(aq)}$
Steps

1. Find the # moles of PbI_2 in 1 litre of the solution using $C = \frac{n}{V}$
2. Make a chart with # moles and ratio
3. Find the # moles of Pb^{2+} and I^- in 1 L of solution using the ratio
4. Find the concentrations of Pb^{2+} and I^- using $C = \frac{n}{V}$
5. Find Ksp using $K_{sp} = \frac{[products]}{[reactants]} = \frac{[C]^c[D]^d}{[A]^a[B]^b}$

The solubility refers to concentration of PbI_2. Assume the solution is 1.00L since the solubility is mol/L.

C_{PbI_2}	0.00130M
n_{PbI_2}	?mol
V	1.00L

$$C_{PbI_2} = \frac{n}{V}$$
$$n_{PbI_2} = C \times V$$
$$n_{PbI_2} = 0.00130M \times 1.00L$$
$$n_{PbI_2} = 0.00130mol$$

	$PbI_{2(s)} \rightleftharpoons$	$Pb^{2+}_{(aq)}+$	$2I^-_{(aq)}$
n	0.00130mol	?mol	?mol
Ratio	1	1	2

$$n_{Pb^{2+}} = 0.00130mol\ PbI_2 \times \frac{1mol\ Pb^{2+}}{1mol\ PbI_2}$$
$$n_{Pb^{2+}} = 0.00130mol$$
$$C_{Pb^{2+}} = \frac{n}{V}$$
$$C_{Pb^{2+}} = \frac{0.00130mol}{1.00L}$$
$$C_{Pb^{2+}} = 0.00130M$$
$$n_{I^-} = 0.00130mol\ PbI_2 \times \frac{2mol\ I^-}{1mol\ PbI_2}$$
$$n_{I^-} = 0.00260mol$$
$$C_{I^-} = \frac{n}{V}$$
$$C_{I^-} = \frac{0.00260mol}{1.00L}$$
$$C_{I^-} = 0.00260M$$
$$K_{sp} = \frac{[products]}{[reactants]} = \frac{[Pb^{2+}]^1[I^-]^2}{1}$$
$$K_{sp} = \frac{[0.00130M]^1[0.00260M]^2}{1}$$
$$K_{sp} = 8.79 \times 10^{-9}$$

The equilibrium constant for dissociation of PbI_2 is 8.79×10^{-9}.

Example 2
For the following reaction, Ksp is 1.1×10^{-18}. If the concentration of Hg^{2+} is 0.010M, what is the concentration of Cl^- required in order to just begin precipitation of $HgCl_2$?

$HgCl_{2(s)} \rightleftharpoons Hg^{2+}_{(aq)} + 2Cl^-_{(aq)}$

This question is asking what concentration of Cl^- is needed to be present in the solution with 0.010M of Hg^{2+} without forming $HgCl_2 \rightarrow$ this means that you need to find concentration of Cl^- at equilibrium.

$$K_{sp} = \frac{[products]}{[reactants]} = \frac{[Hg^{2+}]^1 [Cl^-]^2}{1}$$

$$\sqrt{\frac{K_{sp}}{[Hg^{2+}]^1}} = [Cl^-]$$

$$\sqrt{\frac{1.1 \times 10^{-18}}{[0.010]^1}} = [Cl^-]$$

$$[Cl^-] = 1.04 \times 10^{-8} M$$

The concentration of Cl^- needed to just start precipitation of $HgCl_2$ is 1.04×10^{-8}M.

The common ion effect

Adding a common ion to products will cause equilibrium to shift to the left to produce more reactants

Adding a common ion to reactants will cause equilibrium to shift to the right to produce more products

Example 1
$BaSO_4$ (s) is placed into an aqueous solution. Ksp= 1.1x10⁻¹⁰.
a) What is the solubility of $BaSO_4$ in water?
b) What is the solubility of $BaSO_4$ in 0.010M of $Ba(NO_3)_2$?

a) What is the solubility of $BaSO_4$ in water?
When $BaSO_4$ is placed into water, it dissociates into its ions.
Solubility means you need to find [$BaSO_4$].
Let x be concentration of Ba^{2+} or SO_4^{2-} (since 1-1 ratio)
$BaSO_{4 (s)} \rightleftharpoons Ba^{2+}_{(aq)} + SO_4^{2-}_{(aq)}$

	$BaSO_{4(s)} \rightleftharpoons$	$Ba^{2+}_{(aq)}+$	$SO_4^{2-}_{(aq)}$
C	--------	x	x
Ratio	1	1	1

$$K_{sp} = \frac{[products]}{[reactants]} = \frac{[Ba^{2+}]^1 [SO_4^{2-}]^1}{1}$$

$$K_{sp} = 1.1 \times 10^{-10} = \frac{x^2}{1}$$

$$\sqrt{1.1 \times 10^{-10}} = x$$

Surviving University: First Year Chemistry

$x = 1.0 \times 10^{-5} M$

$[Ba^{2+}] = x = 1.0 \times 10^{-5} M$

$[BaSO_4] = 1.0 \times 10^{-5} M \, Ba^{2+} \times \dfrac{1 mol \, BaSO_4}{1 mol \, Ba^{2+}}$

$[BaSO_4] = 1.0 \times 10^{-5} M$

The solubility of $BaSO_4$ is 1.0×10^{-5}M in water.

b) What is the solubility of BaSO₄ in 0.010M of Ba(NO₃)₂?

In an aqueous solution, $Ba(NO_3)_{2(aq)} \rightarrow Ba^{2+}{}_{(aq)} + 2NO_3{}^-{}_{(aq)}$

Ba^{2+} is a common ion in $BaSO_{4(s)} \rightleftharpoons Ba^{2+}{}_{(aq)} + SO_4{}^{2-}{}_{(aq)}$

$Ba(NO_3)_2$ will be originally in the solution$\rightarrow$ the initial concentration of Ba^{2+} will be 0.010M (since 1-1 ratio of Ba^{2+} in $Ba(NO_3)_2$)

Since $BaSO_4$ dissociates, the equilibrium will be product favoured.

	$BaSO_{4(s)} \rightleftharpoons$	$Ba^{2+}{}_{(aq)} +$	$SO_4{}^{2-}{}_{(aq)}$
I	--------	0.010M	0M
C	--------	+x	+x
E	--------	0.010+x	x

$K_{sp} = \dfrac{[products]}{[reactants]} = \dfrac{[Ba^{2+}]^1 [SO_4^{2-}]^1}{1}$

$K_{sp} = 1.1 \times 10^{-10} = \dfrac{(0.010 + x)(x)}{1}$

Check if $100 \times K_{sp} < C_0$

$100 \times K_{sp} = 100 \times (1.1 \times 10^{-10}) = 1.1 \times 10^{-8} < 0.010 M$

Assume that $0.010 + x \approx 0.010$

$1.1 \times 10^{-10} = \dfrac{(0.010)(x)}{1}$

$\dfrac{1.1 \times 10^{-10}}{(0.010)} = x$

$x = 1.1 \times 10^{-8} M$

$[SO_4^{2-}] = x = 1.1 \times 10^{-8} M$

$[BaSO_4] = 1.1 \times 10^{-8} M \, SO_4^{2-} \times \dfrac{1 mol \, BaSO_4}{1 mol \, SO_4^{2-}}$

$[BaSO_4] = 1.1 \times 10^{-8} M$

The solubility of $BaSO_4$ is 1.1×10^{-8}M in 0.010M of $Ba(NO_3)_2$.

Example 2

An aqueous solution contains 0.015M of Ag⁺₍ₐq₎ and Pb²⁺₍ₐq₎. CrO₄²⁻ is added to the solution in order to form 2 precipitates→ Ag₂CrO₄₍s₎ and PbCrO₄₍s₎. Which compound will precipitate first?

An insoluble compound with the highest Ksp value will precipitate first

Compound	Ksp
Ag_2CrO_4	9×10^{-12}
$PbCrO_4$	1.8×10^{-14}

Since Ag_2CrO_4 has a larger Ksp value, it will precipitate first.

Complex ions

Example 1

$AgCl_{(s)}$ is dissolved in a solution that contains $NH_{3(aq)}$. What is K_{net} for the reaction?

Net:	$AgCl_{(s)} + 2NH_{3(aq)} \rightleftharpoons [Ag(NH_3)_2]^+ + Cl^-_{(aq)}$	$K_{net} = ?$
1.	$AgCl_{(s)} \rightleftharpoons Ag^+_{(aq)} + Cl^-_{(aq)}$	$Ksp = 1.8 \times 10^{-10}$
2.	$Ag^+_{(aq)} + 2NH_{3(aq)} \rightleftharpoons [Ag(NH_3)_2]^+$	$K_{form} = 1.6 \times 10^7$

From part 23 of this book,
$K_{net} = K_1 \times K_2$
$K_{net} = (1.8 \times 10^{-10}) \times (1.6 \times 10^7)$
$K_{net} = 2.9 \times 10^{-3}$
K_{net} for the reaction was 2.9×10^{-3}.

Part 28

Entropy and Free Energy

Spontaneous reaction

Entropy (S)

Standard entropy (ΔS°)

Universe, system, surroundings

Spontaneous reactions

Gibbs free energy

Entropy and Free Energy

Spontaneous reaction

- A spontaneous reaction occurs without energy being added to the system
    - This reaction occurs in the direction of equilibrium
- Most spontaneous reactions are exothermic, some are endothermic

Entropy (S)

- Disorganization of energy (the more dispersed the energy is, the more disorganized it is)
- Spontaneous reaction→ energy becomes dispersed→ entropy ↑
- Exothermic reaction→ energy is dispersed into the surroundings→ spontaneous reaction→ entropy ↑

Microstate- the way that energy is distributed between molecules→ there are many possible microstates

Possible microstate 1		Possible microstate 2		Possible microstate 3

⬤ is a packet of energy

ex.

- The most probable microstate is the one in which 2 packets of energy are in 1 molecule

> Entropy ↑ as the size of container ↑ (the # of available possible microstates ↑, the density of states ↑)
> Entropy ↑ as the temperature ↑
> Entropy ↑ as complexity of molecules ↑
> Entropy ↓ when the number of molecules ↓

energy dispearsal increases
→

$$S_{solid} < S_{liquid} < S_{gas}$$

- When solids and liquids are placed into a solvent, they dissolve spontaneously
    - This is due to high entropy→ energy becomes more dispersed

Surviving University: First Year Chemistry

Reversible process- a reaction can return to reactants without altering its surroundings
- Ex. equilibrium

Irreversible process- a reaction can return to reactants, but its surroundings are altered

$$Reversible\ process:\ dS = \frac{dq}{dT}$$
$$Reversible\ process:\ dS > \frac{dq}{dT}$$
$$During\ a\ phase\ change:\ \Delta S = \frac{q}{T}$$
$$Where\ q_{H_2O} = 40700J/mol$$

Note: ΔS= change in entropy (J/K), q= heat transferred during a phase change (J), T= temperature (K), dS= entropy at a particular instant (J/K), dq= heat being transferred at a particular instant (J), dT= temperature at a particular instant (K)

Standard entropy (ΔS°)

- ΔS° is entropy at **standard conditions**
    - All concentrations are 1.0M
    - Pressures of reactants and products in gaseous states are 1.0 bar
    - Reactants and products are in their standard states (at 298K)

If ΔS° is +ive, the reaction is spontaneous and exothermic

$$\Delta_r S^{\circ} = \Sigma S^{\circ}_{products} - \Sigma S^{\circ}_{reactants}$$

Note: multiply entropy values by stoichiometric coefficients

Note: $\Delta_r S^{\circ}$= entropy of the reaction under standard conditions (J/K•mol rxn), $\Sigma S^{\circ}_{products}$= the sum of entropy values of all of the products (J/K•mol), $\Sigma S^{\circ}_{reactants}$= the sum of entropy values of all of the reactants (J/K•mol)

Example 1
Find $\Delta_r S^{\circ}$ for the following reaction.
$2H_{2\ (g)} + O_{2(g)} \rightarrow 2H_2O_{(l)}$

ΔS° $H_{2(g)}$	130.7J/K•mol
ΔS° $O_{2(g)}$	205.1J/K•mol
ΔS° $H_2O_{(l)}$	69.95J/K•mol
$\Delta_r S^{\circ}$	?J/K• mol rxn

$$\Delta_r S^{\circ} = \Sigma S^{\circ}_{products} - \Sigma S^{\circ}_{reactants}$$

$$\Delta_r S^\circ = \left[\frac{2mol H_2 O}{1mol\ rxn} \times 69.95 J/K \cdot mol\right]$$
$$- \left[\left(\frac{2mol H_2}{1mol\ rxn} \times 130.7 J/K \cdot mol\right)\right.$$
$$\left. + \left(\frac{1mol O_2}{1mol\ rxn} \times 205.1 J/K \cdot mol\right)\right]$$
$$\Delta_r S^\circ = -326.1 J/K \cdot mol\ rxn$$

The standard entropy for the reaction was -326J/K•mol rxn.

Standard entropy of universe, system, and surroundings

From part 5 of this book,

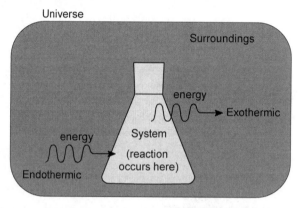

System- where a chemical reaction occurs (ex. flask)→ where reactants are transferred into products

Surroundings- is outside of the system, interacts with the system (ex. air around the flask)

Universe- system + surroundings

Note: standard entropy and enthalpy values can be found at the back of your chemistry textbook

$$\Delta S^\circ_{universe} = \Delta S^\circ_{system} + \Delta S^\circ_{surroundings}$$

$$\text{Where } \Delta S^\circ_{system} = \Sigma S^\circ_{products} - \Sigma S^\circ_{reactants}$$

$$\text{and } \Delta S^\circ_{surroundings} = \frac{\Delta H^\circ_{surroundings}}{T} = -\frac{\Delta_r H^\circ_{system}}{T}$$

$$\text{where } \Delta_r H^\circ = \Sigma \Delta_f H^\circ_{products} - \Sigma \Delta_f H^\circ_{reactants}$$

Note: $\Delta S^\circ_{universe}$ = entropy change of the system and surroundings under standard conditions (J/K•mol rxn), ΔS°_{system} = entropy change of the system under standard conditions (J/K•mol rxn), $\Delta S^\circ_{surroundings}$ = entropy change of the surroundings under standard conditions (J/K•mol rxn), $\Delta_r S°$= entropy of the reaction under standard conditions (J/K•mol rxn), $\Sigma S°_{products}$= the sum of entropy values of all of the products (J/K•mol), $\Sigma S°_{reactants}$= the sum of entropy values of all of the reactants (J/K•mol), $\Delta H°_{surroundings}$= enthalpy change of the surroundings (kJ/K•mol rxn), $\Delta_r H°_{system}$= enthalpy change of the system (kJ/K•mol rxn), T= temperature (K)

Spontaneous or not?

Reaction	$\Delta_r H°_{system}$	$\Delta S°_{system}$	Spontaneous?
exothermic	-ive	+ive	spontaneous
exothermic	-ive	-ive	spontaneous at ↓ temperatures
endothermic	+ive	+ive	spontaneous at ↑ temperatures
endothermic	+ive	-ive	not spontaneous

Example 1

Find $\Delta S°_{universe}$ of dissolving sodium chloride in water under standard conditions (T= 298K). Is this reaction spontaneous?

$NaCl_{(s)} \rightarrow NaCl_{(aq)}$

$\Delta S°_{universe} = \Delta S°_{system} + \Delta S°_{surroundings}$

Steps

1. Find $\Delta S°_{system}$ using $\Delta S°_{system} = \Sigma S°_{products} - \Sigma S°_{reactants}$
2. Find $\Delta_r H°_{system}$ using
   $\Delta_r H°_{system} = \Sigma \Delta_f H°_{products} - \Sigma \Delta_f H°_{reactants}$
3. Find $\Delta S°_{surroundings}$ using $\Delta S°_{surroundings} = -\dfrac{\Delta H°_{system}}{T}$
4. Find $\Delta S°_{universe}$ using $\Delta S°_{universe} = \Delta S°_{system} + \Delta S°_{surroundings}$

Step 1: find $\Delta S°_{system}$

$NaCl_{(s)} \rightarrow NaCl_{(aq)}$

$\Delta S°$ $NaCl_{(s)}$	72.11J/K•mol
$\Delta S°$ $NaCl_{(aq)}$	115.5J/K•mol
$\Delta S°_{system}$	?J/K•mol rxn

$\Delta S°_{system} = \Sigma S°_{products} - \Sigma S°_{reactants}$

$$\Delta S^\circ_{system} = \left[\frac{1 mol \ NaCl_{(aq)}}{1 mol \ rxn} \times 115.5 \ J/K \cdot mol\right]$$

$$- \left[\frac{1 \ mol \ NaCl_{(aq)}}{1 mol \ rxn} \times 72.11 \ J/K \cdot mol\right]$$

$$\Delta S^\circ_{system} = 43.4 \ J/K \cdot mol \ rxn$$

Step 2: find $\Delta_r H^\circ_{system}$

ΔH° NaCl$_{(s)}$	-411.12kJ/mol rxn
ΔH° NaCl$_{(aq)}$	-407.27kJ/mol rxn
$\Delta_r H^\circ_{system}$	?kJ/mol rxn

$$\Delta_r H^\circ_{system} = \Sigma \Delta_f H^\circ_{products} - \Sigma \Delta_f H^\circ_{reactants}$$

$$\Delta_r H^\circ_{system} = \left[\frac{1 mol \ NaCl_{(aq)}}{1 mol \ rxn} \times (-407.27 KJ/mol)\right]$$

$$- \left[\frac{1 mol \ NaCl_{(aq)}}{1 mol \ rxn} \times (-411.12 \ KJ/mol)\right]$$

$$\Delta_r H^\circ_{system} = 3.85 KJ/mol \ rxn$$

Step 3: Find $\Delta S^\circ_{surroundings}$

T	298K
$\Delta_r H^\circ_{system}$	3.85kJ/mol rxn
$\Delta S^\circ_{surroundings}$	?J/K•mol rxn

$$\Delta S^\circ_{surroundings} = -\frac{\Delta H^\circ_{system}}{T}$$

$$\Delta S^\circ_{surroundings} = -\frac{3.85 KJ/mol \ rxn}{298K}$$

$$\Delta S^\circ_{surroundings} = -0.0129 KJ/K \cdot mol \ rxn$$

Need to convert from kJ to J

$$\Delta S^\circ_{surroundings} = -0.0129 KJ/K \cdot mol \ rxn \times \frac{1000J}{1KJ}$$

$$\Delta S^\circ_{surroundings} = -12.9 J/K \cdot mol \ rxn$$

Step 4: Find $\Delta S^\circ_{universe}$

$\Delta S^\circ_{universe}$	?J/K•mol rxn
ΔS°_{system}	43.4J/K•mol rxn
$\Delta S^\circ_{surroundings}$	-12.9J/K•mol rxn

Surviving University: First Year Chemistry

$$\Delta S^{\circ}_{universe} = \Delta S^{\circ}_{system} + \Delta S^{\circ}_{surroundings}$$
$$\Delta S^{\circ}_{universe} = 43.4 J/K \cdot mol + (-12.9 J/K \cdot mol)$$
$$\Delta S^{\circ}_{universe} = 30.5 J/K \cdot molrxn$$

The entropy of universe of the reaction was 30.5 J/K•mol rxn. Since entropy is a positive value, the reaction was spontaneous.

Gibbs free energy

- Total energy change of the system when pure reactants are completely converted into pure products
- $\Delta_r G^{\circ}$ is change in free energy under standard conditions
  - All concentrations are 1.0M
  - Pressures of reactants and products in gaseous states are 1.0 bar
  - Reactants and products are in their standard states (at 298K)
- $\Delta_r G$ is change in free energy, but not under standard conditions

$$\Delta_r G^{\circ} = \Sigma\Delta_f G^{\circ}_{products} - \Sigma\Delta_f G^{\circ}_{reactants}$$

$$\Delta G^{\circ} = \Delta H^{\circ} - T\Delta S^{\circ} = -RT\ln K$$

If $aA + bB \rightleftharpoons cC + dD$

$$K = \frac{[products]}{[reactants]} = \frac{[C]^c[D]^d}{[A]^a[B]^b}$$

And $\Delta_r H^{\circ} = \Sigma\Delta_f H^{\circ}_{products} - \Sigma\Delta_f H^{\circ}_{reactants}$

Note: $\Delta_r G^{\circ}$= change in free energy of the reaction (kJ/mol•rxn), $\Delta_f G^{\circ}_{products}$= change in free energy of products (kJ/mol•rxn), $\Delta_f G^{\circ}_{reactants}$= change in free energy of reactants (kJ/mol•rxn), ΔH°= enthalpy change of reaction (kJ/mol•rxn), T= temperature (K), ΔS°= change in entropy of the reaction (kJ/K•mol•rxn), K= equilibrium constant, $\Delta_f H^{\circ}_{products}$= enthalpy change of products (kJ/mol•rxn), $\Delta_f H^{\circ}_{reactants}$= enthalpy change of reactants (kJ/mol•rxn)

$$\Delta_r G = \Delta_r G^{\circ} + RT\ln Q$$

If $aA + bB \rightleftharpoons cC + dD$

$$Q = \frac{[products]}{[reactants]} = \frac{[C]^c[D]^d}{[A]^a[B]^b}$$

And $R = 8.3145 \frac{J}{K \cdot mol}$

Surviving University: First Year Chemistry

Note: $\Delta_r G°$= change in free energy of the reaction under standard conditions (kJ/mol•rxn), : $\Delta_r G$= change in free energy of the reaction under non-standard conditions (kJ/mol•rxn), T= temperature (K), Q= reaction quotient, R= gas constant

$\Delta G°$ of a free element (ex. O_2)= 0 kJ/mol•rxn				

Q	K	ΔG	Product/reactant favoured	Spontaneous?
Q<K	K>>1	ΔG<0	product	yes
Q=K	K=1	ΔG=0	-----------	-----------
Q>K	K<<1	ΔG>0	reactant	no

Example 1
a) Find $\Delta_r G°$ for the following reaction of ethyne at 298K. Is the reaction spontaneous?
b) At what temperature does $\Delta_r G°$ change from being -ive to being +ive?
$C_2H_{2(g)}$+ 5/2 $O_{2(g)}$→ 2$CO_{2(g)}$+$H_2O_{(g)}$

a) Find $\Delta_r G°$ for the following reaction of ethyne at 298K. Is the reaction spontaneous?
Steps
1. Find $\Delta_r H°_{system}$ using $\Delta_r H°_{system} = \Sigma\Delta_f H°_{products} - \Sigma\Delta_f H°_{reactants}$
2. Find $\Delta S°_{system}$ using $\Delta S°_{system} = \Sigma S°_{products} - \Sigma S°_{reactants}$
3. Find $\Delta_r G°$ using $\Delta G° = \Delta H° - T\Delta S°$
Step 1: find $\Delta_r H°_{system}$
$C_2H_{2(g)}$+ 5/2 $O_{2(g)}$→ 2$CO_{2(g)}$+$H_2O_{(g)}$

ΔH° $C_2H_{2(g)}$	226.73kJ/mol
ΔH° $O_{2(g)}$	0 kJ/mol
ΔH° $CO_{2(g)}$	-393.509kJ/mol
ΔH° $H_2O_{(g)}$	-241.83kJ/mol
$\Delta_r H°_{system}$	?kJ/mol rxn

$\Delta_r H°_{system} = \Sigma\Delta_f H°_{products} - \Sigma\Delta_f H°_{reactants}$

Surviving University: First Year Chemistry

$$\Delta_r H^{\circ}_{system} = \left[\frac{2mol\ CO_2}{1mol\ rxn} \times (-393.509KJ/mol) + \frac{1mol\ H_2O}{1mol\ rxn}\right.$$
$$\times (-241.83KJ/mol)]\Big]$$
$$-\left[\frac{1mol\ C_2H_2}{1mol\ rxn} \times (226.73KJ/mol) + \frac{\frac{5}{2}mol\ O_2}{1mol\ rxn}\right.$$
$$\times (0KJ/mol)\Big]$$

$\Delta_r H^{\circ}_{system} = -1256KJ/molrxn$

Step 2: find $\Delta S^{\circ}_{system}$

$\Delta S^{\circ}\ C_2H_{2(g)}$	200.94J/K•mol
$\Delta S^{\circ}\ O_{2(g)}$	205.07J/K•mol
$\Delta S^{\circ}\ CO_{2(g)}$	213.74J/K•mol
$\Delta S^{\circ}\ H_2O_{(g)}$	188.84J/K•mol
$\Delta_r S^{\circ}_{system}$	?kJ/mol rxn

$\Delta S^{\circ}_{system} = \Sigma S^{\circ}_{products} - \Sigma S^{\circ}_{reactants}$

$$\Delta S^{\circ}_{system} = \left[\frac{2mol\ CO_2}{1mol\ rxn} \times (213.74J/K \cdot mol) + \frac{1mol\ H_2O}{1mol\ rxn}\right.$$
$$\times (188.84J/K \cdot mol)]\Big]$$
$$-\left[\frac{1mol\ C_2H_2}{1mol\ rxn} \times (200.94J/K \cdot mol) + \frac{\frac{5}{2}mol\ O_2}{1mol\ rxn}\right.$$
$$\times (205.07\ J/K \cdot mol)\Big]$$

$\Delta S^{\circ}_{system} = -97.3J/K \cdot mol\ rxn$

$\Delta S^{\circ}_{system} = -97.3J/K \cdot mol\ rxn \times \frac{1KJ}{1000J}$

$\Delta S^{\circ}_{system} = -0.0973KJ/K \cdot mol\ rxn$

Step 3: find $\Delta_r G^{\circ}$

$\Delta G^{\circ} = \Delta H^{\circ} - T\Delta S^{\circ}$

ΔG°	?kJ/mol
$\Delta S^{\circ}_{system}$	-0.0947kJ/K•mol rxn
$\Delta_r H^{\circ}_{system}$	-1256kJ/mol rxn

T	298K

$$\Delta G° = \Delta H° - T\Delta S°$$
$$\Delta G° = -1256 kJ/mol\ rxn - \left(298K \times (-0.0947 kJ/K \cdot mol\ rxn)\right)$$
$$\Delta G° = -1227 kJ/mol\ rxn$$

The free energy in the reaction is -1227kJ/molrxn. Since the value is negative, the reaction is spontaneous.

b) At what temperature does $\Delta_r G°$ change from being -ive to being +ive?
$$\Delta G° = \Delta H° - T\Delta S°$$
$\Delta G°$ changes from + ive to − ive when its value is equal to 0. Sub in $\Delta G° = 0$.
$$0 = \Delta H° - T\Delta S°$$
Rearrange and solve for temperature.
$$T\Delta S° = \Delta H°$$
$$T = \frac{\Delta H°}{\Delta S°}$$

$\Delta S°_{system}$	-0.0973kJ/K•mol rxn
$\Delta_r H°_{system}$	-1256kJ/molrxn
T	?K

$$T = \frac{-1256\ KJ/molrxn}{-0.0973\ KJ/K \cdot mol\ rxn}$$
$$T = 1.29 \times 10^4\ K$$

The free energy changes from being –ive (spontaneous) to being +ive (not spontaneous) at 1.29x10⁴K.

Example 2

$AgCl_{(s)}$ dissociates when placed into water. What is ΔG° for dissociation of silver chloride at 298K? Is this reaction spontaneous?

$Ag^+_{(aq)} + Cl^-_{(aq)} \rightarrow Ag_{(s)}$ ① $K_{sp} = 1.8 \times 10^{-10}$

When an ionic compound is placed into water, it dissociated into its ions→ so the reaction is

$Ag_{(s)} \rightarrow Ag^+_{(aq)} + Cl^-_{(aq)}$ ②

The dissociation is in the opposite direction than the reaction given in this problem. Since the direction is reversed, K_{sp} for reaction ① will be different than that for reaction ②.

From part 23 of this book, $K_{new} = \frac{1}{K_{old}}$

$$K_2 = \frac{1}{K_1}$$

Surviving University: First Year Chemistry

$$K_2 = \frac{1}{1.8 \times 10^{-10}}$$

$$K_2 = 5.6 \times 10^9$$

$$\Delta G° = -RTlnK$$

$$\Delta G° = -(8.3145 \frac{J}{K \cdot mol})(298K)ln(5.6 \times 10^9)$$

$$\Delta G° = -5.6 \times 10^4 J/mol\ rxn$$

ΔG° for dissociation of silver chloride was -5.6x10⁴J/mol rxn. Since ΔG° has a negative value, the reaction is spontaneous.

Example 3

The following reaction has equilibrium constant of 7.99x10⁻². At 1073K, the concentrations are found to be the following: [CO]= 0.500M, [H₂]= 4.25x10⁻²M, and [H₂O]= 0.150M. Find ΔG for this reaction. Is this reaction spontaneous?

$C_{(s)} + H_2O_{(g)} \rightleftharpoons CO_{(g)} + H_{2(g)}$

You know $\Delta_r G = \Delta_r G° + RTlnQ$ ①

and $\Delta G° = -RTlnK$ ②

Sub ② into ①

$\Delta_r G = -RTlnK + RTlnQ$

$\Delta_r G = RTlnQ - RTlnK$

Factor out RT

$\Delta_r G = RT(lnQ - lnK)$

Using properties of lns: $lnQ - lnK$ is the same thing as $ln\frac{Q}{K}$

$$\Delta_r G = RT(ln\frac{Q}{K})$$

Find Q by plugging in all of the other known values into the reaction quotient expression.

$$Q = \frac{[products]}{[reactants]}$$

$$Q = \frac{[CO]^1[H_2]^1}{[H_2O]^1}$$

$$Q = \frac{[0.500M]^1[4.25 \times 10^{-2}M]^1}{[0.150M]^1}$$

$$Q = 0.142$$

Q	0.142
T	1073K
K	7.99x10⁻²
ΔG	?kJ/mol

Surviving University: First Year Chemistry

| R | 8.3145J/K•mol |

$$\Delta_r G = \left(8.3145\frac{J}{K \cdot mol}\right)(1073K)(ln\frac{0.142}{7.99 \times 10^{-2}})$$
$$\Delta_r G = 5130J/mol\ rxn$$

The free energy of the reaction was 5130 J/mol rxn. Since it is a positive value, the reaction was not spontaneous.

Example 4

Find the equilibrium constant at 298K for the following reaction.
$\Delta G° = 163.2kJ/mol$.

$3O_{2(g)} \rightleftharpoons 2O_{3(g)}$
Find K using $\Delta G° = -RTlnK$

T	298K
K	?
ΔG°	163.2kJ/mol
R	8.3145J/K•mol

Need to convert ΔG° into J/mol.

$$\Delta G° = -163.2 kJ/K \cdot mol \times \frac{1000J}{1kJ}$$
$$\Delta G° = -163200J/K \cdot mol$$
$$\Delta G° = -RTlnK$$
$$\frac{\Delta G°}{-RT} = lnK$$
$$e^{\frac{\Delta G°}{-RT}} = K$$
$$K = e^{-\frac{163200J/molrxn}{\left(8.3145\frac{J}{K \cdot mol}\right)(298K)}}$$
$$K = 2.48 \times 10^{-29}$$

The equilibrium constant for the reaction is 2.48×10^{-29}.

Surviving University: First Year Chemistry

Part 29

Redox Reactions

Galvanic cell

Cell notation

Electromotive force

Standard cell potential

Cell potential under non-standard

conditions

Measuring pH using cell potential

Free energy and equilibrium constant

Spontaneous or not?

Battery types

Electrolytic cell

Surviving University: First Year Chemistry

Redox Reactions

See part 3 for oxidation-reduction, oxidation states, balancing redox reactions

Galvanic cell

Galvanic cell- a chemical change is used to produce a current

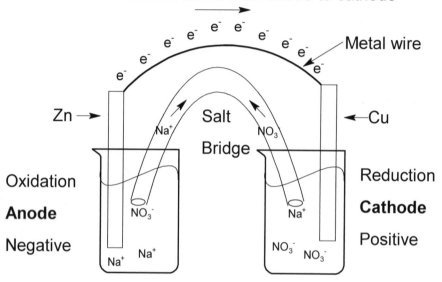

Salt bridge- allows anions and cations to move between 2 compartments to balance the charge
Anode- where oxidation occurs
Cathode- where reduction occurs
- Electrons move through the metal wire from anode to cathode

Surviving University: First Year Chemistry

Cell notation

Example 1

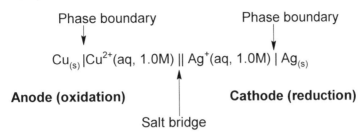

Phase boundary   Phase boundary

$$Cu_{(s)} | Cu^{2+}(aq, 1.0M) \| Ag^{+}(aq, 1.0M) | Ag_{(s)}$$

Anode (oxidation)   **Cathode (reduction)**

Salt bridge

The half-reactions from cell notation have to be balanced!

Oxidation half-reaction	$Cu \rightarrow Cu^{2+} + 2e^{-}$
Reduction half-reaction	$Ag^{+} + e^{-} \rightarrow Ag$

- Charge balance

Oxidation half-reaction	$Cu \rightarrow Cu^{2+} + 2e^{-}$
Reduction half-reaction	$(Ag^{+} + e^{-} \rightarrow Ag)$ **x2** $= 2Ag^{+} + 2e^{-} \rightarrow 2Ag$

Add the 2 half-reactions
$Cu + 2Ag^{+} + 2e^{-} \rightarrow 2Ag + Cu^{2+} + 2e^{-}$
$Cu + 2Ag^{+} + \cancel{2e^{-}} \rightarrow 2Ag + Cu^{2+} + \cancel{2e^{-}}$
$Cu_{(s)} + 2Ag^{+}_{(aq)} \rightarrow 2Ag_{(s)} + Cu^{2+}_{(aq)}$
If you do not understand this example, refer to part 3 of this book for balancing redox reactions.

Electromotive force

- **Electromotive force** causes electrons to move from anode to cathode
- Electromotive force is created due to potential difference between 2 electrodes
  - Each metal strip has a different charge $\rightarrow$ 1 metal strip loses electrons, 1 metal strip gains electrons

Standard cell potential (E°)

- **Standard conditions**
  - All concentrations are 1.0M
  - Pressure of reactants and products in gaseous states is 1.0 bar

> ○ Reactants and products are in their standard states (at 298K)

Standard cell potential (E°)- measures the tendency of reactants to form products under standard conditions

- Values for each reaction are usually given at the back of your chemistry textbook

Standard hydrogen cell- has E°= 0.0V

- Best oxidizing agents have the highest E° values
- Best reducing agents have the lowest E° values

$$E_{cell}^{\circ} = E_{cathode}^{\circ} + E_{anode}^{\circ}$$

Spontaneous: E° is +ive

Not spontaneous: E° is -ive

Note: half-reactions are in a table at the back of your chemistry textbook. The half-reactions are given as reduction reactions→ to convert to oxidation reaction, reverse the sign of E° (from +ive to –ive or from –ive to +ive)

If a half-reaction is multiplied by a coefficient, E° value is <u>not</u> multiplied by that coefficient

Example 1

Find the standard cell potential for the following reaction. Is this reaction spontaneous?

$Sn^{2+}_{(aq)} + Ag_{(s)} \rightarrow Sn_{(s)} + Ag^{+}_{(aq)}$

This equation is not balanced→ need to balance the equation.

The exact oxidation and reduction reactions can be found in a table at the back of your chemistry textbook.

	Reaction	E° (V)
Oxidation half-reaction	$Ag_{(s)} \rightarrow Ag^{+}_{(aq)} + e^{-}$ When the half-reactions are added together, electrons need to cancel out $(Ag_{(s)} \rightarrow Ag^{+}_{(aq)} + e^{-})$ **x 2** $= 2Ag_{(s)} \rightarrow 2Ag^{+}_{(aq)} + 2e^{-}$	-0.799
Reduction half-reaction	$Sn^{2+}_{(aq)} + 2Ag_{(s)} \rightarrow Sn_{(s)} + 2Ag^{+}_{(aq)}$ Add the 2 half-reactions $2Ag_{(s)} + Sn^{2+}_{(aq)} + 2Ag_{(s)} \rightarrow 2Ag^{+}_{(aq)} + 2e^{-} + Sn_{(s)} + 2Ag^{+}_{(aq)}$ electrons cancel out	-0.14
Overall reaction	$Sn^{2+}_{(aq)} + 2Ag_{(s)} \rightarrow Sn_{(s)} + 2Ag^{+}_{(aq)}$	?

Note: the reaction in a table in the back of your chemistry textbook is $Ag^{+}_{(aq)} + e^{-} \rightarrow Ag_{(s)}$ with E°=0.799V. In order to make it an oxidation, the

Surviving University: First Year Chemistry

direction of the reaction has to be reversed and the sign of E° has to be changed from 0.799V to -0.799V.

$$E^\circ_{cell} = E^\circ_{cathode} + E^\circ_{anode}$$
$$E^\circ_{cell} = -0.799\ V + (-0.14\ V)$$
$$E^\circ_{cell} = -0.939\ V$$

The cell potential is -0.939V. The reaction is not spontaneous since E°cell is negative.

Cell potential under non-standard conditions (E)

- When the concentration of each aqueous solution is not 1.0M or the pressure of reactants and products in gaseous states is not 1.0 bar or reactants and products are not in their standard states
  - Then the **Nerst equation** is used to find the cell potential

Nerst equation: $E = E^\circ - \dfrac{RT}{nF} \ln Q$

Where $F = 9.6485338 \times 10^4\, C/mol$

$$R = 8.3145\ \frac{J}{K \cdot mol}$$

If $aA + bB \rightleftharpoons cC + dD$

$$Q = \frac{[products]}{[reactants]} = \frac{[C]^c[D]^d}{[A]^a[B]^b}$$

Note: E= cell potential under non-standard conditions (V), E°= cell potential under standard conditions (V), T= temperature (K), n= # of electrons exchanged, F= Faraday's constant, R= gas constant, Q= reaction quotient

Example 1
Half of a galvanic cell contains 4.8×10^{-3}M solution of $Cu(NO_3)_2$. The other half of the cell contains 0.40M solution of $Zn(NO_3)_2$. Find the cell potential at 298K. Is this reaction spontaneous?
$Cu^{2+}_{(aq)} + Zn_{(s)} \rightarrow Cu_{(s)} + Zn^{2+}_{(aq)}$
Steps
1. Write oxidation and reduction half-reactions
2. Find E° using $E^\circ_{cell} = E^\circ_{cathode} + E^\circ_{anode}$
3. Find the reaction quotient using $Q = \dfrac{[products]}{[reactants]}$
4. Find E using $E = E^\circ - \dfrac{RT}{nF} \ln Q$

The oxidation and reduction reactions can be found in a table at the back of your chemistry textbook.

Surviving University: First Year Chemistry

	Reaction	E° (V)
Oxidation half-reaction	$Zn_{(s)} \rightarrow Zn^{2+}_{(aq)} + 2e^{-}$	0.763
Reduction half-reaction	$Cu^{2+}_{(aq)} + 2e^{-} \rightarrow Cu_{(s)}$	0.337
Overall reaction	$Cu^{2+}_{(aq)} + Zn_{(s)} \rightarrow Cu_{(s)} + Zn^{2+}_{(aq)}$	?

Note: the reaction in a table at the back of your chemistry textbook is $Zn^{2+}_{(aq)} + 2e^{-} \rightarrow Zn_{(s)}$ with E°=-0.763V. In order to make it an oxidation, the direction of the reaction has to be reversed and the sign of E° has to be changed from -0.763V to 0.763V.

$$E^{\circ}_{cell} = E^{\circ}_{cathode} + E^{\circ}_{anode}$$
$$E^{\circ}_{cell} = 0.763V + 0.337V$$
$$E^{\circ}_{cell} = 1.100V$$

Now you need to find the reaction quotient. Solids do not appear in the reaction quotient expression.

$Cu^{2+}_{(aq)} + Zn_{(s)} \rightarrow Cu_{(s)} + Zn^{2+}_{(aq)}$

$$Q = \frac{[Zn^{2+}]}{[Cu^{2+}]}$$
$$Q = \frac{[0.40M]}{[4.8 \times 10^{-3}M]}$$
$$Q = 83.3$$
$$E = E^{\circ} - \frac{RT}{nF} lnQ$$

Since there are 2 electrons transferred (Zn loses 2 electrons and Cu gains 2 electrons), n=2

$$E = 1.100\,V - \frac{8.3145 \frac{J}{K \cdot mol} \times 298K}{2 \times (9.6485338 \times 10^4 \frac{C}{mol})} \ln(83.3)$$

$$E = 1.043V$$

The cell potential was 1.043V. Since E is +ive, the reaction is spontaneous.

Measuring pH using the cell potential in a galvanic cell

Example 1
Cell potential at 298K for Ag/AgCl electrode was measured to be 0.34V. The pressure of hydrogen gas was 1.00atm. The concentration of Cl⁻ was found to be 3.5M. What is the pH of this solution?

The Ag/AgCl reduction half-reaction is $2AgCl_{(s)} + 2e^{-} \rightarrow 2Ag_{(s)} + 2Cl^{-}_{(aq)}$
Steps
1. Write the oxidation and reduction half-reactions
2. Find E° using $E^{\circ}_{cell} = E^{\circ}_{cathode} + E^{\circ}_{anode}$

Surviving University: First Year Chemistry

3. Find the reaction quotient using $Q = \frac{[products]}{[reactants]}$
4. Find [H⁺] using $E = E° - \frac{RT}{nF} lnQ$
5. Find pH using $pH = -\log[H^+]$

Since there is Ag/AgCl electrode and hydrogen gas is involved, then 1 half-reaction should involve AgCl and 1 half-reaction should involve hydrogen gas. The exact oxidation and reduction reactions can be found in a table at the back of your chemistry textbook.

	Reaction	E° (V)
Oxidation half-reaction	$H_{2\,(g)} \rightarrow 2H^+_{(aq)} + 2e^-$	0.00
Reduction half-reaction	$2AgCl_{(s)} + 2e^- \rightarrow 2Ag_{(s)} + 2Cl^-_{(aq)}$	0.22
Overall reaction	$H_{2\,(g)} + 2AgCl_{(s)} \rightarrow 2Ag_{(s)} + 2H^+_{(aq)} + 2Cl^-_{(aq)}$	?

$E°_{cell} = E°_{cathode} + E°_{anode}$
$E°_{cell} = 0.00V + 0.22V$
$E°_{cell} = 0.22V$

Now you need to find reaction quotient. Solids do not go into the reaction quotient expression.

$H_{2\,(g)} + 2AgCl_{(s)} \rightarrow 2Ag_{(s)} + 2H^+_{(aq)} + 2Cl^-_{(aq)}$

$$Q = \frac{[H^+]^2[Cl^-]^2}{P_{H_2}}$$

You know that using $pH = -\log[H^+]$. So you need to find [H⁺].

$$E = E° - \frac{RT}{nF} lnQ$$

$$E = E° - \frac{RT}{nF} \ln\left(\frac{[H^+]^2[Cl^-]^2}{P_{H_2}}\right)$$

Since there are 2 electrons transferred, n=2

$$0.34V = 0.22V - \frac{8.314\frac{J}{K \cdot mol} \times 298K}{2 \times (9.6485338 \times 10^4 \frac{C}{mol})} \ln\left(\frac{[H^+]^2[3.5\,M]^2}{1.00atm}\right)$$

$$0.34V = 0.22V - \frac{8.314\frac{J}{K \cdot mol} \times 298K}{2 \times (9.6485338 \times 10^4 \frac{C}{mol})} \ln\left([H^+]^2 \times 12.25\right)$$

$$0.34V - 0.22V = -\frac{8.314\frac{J}{K \cdot mol} \times 298K}{2 \times (9.6485338 \times 10^4 \frac{C}{mol})} \ln\left([H^+]^2 \times 12.25\right)$$

$$\frac{0.34V - 0.22V}{-\frac{8.314\frac{J}{K \cdot mol} \times 298K}{2 \times (9.6485338 \times 10^4 \frac{C}{mol})}} = \ln\left([H^+]^2 \times 12.25\right)$$

$$e^{\dfrac{0.34V-0.22V}{-\dfrac{8.314\frac{J}{K\cdot mol}\times298K}{2\times(9.6485338\times10^4\frac{C}{mol})}}} = [H^+]^2 \times 12.25$$

$$\dfrac{e^{\dfrac{0.34V-0.22V}{-\dfrac{8.314\frac{J}{K\cdot mol}\times298K}{2\times(9.6485338\times10^4\frac{C}{mol})}}}}{12.25} = [H^+]^2$$

$$[H^+] = \sqrt{\dfrac{e^{\dfrac{0.34V-0.22V}{-\dfrac{8.314\frac{J}{K\cdot mol}\times298K}{2\times(9.6485338\times10^4\frac{C}{mol})}}}}{12.25}}$$

$$[H^+] = 2.67 \times 10^{-3}M$$
$$pH = -log[H^+]$$
$$pH = -log[2.67 \times 10^{-3}M]$$
$$pH = 2.57$$

The pH of the solution was 2.57.

Free energy (ΔG) and the equilibrium constant

- Free energy is the maximum amount of work that the galvanic cell does on its surroundings when it produces electricity
- ΔG°- free energy at standard conditions
  - All concentrations are 1.0M
  - Pressure of reactants and products in gaseous states is 1.0 bar
  - Reactants and products are in their standard states (at 298K)
- ΔG- free energy at non-standard conditions

$$\Delta G° = -nFE° = -RTlnK$$
$$\Delta G = -nFE = -RTlnK$$
$$\text{Where } F = 9.6485338 \times 10^4 C/mol$$
$$R = 8.3145 \frac{J}{K \cdot mol}$$
$$\text{If } aA + bB \rightleftharpoons cC + dD$$
$$K = \frac{[products]}{[reactants]} = \frac{[C]^c[D]^d}{[A]^a[B]^b}$$

Note: ΔG°- free energy at standard conditions (kJ), ΔG- free energy at non-standard conditions (kJ), n= # of moles of electrons transferred, F= Faraday's constant, T= temperature (K), R= gas constant, K= equilibrium constant

Surviving University: First Year Chemistry

Example 1

Find the free energy under standard conditions and the equilibrium constant for the following reaction.

$Ag^+_{(aq)} + Br^-_{(aq)} \rightleftharpoons AgBr_{(s)}$

The oxidation half-reaction is $Ag_{(s)} + Br^-_{(aq)} \rightarrow AgBr_{(s)} + e^-$ *where E°=-0.0713V*

Steps

1. Write the oxidation and reduction half-reactions
2. Find E° using $E^{\circ}_{cell} = E^{\circ}_{cathode} + E^{\circ}_{anode}$
3. Find free energy using $\Delta G^{\circ} = -nFE^{\circ}$
4. Find K using $\Delta G^{\circ} = -RTlnK$

The exact oxidation and reduction reactions can be found in a table at the back of your chemistry textbook.

	Reaction	E° (V)
Oxidation half-reaction	$Ag_{(s)} + Br^-_{(aq)} \rightarrow AgBr_{(s)} + e^-$	-0.0713
Reduction half-reaction	$Ag^+_{(aq)} + e^- \rightarrow Ag_{(s)}$	0.7994
Overall reaction	$Ag^+_{(aq)} + Br^-_{(aq)} \rightleftharpoons AgBr_{(s)}$	?

$E^{\circ}_{cell} = E^{\circ}_{cathode} + E^{\circ}_{anode}$

$E^{\circ}_{cell} = -0.0713V + 0.7994V$

$E^{\circ}_{cell} = 0.7281V$

$\Delta G^{\circ} = -nFE^{\circ}$

Since there is 1 electron transferred, n=1

$\Delta G^{\circ} = -(1mol)\left(9.6485338 \times 10^4 \frac{C}{mol}\right)(0.7281V)$

$\Delta G^{\circ} = 70250J$

$\Delta G^{\circ} = -RTlnK$

Rearrange for K.

$\frac{\Delta G^{\circ}}{-RT} = lnK$

$K = e^{\frac{\Delta G^{\circ}}{-RT}}$

$K = e^{-\frac{70250J}{\left(8.3145\frac{J}{K \cdot mol}\right)(298K)}}$

$K = 4.85 \times 10^{-13}$

The equilibrium constant is 4.85x10⁻¹³.

Spontaneous or not?

	E°	ΔG°	K
Product favoured	>0	<0	>>1

(spontaneous)			
At equilibrium	0	0	1
Reactant favoured (not spontaneous)	<0	>0	<<1

Note: E°= standard cell potential (V), ΔG°= free energy (J), K= equilibrium constant

Battery types

Primary battery- redox reaction cannot be restored by recharging the battery

Secondary battery- redox reaction can be restored by recharging the battery

Electrolytic cell

Electrolytic cell- a current is used to produce chemical change
- Electrolytic cell has reversed polarity comparing to a galvanic cell (anode is +ive, cathode is −ive)

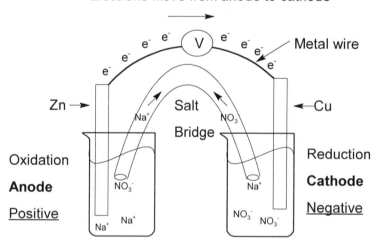

Electrons move from anode to cathode

Cations move from anode to cathode

Anions move from cathode to anode

Current- the amount of charge flowing through an area in a specific period of time

Surviving University: First Year Chemistry

$$I = \frac{q}{t}$$
$$F = 9.6485338 \times 10^4 C/mol$$
$$n = \frac{q}{F}$$

Note: I= current (A), q= charge (C), t= time (s), F= Faraday's constant, n= # moles (mol)

Example 1

1.50 amperes flow through $Ag^+_{(aq)}$ in a time of 900s. What is the mass of Ag metal deposited?

Steps

1. Find charge using $I = \frac{q}{t}$
2. Find # moles deposited using Faraday's constant $n = \frac{q}{F}$
3. Find mass using $n = \frac{m}{M}$

I	1.50A
q	?C
t	900s
n	?mol
M	107.86g/mol
m	?g

$$I = \frac{q}{t}$$
$$q = I \times t$$
$$q = 1.50A \times 900s$$
$$q = 1350C$$
You know that $F = 9.6485338 \times 10^4 C/mol$
$$n = \frac{q}{F}$$
$$n = \frac{1350C}{9.6485338 \times 10^4 C/mol}$$
$$n = 0.0140mol$$
$$n = \frac{m}{M}$$
$$m = n \times M$$
$$m = 0.0140mol \times 107.86g/mol$$
$$m = 1.51g$$
The mass of silver deposited was 1.51g.

Equations and Constants

Part 1: Basic Concepts of Chemistry

Equation/constant	
$$\rho = \frac{m}{V}$$ $$\rho_{H_2O} = 1 g/mL$$	ρ= density (g/mL or g/L or mg/mL or mg/L or kg/mL or kg/L) ρ_{H2O}= density of water (g/mL) m= mass (g or mg or kg) V= volume (mL or L)
$$1L = 1000cm^3$$ $$1mL = 1cm^3 = 1cc$$ $$1\ angstrom = 1Å = 10^{-10}m$$	
$$New\ Units = original\ units \times \frac{new\ units}{original\ units}$$	
$Temperature\ in\ Kelvin$ $$= (Temperature\ in\ °C + 273.15°C) \times \frac{1K}{1°C}$$ $Temperature\ in\ °C$ $$= (Temperature\ in\ K - 273.15K) \times \frac{1°C}{1K}$$	
$Error = experimental\ value$ $\qquad - accepted\ value$ $\% Error$ $$= \frac{|experimental\ value - accepted\ value|}{accepted\ value}$$ $\times 100\%$	| | means absolute value (all negative values become positive) Experimental value comes from the lab Accepted value comes from calculations Error measures the discrepancy between data obtained in the lab and data calculated

Part 2: Atoms, Molecules, and Ions

	Mass
Electron (e⁻)	9.109×10^{-28}g
Proton (p)	1.673×10^{-24}g
Neutron (n)	1.675×10^{-24}g

Equation/constant	
$\% \ abundance = \dfrac{\# \ atoms \ in \ a \ specific \ isotope}{total \ \# \ of \ atoms \ in \ all \ isotopes} \times 100\%$ $100\% = \% \ abundance \ of \ isotope \ 1$ $+ \ \% \ abundance \ of \ isotope \ 2 + \cdots$	% abundance is measured experimentally using a mass spectrometer
$1 amu = 1u = 1.66054 \times 10^{-24} g$	amu= u= atomic mass unit
$Atomic \ weight = \dfrac{\% A_1}{100\%} \times m_1 + \dfrac{\% A_2}{100\%} \times m_2 + \dfrac{\% A_3}{100\%} \times m_3 + \cdots$	$\%A_1$= percentage abundance of isotope 1 m_1= mass of isotope 1 (u)
$Force = \dfrac{q_1 \times q_2}{r^2}$	q_1= magnitude of charge of the first charge (Coulombs) q_2= magnitude of charge of the second charge (Coulombs) r= distance between charges (m)
$1 \ mol = 6.0221415 \times 10^{23} particles$ $Avogadro's \ number = \ 6.0221415 \times 10^{23} particles/mol$ $\# \ particles = n \times 6.0221415 \times 10^{23} particles/mol$	n= number of moles (mol)
$n = \dfrac{m}{M}$	n= number of moles (mol) m= mass (g) M= molar mass (g/mol)
$\% \ composition = \dfrac{mass \ of \ an \ element}{mass \ of \ a \ molecule} \times 100\%$ $\% \ composition$ $= \dfrac{\# \ atoms \ of \ element \ in \ a \ molecule \ \times \ M \ of \ an \ element}{M \ of \ a \ molecule}$ $\times 100\%$	M= molar mass (g/mol)

Part 4: Stoichiometry

Equation/constant	
$\% \ yield = \dfrac{actual \ yield}{theoretical \ yield} \times 100\%$	

$Atom\ efficiency$ $= \dfrac{\#\ of\ atoms\ of\ an\ element\ in\ a\ desired\ product}{\#of\ atoms\ of\ an\ element\ in\ reactants}$ $\times 100\%$	
$OAE = \dfrac{mass\ of\ a\ desired\ product}{total\ mass\ of\ all\ products} \times 100\%$	OAE= overall atom efficiency
$E\ factor = \dfrac{mass\ of\ waste}{mass\ of\ a\ desired\ product}$	
$Purity = \dfrac{mass\ obtained\ in\ a\ lab}{mass\ calculated} \times 100\%$	
$C = \dfrac{n}{V}$	C= concentration of solution (mol/L or M) n= # moles (mol) V= volume (L)
$C_1 V_1 = C_2 V_2$	C_1 is the original concentration of the solution (M) V_1 is the original volume of the solution (L) C_2 is the final concentration of the solution (M) V_2 is the final volume of the solution (L)

Part 5: Chemical Reactivity

Equation/constant	
$1\ cal = 4.184\ J$ $1\ dietary\ calorie = 1000\ cal$	
$\Delta U = q + W$	ΔU= change of energy in the system (J) q= energy absorbed/released by system (J) W= work done by or on the system (J)
$Specific\ heat\ capacity\ of\ H_2O = 4.18\ J/g \cdot K$	
$q = m \times C_p \times \Delta T$ Where $\Delta T = T_f - T_i$	Note: the temperature must be in Kelvin q= energy gained/lost in the chemical reaction (J) m= mass of substance (g) C_p= specific heat capacity (J/g•K) Δ T= change in temperature (K) T_f= final temperature of the system (K)

	T_i= initial temperature of the system (K)
$$q_1 + q_2 + q_3 \ldots = 0$$ Where $q = m \times C_p \times \Delta T$ where $\Delta T = T_f - T_i$	q_1= energy gained/lost in the 1st chemical reaction (J) q_2= energy gained/lost in the 2nd chemical reaction (J) q_3= energy gained/lost in the 3rd chemical reaction (J) m= mass of substance (g) C_p= specific heat capacity (J/g·K) ΔT= change in temperature (K) T_f= final temperature of the system (K) T_i= initial temperature of the system (K)
$$q = n \times \Delta H$$	q= energy gained/lost during a phase change (J) n= # of moles of a substance ΔH= heat of transition (J/mol)
$$\Delta H = \Delta U + P\Delta V$$ $$\Delta H = H_f - H_i$$	ΔH= enthalpy (J) ΔU= change in energy of the system (J) P= pressure of the system (kPa) ΔV= change in volume (L)
$$q_{reaction} = -q_{calorimeter}$$ $$q_{calorimeter} = c_{calorimeter}\Delta T \text{ where}$$ $$\Delta T = T_f - T_i$$ where $c_{calorimeter} \cong m_{solution}c_{solution}$	Note: the temperature must be in Kelvin $q_{reaction}$= energy gained/lost during a chemical reaction (J), $q_{calorimeter}$= energy gained/lost by the calorimeter during a chemical reaction (J) $c_{calorimeter}$= specific heat capacity of the calorimeter (J/g·K) ΔT= change in temperature (K) T_f= final temperature of the system (K) T_i= initial temperature of the system (K) $m_{solution}$= mass of solution inside of the calorimeter (g) $c_{solution}$= specific heat capacity of solution inside of the calorimeter (J/g·K)

Surviving University: First Year Chemistry

$\Delta_r H° = \Sigma\Delta_f H°_{products} - \Sigma\Delta_f H°_{reactants}$	The enthalpy value for elements (ex. O_2) is 0kJ/mol Multiply $\Delta_f H°_{product}$ and $\Delta_f H°_{reactant}$ of each compound by its stoichiometric coefficient $\Sigma\Delta_f H°_{products}$= enthalpy of products (kJ/mol) $\Sigma\Delta_f H°_{reactants}$= enthalpy of reactants (kJ/mol) $\Delta_r H°$= enthalpy of the reaction (kJ/mol) Note: $\Delta_f H°$ values for each reactant/product can be found in a table at the back of your chemistry textbook.
$\Delta_r H° = \Delta H°_1 + \Delta H°_2 + \cdots$	$\Delta_r H°$= enthalpy of the reaction (kJ/mol) $\Delta H°_1$= enthalpy of step 1 of the reaction (kJ/mol) $\Delta H°_1$= enthalpy of step 2 of the reaction (kJ/mol)
$\Delta_r H° = \Sigma energy\ to\ break\ bonds$ $- \Sigma energy\ to\ make\ bonds$	Multiply $\Sigma energy\ to\ break\ bonds$ and $\Sigma energy\ to\ make\ bonds$ of each bond by the number that particular bond broken/formed Note: energy to break and to make bonds can be found at the back of your chemistry textbook. $\Delta_r H°$= enthalpy of the reaction (kJ/mol)

Part 6: Structure of Atoms

Equation/constant	
$c = \lambda v$	c= speed of light (3.00×10^8m/s) λ= wavelength (m) v= frequency (Hz= 1/s or s^{-1})
$E = nhv = \dfrac{hc}{\lambda}$ where $h = 6.626 \times 10^{-34} J \cdot s/photon$ $1nm = 1 \times 10^{-9}m$	E= energy (J) n= +ive integer h= Planck's constant v = frequency (Hz) c= speed of light (3.00×10^8m/s) λ= wavelength (m)
$\Delta E = E_{higher} - E_{lower} = \Delta nhv$	E= energy (J) E_{higher}= energy of the higher level (J) E_{lower}= energy of lower level (J) Δn= change in energy levels (ex. from

	level 3 to level 1→ $\Delta n = n_{final} - n_{initial} = 3-1 = 2$)
	h= Planck's constant ($6.626 \times 10^{-34} J \cdot s/photon$)
	v = frequency (Hz= 1/s or s^{-1})
$E = \dfrac{hcN}{\lambda}$ where $h = 6.626 \times 10^{-34} J \cdot s/photon$ $N = 6.02 \times 10^{23} J/mol$	c= speed of light (3.00×10^8 m/s)
	h= Planck's constant
	E= energy (J)
	λ= wavelength (m)
$\dfrac{1}{\lambda} = R \left(\dfrac{1}{2^2} - \dfrac{1}{n^2} \right)$ when n>2 $R = 1.097 \times 10^7 m^{-1}$	λ= wavelength (m)
	R= Rydberg constant (m^{-1})
	n= integer
$E_n = -\dfrac{hcR}{n^2}$	n= energy level
	R= Rydberg constant (1.097×10^7 m^{-1})
	c= speed of light (3.00×10^8 m/s)
	h= Planck's constant ($h = 6.626 \times 10^{-34} J \cdot s/photon$)
$\Delta E = E_{final} - E_{initial}$ $= -N_A Rhc \left(\dfrac{1}{n_{final}^2} - \dfrac{1}{n_{initial}^2} \right)$ Where $N_A Rhc = 1312 kJ/mol$	ΔE= change in energy (energy absorbed/released) (kJ/mol)
	E_{final}= energy of the final energy level (J)
	$E_{initial}$= energy of the initial energy level
	n= energy level
$\lambda = \dfrac{h}{mv}$	λ= wavelength (m)
	h= Planck's constant ($h = 6.626 \times 10^{-34} J \cdot s/photon$)
	m= mass of an electron (9.1094×10^{-31} kg)
	v= velocity (m/s)

Part 7: Quantum Mechanics

Equation/constant	
Maximum number of electrons in a shell $= 2n^2$ Number of orbitals (m_l) in a shell $= n^2$	n= shell #
Maximum number of electrons in a subshell $= 2(2l + 1)$ Number of orbitals (m_l) in a subshell $= 2l + 1$	l= subshell #

Surviving University: First Year Chemistry

Part 9: Bonding and Molecular Structure

Equation/constant	

$$Formal\ charge\ of\ atom\\ = Group\ \#\ of\ atom\\ - \left[LPE + \frac{1}{2}(BE)\right]$$	Group # refers to the number of valence electrons present in an atom
	LPE= number of electrons which are not bonded in an atom (called lone electrons)
	BE= number of electrons which are bonded (called bonded electrons)

$$Formal\ charge\ of\ atom\ in\ the\ resonance\ hybrid\\ = \frac{Formal\ charge\ of\ atom\ in\ structure\ \#1 + Formal\ charge\ of\ atom\ in\ structure}{\#\ resonance\ structures}$$	
$$Bond\ order\\ = \frac{1}{2}\\ \times \frac{\#\ of\ delocalized\ e^-}{\#\ of\ bonds\ over\ which\ e^-\ are\ delocalized}$$	

Part 10: Orbital hybridization and molecular orbitals

Equation/constant	
$$Bond\ order = \frac{1}{2}(\#\ e^-\ in\ bonding\ MO\\ - \#\ e^-\ in\ antibonding\ MO)$$	MO= molecular orbitals

Part 12: Colligative properties

Equation/constant	
$$P_A = X_A P_A^{\circ}\\ \Delta P_A = -X_B P_A^{\circ}\\ where\ X_A = \frac{n_A}{n_T} = 1 - X_B\\ where\ n_T = n_A + n_B + \cdots\\ P_T = P_A + P_B = X_A P_A^{\circ} + X_B P_B^{\circ}$$	P°_A= pressure created by pure liquid A (atm) P_A= partial vapor pressure created by pure liquid A (atm) X_A= mole fraction of liquid A X_B= mole fraction of liquid B ΔP_A= change in partial vapor pressure created by pure liquid A (atm) n_A= # moles of liquid A (mol) n_B= # moles of liquid B (mol)
$$\Delta T_B = k_b \times m_{solute}\\ k_b\ for\ water = 0.5°C/m$$	ΔT_B= difference in boiling point between the solvent and the dissolved solution (°C or K) k_b= the solvent's boiling-point elevation constant (°C/m) m_{solute}= molal concentration of a solution (mol/kg)

Surviving University: First Year Chemistry

$molality_{solute} = \dfrac{n_{solute}}{mass_{solvent}}$	Note: mass must be in kg
	molality= molality of solute (mol/kg or m)
	n= # moles (mol)
	m= mass of solvent (kg)

$\Delta T_f = -k_f \times m_{solute}$ $k_f \ for \ water = \ 1.9°C/m$ $= 1.86K/m$	ΔT_f= difference in freezing point between the solvent and the dissolved solution (°C or K) k_f= the solvent's freezing-point depression constant (°C/m or K/m) m_{solute}= molal concentration of a solution (mol/kg)

$\Pi = CRT$
where $C = \dfrac{n}{V}$
$R = 8.314 \dfrac{L \cdot kPa}{K \cdot mol}$
	Π= osmotic pressure (atm)
	C= concentration of solution (mol/L or M)
	n= # moles (mol)
	V= volume (L)
	R= gas constant
	T= temperature (K)

Part 13: Nuclear Chemistry

Equation/constant	
$1 Bq = 1 \ disintegration/second$ $1 \ amu = 1.66058 \times 10^{-27} kg$	
$\Delta m = \Sigma mass \ of \ products$ $- \Sigma mass \ of \ reactants$	Δm= mass defect or excess mass (kg or amu)
$E_b = \Delta m c^2$	Δm= mass difference (kg/mol) c= 3.00×10^8 m/s (the speed of light) E_b= nuclear binding energy (J/mol)
$E_b \ in \dfrac{MeV}{amu} = \left(\dfrac{E_b \ in \frac{J}{amu}}{\frac{1.6029 \times 10^{-19} J}{eV}} \right)$ $E_b = \Delta m \ \times 931.5 \ MeV/amu$	Δm= mass difference (kg/mol) E_b= nuclear binding energy (J/mol)
$\left(\dfrac{\Delta N}{\Delta t} \right) \propto N$	ΔN= change in the number of atoms Δt= change in time (s or min or h) N= # of atoms
$ln \left(\dfrac{N}{N_0} \right) = -kt$	ln = natural logarithm t= time (s or min or h) k= rate constant N_0= number of atoms at the beginning of the decay N= number of atoms after a specific period of time

$$ln\left(\frac{A}{A_0}\right) = -kt$$	A_0= activity of the sample at the beginning of decay (Bq) A= activity after a specific period of time (Bq) k= rate constant t= time (s or min or h)
$$t_{1/2} = \frac{\ln 2}{k}$$	$t_{1/2}$= half life (s or min or h or days) k=rate constant
$$A = A_0 \times \left(\frac{1}{2}\right)^n$$ where $n = \frac{t}{t_{1/2}}$	A_0= activity of the sample at the beginning of decay (Bq) A= activity after a specific period of time (Bq) n= # of half-lives (can be a fraction) t= time (s or min or h or days) $t_{1/2}$= half life (s or min or h or days)

Part 15: Hydrocarbons

Equation/constant	
If the number of π electrons in the ring(s) and free available pairs of a molecule= 4n+2, then the molecule has aromatic properties	n is an integer (n= 0, 1, 2, 3, ...)

Part 20: Investigative tools

Equation/constant	
$$v = \frac{1}{\lambda}$$	v= wavenumber (cm^{-1}) λ= wavelength (cm)
$$[\alpha]_D = \frac{\alpha}{l \times c}$$	$[\alpha]_D$= specific rotation (°) α= observed rotation (°) l= length of sample (dm) c= concentration of sample (g/mL)

Part 21: Gases

Equation/constant	
$1atm = 760mm\,Hg = 101.325kPa = 1bar$ $= 760torr$	
$$P_1V_1 = P_2V_2$$ $$\frac{V_1}{T_1} = \frac{V_2}{T_2}$$ $$\frac{P_1V_1}{T_1} = \frac{P_2V_2}{T_2}$$ $$PV = nRT$$ where $R = 0.082057 \frac{L\cdot atm}{K\cdot mol}$	V_1 = volume in scenario 1 (L) V_2= volume in scenario 2 (L) P_1= pressure in scenario 1 (atm) P_2= pressure in scenario 2 (atm) T_1= temperature in scenario 1 (K) T_2= temperature in scenario 2 (K) P= pressure in the container (atm)

Surviving University: First Year Chemistry

	V= volume of the container (L) n= number of moles of gas in the container (mol) T= temperature inside of the container (K)
$$P_T = P_A + P_B + \cdots$$	P_T = total pressure created by all gases (atm) P_A= pressure created by gas A (atm) P_B= pressure created by gas B (atm)

$$X = \frac{n_A}{n_T}$$
where $n_T = n_A + n_B + \cdots$
	n_A= # moles of gas A (mol)
	n_B= # moles of gas B (mol)
	n_T= total # moles of gas in container (mol)
	X= mole fraction

$P_T V_T = n_T RT$ where
$$P_1 = X_1 P_T$$
$$P_2 = X_2 P_T$$
	P_T= the total pressure present in a container (atm)
	V_T= the total volume of a container (L)
	n_T= the total # moles of gas in a container (mol)
	T= the temperature in a container (K)
	R=0.082057L•atm/K•mol
	P_1= the pressure exerted by gas 1 (atm)
	P_2= the pressure exerted by gas 2 (atm)
	X_1= the mole fraction of gas 1
	X_2= the mole fraction of gas 2

$$K = \frac{1}{2}mv^2$$ $$\sqrt{\bar{u}^2} = \sqrt{\frac{3RT}{M}}$$ where $R = 8.3145 \frac{J}{K \cdot mol}$ The value of R is different (from what was used in PV=nRT) since the units are J/K•mol (not L•atm/K•mol)	M must be in kg/mol, T must be in K K= kinetic energy of molecules (J) m=mass of molecules (kg) v= speed of molecules (m/s) ū= mean square speed (rms) (average speed of molecules) (m/s) T= temperature (K) M= molar mass (kg/mol)
$$\frac{Rate\ for\ A}{Rate\ for\ B} = \sqrt{\frac{M_B}{M_A}}$$	Rate for A= rate of effusion for gas A Rate for B= rate of effusion for gas B M_A= molar mass of gas A (g/mol)

	M_B= molar mass of gas B (g/mol)

Part 22: Chemical kinetics

Equation/constant	
$Rate\ of\ a\ reaction = \dfrac{change\ in\ concentration}{change\ in\ time}$ $= \dfrac{d[conc]}{dt} = \dfrac{[C]_f - [C]_i}{t_f - t_i}$	$[C]_f$= final concentration (M) $[C]_i$= initial concentration (M) t_f= final time (s or min or h) t_i= initial time (s or min or h)
If $aA + bB \rightarrow cC + dD$ $-\dfrac{1}{a}\dfrac{d[A]}{dt} = -\dfrac{1}{b}\dfrac{d[B]}{dt} = \dfrac{1}{c}\dfrac{d[C]}{dt} = \dfrac{1}{d}\dfrac{d[D]}{dt}$	Note: lower case letters represent stoichiometric coefficients, upper case letters represent molecules, brackets represent concentrations (M) Note: negative signs mean that reactants are disappearing; positive signs mean that products are appearing
$Rate = k[A]^m[B]^n$ $Overall\ reaction\ order = m + n$	Only concentrations of reactants go into the rate equation m and n are not stoichiometric coefficients→ they are determined experimentally k= rate constant [A]= the concentration of reactant A (M) [B]= concentration of reactant B (M) m= reaction order for reactant A n= reaction order for reactant B
$\dfrac{Rate_2}{Rate_1} = \dfrac{k[X_2]^m[Y_2]^n}{k[X_1]^m[Y_1]^n}$	$Rate_2$= rate in trial 2 (M/s) $Rate_1$= rate in trial 1 (M/s) k= rate constant $[X_2]$= concentration of 1st reactant in trial 2 (M) $[X_1]$= concentration of 1st reactant in trial 1 (M) $[Y_2]$= concentration of 2nd reactant in trial 2 (M) $[Y_1]$= concentration of 2nd reactant in trial 1 (M) m= order for X n= order for Y
$t_{1/2} = \dfrac{ln\ 2}{k}$	$t_{1/2}$= half-life (s or min or h or days) k= rate constant (s^{-1} or min^{-1} or h^{-1} or days^{-1})

Surviving University: First Year Chemistry

$$k = Ae^{\frac{-E_a}{RT}}$$ where $R = 8.3145 \times 10^{-3} \frac{KJ}{K \cdot mol}$	Temperature must be in Kelvin k= rate constant (s^{-1} or min^{-1} or h^{-1}) A= frequency of collisions E_a= activation energy (kJ) T= temperature (K)
$$\ln\left(\frac{k_1}{k_2}\right) = -\frac{E_a}{R}\left(\frac{1}{T_2} - \frac{1}{T_1}\right)$$ Note: $\ln\left(\frac{k_1}{k_2}\right) = lnk_1 - lnk_2$ where $R = 8.3145 \times 10^{-3} \frac{KJ}{K \cdot mol}$	Temperature must be in Kelvin k_1= rate constant at temperature 1 (s^{-1} or min^{-1} or h^{-1}) k_2= rate constant at temperature 2 (s^{-1} or min^{-1} or h^{-1}) E_a= activation energy (kJ), T_1= temperature 1 (K) T_2= temperature 2 (K)

Part 23: Chemical equilibrium

Equation/constant	
If $aA + bB \rightleftharpoons cC + dD$ $$K_c = \frac{[products]}{[reactants]} = \frac{[C]^c[D]^d}{[A]^a[B]^b}$$ Solids and liquids <u>never</u> appear in the equilibrium expression! $$K_p = \frac{[products]}{[reactants]} = \frac{P_C^c P_D^d}{P_A^a P_B^b}$$	K_c= equilibrium constant for an aqueous solution (no units) K_p= equilibrium constant for a gaseous solution (no units) []= concentration (M) P= pressure (atm)
If $aA + bB \rightleftharpoons cC + dD$ $$Q_c = \frac{[products]}{[reactants]} = \frac{[C]^c[D]^d}{[A]^a[B]^b}$$ Solids and liquids <u>never</u> appear in the reaction quotient expression! $$Q_p = \frac{[products]}{[reactants]} = \frac{P_C^c P_D^d}{P_A^a P_B^b}$$	Q_c= reaction quotient for an aqueous solution (no units) Q_p= reaction quotient for a gaseous solution (no units) []= concentration (M) P= pressure (atm)
$$K_{new} = \frac{1}{K_{old}}$$	K_{new}= equilibrium constant for the new reaction K_{old}= equilibrium constant for the original reaction
$$K_{net} = K_1 \times K_2$$	K_{net}= equilibrium constant for the overall reaction K_1= equilibrium constant for reaction 1 K_2= equilibrium constant for reaction 2
$$K_{new} = (K_{old})^n$$	n= # that the reaction is multiplied by K_{new}= equilibrium constant for the

	new reaction
	K_{old}= equilibrium constant for the original reaction

Part 24: Acids and bases

Equation/constant	
$K_w = [H_3O^+][OH^-] = 1.0 \times 10^{-14} \, at \, 298K$	K_w= autoionization constant for water
$pH = -log[H_3O^+]$ and $[H_3O^+] = 10^{-pH}$ $pOH = -log[OH^-]$ and $[OH^-] = 10^{-pOH}$ $pKw = 14 = pH + pOH$	
If $aA + bB \rightleftharpoons cC + dD$ $K_a = \dfrac{[products]}{[reactants]} = \dfrac{[C]^c[D]^d}{[A]^a[B]^b}$ $K_b = \dfrac{[products]}{[reactants]} = \dfrac{[C]^c[D]^d}{[A]^a[B]^b}$	K_a= acid equilibrium constant K_b= base equilibrium constant
$pKa = -logKa$ and $Ka = 10^{-pKa}$ $pKb = -logKb$ and $Kb = 10^{-pKb}$ $pKa + pKb = 14$ $Kw = Ka \times Kb = 1.0 \times 10^{-7} \, at \, 298K$	K_a= acid equilibrium constant K_b= base equilibrium constant
$\% \, protonated = \dfrac{[conjugate \, acid]}{[base]} \times 100\%$	

Part 25: Buffers

Equation/constant	
$[H_3O^+] = \dfrac{[acid]}{[conjugate \, base]} \times Ka$ $[OH^-] = \dfrac{[base]}{[conjugate \, acid]} \times Kb$	K_a= acid equilibrium constant K_b= base equilibrium constant
$pH = pKa + log\dfrac{[conjugate \, base]}{[acid]}$	

Part 26: Titrations

Equation/constant	
At the halfway point $[H_3O^+] = Ka$ and $pH = pKa$	K_a= acid equilibrium constant
At equivalence point [acid]=[base]	
$[H_3O^+] = \dfrac{[acid \, remaining]}{[conjugate \, base \, produced]} \times Ka$ $pH = pKa + log\dfrac{[conjugate \, base \, produced]}{[acid \, remaining]}$	K_a= acid equilibrium constant

Surviving University: First Year Chemistry

$pH = -log[H_3O^+]$	

Part 27: Solubility

Equation/constant	
If $aA + bB \rightleftharpoons cC + dD$ $$K_{sp} = \frac{[products]}{[reactants]} = \frac{[C]^c[D]^d}{[A]^a[B]^b}$$ Solids and liquids never appear in the Ksp expression!	Ksp= solubility product constant, lower case letters represent stoichiometric coefficients, upper case letters represent molecules, brackets represent concentrations (M)
If $aA + bB \rightleftharpoons cC + dD$ $$Q = \frac{[products]}{[reactants]} = \frac{[C]^c[D]^d}{[A]^a[B]^b}$$ Solids and liquids never appear in the reaction quotient expression!	Q= reaction quotient, lower case letters represent stoichiometric coefficients, upper case letters represent molecules, brackets represent concentrations (M)

Part 28: Entropy and free energy

Equation/constant	
$$q_{H_2O} = 40700 J/mol$$	q= heat transferred during a phase change (J)
$$\Delta_r S^\circ = \Sigma S^\circ_{products} - \Sigma S^\circ_{reactants}$$	Multiply entropy values by stoichiometric coefficients $\Delta_r S^\circ$= entropy of the reaction under standard conditions (J/K•mol rxn) $\Sigma S^\circ_{products}$= the sum of entropy values of all of the products (J/K•mol) $\Sigma S^\circ_{reactants}$= the sum of entropy values of all of the reactants (J/K•mol)
$$\Delta S^\circ_{universe} = \Delta S^\circ_{system} + \Delta S^\circ_{surroundings}$$ where $\Delta S^\circ_{system} = \Sigma S^\circ_{products} - \Sigma S^\circ_{reactants}$ $$\Delta S^\circ_{surroundings} = \frac{\Delta H^\circ_{surroundings}}{T}$$ $$= -\frac{\Delta_r H^\circ_{system}}{T}$$ $$\Delta_r H^\circ = \Sigma \Delta_f H^\circ_{products} - \Sigma \Delta_f H^\circ_{reactants}$$	$\Delta S^\circ_{universe}$= entropy change of the system and surroundings under standard conditions (J/K•mol rxn) ΔS°_{system}= entropy change of the system under standard conditions (J/K•mol rxn) $\Delta S^\circ_{surroundings}$= entropy change of the surroundings under standard conditions (J/K•mol rxn) $\Delta_r S^\circ$= entropy of the reaction under standard conditions (J/K•mol rxn) $\Sigma S^\circ_{products}$= the sum of entropy values of all of the products (J/K•mol) $\Sigma S^\circ_{reactants}$= the sum of entropy values of all of the reactants (J/K•mol) $\Delta H^\circ_{surroundings}$= enthalpy change of

	the surroundings (kJ/K•mol rxn) $\Delta_r H^\circ_{system}$= enthalpy change of the system (kJ/K•mol rxn) T= temperature (K)
$\Delta_r G^\circ = \Sigma \Delta_f G^\circ_{products} - \Sigma \Delta_f G^\circ_{reactants}$ $\Delta G^\circ = \Delta H^\circ - T\Delta S^\circ = -RTlnK$ If $aA + bB \rightleftharpoons cC + dD$ $K = \dfrac{[products]}{[reactants]} = \dfrac{[C]^c[D]^d}{[A]^a[B]^b}$ $\Delta_r H^\circ = \Sigma \Delta_f H^\circ_{products} - \Sigma \Delta_f H^\circ_{reactants}$	$\Delta_r G^\circ$= change in free energy of the reaction (kJ/mol•rxn) $\Delta_f G^\circ_{products}$= change in free energy of products (kJ/mol•rxn) $\Delta_f G^\circ_{reactants}$= change in free energy of reactants (kJ/mol•rxn) ΔH°= enthalpy change of reaction (kJ/mol•rxn) T= temperature (K) ΔS°= change in entropy of the reaction (kJ/K•mol•rxn) K= equilibrium constant $\Delta_f H^\circ_{products}$= enthalpy change of products (kJ/mol•rxn) $\Delta_f H^\circ_{reactants}$= enthalpy change of reactants (kJ/mol•rxn)
$\Delta_r G = \Delta_r G^\circ + RTlnQ$ If $aA + bB \rightleftharpoons cC + dD$ $Q = \dfrac{[products]}{[reactants]} = \dfrac{[C]^c[D]^d}{[A]^a[B]^b}$ and $R = 8.3145 \dfrac{J}{K \cdot mol}$	$\Delta_r G^\circ$= change in free energy of the reaction under standard conditions (kJ/mol•rxn) $\Delta_r G$= change in free energy of the reaction under non-standard conditions (kJ/mol•rxn) T= temperature (K) Q= reaction quotient R= gas constant
ΔG° of a free element (ex. O_2)= 0 kJ/mol•rxn	

Part 29: Redox reactions

Equation/constant	
$E^\circ_{cell} = E^\circ_{cathode} + E^\circ_{anode}$	E°= cell potential under standard conditions (V) E$_{cathode}$°= cell potential at the cathode under standard conditions (V) E$_{anode}$°= cell potential at the anode under standard conditions (V)
$E = E^\circ - \dfrac{RT}{nF}lnQ$ $F = 9.6485338 \times 10^4 C/mol$	E= cell potential under non-standard conditions (V) E°= cell potential under standard

Surviving University: First Year Chemistry

$R = 8.3145 \dfrac{J}{K \cdot mol}$ If $aA + bB \rightleftharpoons cC + dD$ $Q = \dfrac{[products]}{[reactants]} = \dfrac{[C]^c[D]^d}{[A]^a[B]^b}$	conditions (V) T= temperature (K) n= # of electrons exchanged F= Faraday's constant R= gas constant Q= reaction quotient
$\Delta G° = -nFE° = -RTlnK$ $\Delta G = -nFE = -RTlnK$ $F = 9.6485338 \times 10^4 C/mol$ $R = 8.3145 \dfrac{J}{K \cdot mol}$ If $aA + bB \rightleftharpoons cC + dD$ $K = \dfrac{[products]}{[reactants]} = \dfrac{[C]^c[D]^d}{[A]^a[B]^b}$	ΔG°- free energy at standard conditions (kJ) ΔG- free energy at non-standard conditions (kJ) n= # of moles of electrons transferred F= Faraday's constant T= temperature (K) R= gas constant K= equilibrium constant
$I = \dfrac{q}{t}$ $F = 9.6485338 \times 10^4 C/mol$ $n = \dfrac{q}{F}$	I= current (A) q= charge (C) t= time (s) F= Faraday's constant n= # moles (mol)

Summary of Organic Chemistry Reactions

Reactions of alkanes ($R_3C\!-\!CR_3$)

Reaction name	General reaction	Used to produce
Elimination		Alkene
Substitution		Alcohol Haloalkane Ether

Reactions of alkenes ($R_2C\!=\!CR_2$)

- Double bond is broken apart to produce a single bond

Reaction name	General reaction	Used to produce
Addition		Alkane Haloalkane Alcohol
Substitution		Alcohol Haloalkane

Reactions of aromatic compounds ( )

Reaction name	General reaction	Used to produce
Addition	Is unlikely to occur!	-

Surviving University: First Year Chemistry

	⬡ + (A)–(B) ⟶̸ No reaction Ex. ⬡ + HCl ⟶̸ No reaction Ex. ⬡ + H_3O^+ ⟶̸ No reaction	
Electrophilic Substitution	(structure) + Electrophile⁺ ⟶ (structure) + H⁺	Derivative of benzene

Reactions of alcohols (R_3C—OH)

Reaction name	General reaction	Used to produce
Oxidation	R—C(OH)(H)—R →(oxidation)→ R—C(=O)—R	Aldehyde Ketone
Esterification	R—C(=O)—OH + HO—R ⟶ H_2O + R—C(=O)—O—R	Ester

Reactions of aldehydes (R—C(=O)—H)

Reaction name	General reaction	Used to produce
Oxidation	R—C(=O)—H →(oxidation)→ R—C(=O)—OH	Carboxylic acid

Reduction	reduction: R–CHO → R–CH(OH)H	Primary alcohol
Tautomeri-zation	Keto form (Aldehyde or Ketone) ⇌ Enol form (Enol-keto equilibrium)	Enol
Nucleophilic addition	R–CO–R + Nucleophile + H⁺ ⇌ R–C(OH)(Nucleophile)R	Depends on nucleophile

Reactions of ketones (R–CO–R)

Reaction name	General reaction	Used to produce
Oxidation	Do not undergo oxidation reaction! R–CO–R —oxidation→ No reaction. No H atom!	-
Reduction	R–CO–R —reduction→ R–CH(OH)–R	Secondary alcohol
Tautomeri-zation	Keto form (Aldehyde or Ketone) ⇌ Enol form (Enol-keto equilibrium)	Enol

Surviving University: First Year Chemistry

Nucleophilic addition	$R\overset{O}{\underset{R}{\parallel}}$ + Nucleophile + H⁺ ⇌ $R\overset{OH}{\underset{R}{\mid}}$Nucleophile	Depends on nucleophile

Reactions of carboxylic acids ($R\overset{O}{\underset{}{\parallel}}OH$)

Reaction name	General reaction	Used to produce
Reduction	$R\overset{O}{\underset{OH}{\parallel}}$ —reduction→ $R\!-\!\overset{OH}{\underset{H}{\mid}}\!-\!H$	Primary alcohol
Esterification	$R\overset{O}{\underset{O\boxed{H}}{\parallel}}$ + $\boxed{HO}\!-\!R$ → $\boxed{H_2O}$ + $R\overset{O}{\underset{}{\parallel}}O\!-\!R$	Ester

Reactions of esters ($R\overset{O}{\underset{}{\parallel}}OR$)

Reaction name	General reaction	Used to produce
Reduction	$R\overset{O}{\underset{OR}{\parallel}}$ —reduction→ $R\!-\!\overset{OH}{\underset{H}{\mid}}\!-\!H$	Secondary alcohol
Hydrolysis	$\boxed{H_2O}$ + $R\overset{O}{\underset{}{\parallel}}O\!-\!R$ → $R\overset{O}{\underset{O\boxed{H}}{\parallel}}$ + $\boxed{HO}\!-\!R$	Carboxylic acid Alcohol

__Some Tips for Studying__

These are some strategies which I used during university.

- You are in control of your study habits
  - The effort that you put into your work is what you will get out of it
- Study every day
  - Practice makes perfect
- Have a positive mind set
  - Do NOT listen to people who tell you that the course is hard or that you will fail. They are complaining because they did not put in the work and did not do well. A student with 80-95% in the class will not tell you that the course is impossible.
  - Look at it this way: if the course is impossible and is mandatory for your program, how is it that people graduate from your program? They put in the work!
- Come to every lecture
  - Professors will often "hint" to the type of problems that will be on the midterm/exam
  - The amount of time a professor spends on a concept will indicate its importance
- Use flashcards
  - This makes memorizing fun!
    - ex. memorizing polyatomic ions
  - You can either make your own flashcards (from paper) or use free online resources (search for "free flashcards online")
- Plan your study sessions
  - Assign the amount of content that you need to cover that day <u>before</u> starting to study
    - If you know that there is more to be covered, you will be less likely to waste time. Once the work is done, you can relax and have fun!
- Memorizing vs understanding
  - Understanding is crucial. If you do not understand the concepts, do not memorize them. Ask for someone to explain the concepts to you (your classmates, TA, professor, online forums).

- o Tag the questions/concepts that you do not understand with a sticky note
  - ▪ Write down (on a sticky note) the exact question that you will ask your classmate/TA/professor
  - ▪ This prevents you from
    - • Having problems with finding the question
    - • Forgetting what you wanted to ask your classmate/TA/professor
- o Memorize only content that must be memorized
  - ▪ ex. names of polyatomic ions
  - ▪ ex. names of molecular shapes for VSEPR model
  - ▪ ex. equations (if they are not provided to you on the exam)
- ▪ Have study groups
  - o Make sure that your time is spent productively. If you talk about your haircut rather than hybridization, you are wasting your time (this is not studying!!!).
  - o Try to pick a group with a variety of people. The concept that 1 person does not understand, another person might understand.
  - o Avoid studying in a group where you are the only person who understands the concepts and everyone else knows little/nothing. This will not help you increase your knowledge in areas that you do not understand.
  - o Avoid studying in a group that has a negative mind set about the class. I find that it is harder for me to put in the work when people around me are constantly complaining about the class. Do not complain and focus on doing the work!!!
  - o Make sure that everyone is involved in the discussion
- ▪ Do all of the assigned problems/assignments
  - o Make a list of questions that you did not know or want to go over. Make sure to go over them before the exam.
- ▪ Before the exam
  - o 1 week before the midterm/exam
    - ▪ Make a schedule of the content that you will cover each day
    - ▪ Leave time to redo all of the problems that you are not confident about
  - o The week before the midterm/exam
    - ▪ Read your notes
      - • Understand the concepts

- Redo all of the assigned problems
- Redo all of the problems done in class
- Memorize important concepts
- Ask for help
- Make a summary page(s) of everything that you do not know or are not confident about

Saturday	Sunday	Monday	Tuesday	Wednesday	Thursday	Friday
Chapters 1, 2	Chapter 3	Chapter 4	Chapter 5	New material covered in class	Review	Midterm

- o The day of the midterm/exam
  - Read over the solutions to problems which you are not confident about
  - Study the summary page(s)→ it is crucial to keep the concepts that you are not confident about fresh in your mind
- During the midterm/exam
  - o Do not panic!!!
  - o When you receive the exam, skim over the questions (do not fully read them)
    - Look at
      - How many questions are present
      - The type of problems
      - Approximate length of answers (ex. ½ page)
  - o Do not forget about time
    - You might panic when you realize that there are 15 minutes left and you have completed 2 out of 6 problems.
  - o Approximate how much time you will need for each question
    - Leave 10-20 minutes to review your work
      - This also serves as a safety net. If you are having difficulties with a problem, this gives you additional 10-20 minutes to go back to that problem.

Total amount of time	100 minutes
Multiple choice	30 minutes
4 Problems	60 minutes (~15 minutes/problem)
Review	10 minutes

Good luck!!! Study hard!!! ☺

Surviving University: First Year Chemistry

Index

Surviving University: First Year Chemistry

Surviving University: First Year Chemistry

Surviving University: First Year Chemistry

Works Cited

Content and examples

Dr. Caron, Francois. "CHMI 1006 lectures." Laurentian University. Sudbury, ON, Canada. September-December 2008. Performance.

Dr. Munro, Joy Gray. "CHMI 1007 lectures." Laurentian University. Sudbury, ON, Canada. January- April 2009. Performance.

John Kotz, Paul Treichel, and John Townsend. *Chemistry and Chemical Reactivity*. 7th ed. Belmount, CA, United States of America: The Thomson Corporation, 2009. Print.

Peter Mahaffy, Bob Bucat, Roy Tasker, John Kotz, Paul Treichel, Gabriela Weaver, and John McMurry. *Chemistry: Human Activity, Chemical Reactivity*. 1st Canadian ed. United States of America. Nelson Education Ltd. 2011. Print.

Drawings

ADC/ChemSketch. Advanced Chemistry Development, Inc. Toronto, ON, Canada. 2009.

Surviving University: First Year Chemistry

About the Author

Maria Sokolova

Photographer: Terri Scherzinger

Maria Sokolova is a fourth year biomedical biology student at Laurentian University in Sudbury, Ontario, Canada. Maria discovered her interest in sciences while taking a grade 11 high school chemistry course. Ever since then she has been fascinated by biology and chemistry.

Maria began to write stories at age 6 and tutoring at age 14. In the last 3 years, she has privately tutored dozens of high school and university students in chemistry, mathematics, physics, anatomy, and biology. Her enthusiasm for chemistry, teaching, and writing drove her to write this book in the summer after her first year of university. The goal for this study guide is to ease the students' transition between high school and university by presenting the material in a simple way from a student's point of view.

After completing her bachelor's degree, Maria plans to attend medical school or pursue graduate work in biological sciences.

Surviving University: First Year Chemistry

Periodic Table of the Elements

Atomic number (# of protons= # of electrons in a neutral atom)

Atomic weight (average mass of all isotopes of an element)

	1
Symbol →	H
	1.01

1	2	3	4	5	6	7	8	9	10	11	12	13	14	15	16	17	18
1 H 1.01																	2 He 4.00
3 Li 6.94	4 Be 9.01											5 B 10.81	6 C 12.01	7 N 14.01	8 O 16.00	9 F 19.00	10 Ne 20.18
11 Na 22.99	12 Mg 24.30											13 Al 26.98	14 Si 28.09	15 P 30.97	16 S 32.07	17 Cl 35.45	18 Ar 39.95
19 K 39.10	20 Ca 40.08	21 Sc 44.96	22 Ti 47.87	23 V 50.94	24 Cr 52.00	25 Mn 54.94	26 Fe 55.85	27 Co 58.93	28 Ni 58.69	29 Cu 63.55	30 Zn 65.39	31 Ga 69.72	32 Ge 72.61	33 As 74.92	34 Se 78.96	35 Br 79.90	36 Kr 83.80
37 Rb 85.47	38 Sr 87.62	39 Y 88.91	40 Zr 91.22	41 Nb 92.91	42 Mo 95.94	43 Tc 97.91	44 Ru 101.1	45 Rh 102.9	46 Pd 106.4	47 Ag 107.9	48 Cd 112.4	49 In 114.8	50 Sn 118.7	51 Sb 121.8	52 Te 127.6	53 I 126.9	54 Xe 131.3
55 Cs 132.9	56 Ba 137.3	57 La 138.9	72 Hf 178.5	73 Ta 180.9	74 W 183.8	75 Re 186.2	76 Os 190.2	77 Ir 192.2	78 Pt 195.1	79 Au 197.0	80 Hg 200.6	81 Tl 204.4	82 Pb 207.2	83 Bi 209.0	84 Po 209.0	85 At 210.0	86 Rn 222.0
87 Fr 223.0	88 Ra 226.0	89 Ac 227.0	104 Rf 261.1	105 Db 262.1	106 Sg 263.1	107 Bh 264.1	108 Hs 265.1	109 Mt 266.1	110 Ds 269.1	111 Rg 272.1	112 Cn 277.1						

Lanthanides

58 Ce 140.1	59 Pr 140.9	60 Nd 144.2	61 Pm 144.9	62 Sm 150.4	63 Eu 152.0	64 Gd 157.2	65 Tb 158.9	66 Dy 162.5	67 Ho 164.9	68 Er 167.3	69 Tm 168.9	70 Yb 173.0	71 Lu 175.0

Actinides

90 Th 232.0	91 Pa 231.0	92 U 238.0	93 Np 237.0	94 Pu 244.1	95 Am 243.1	96 Cm 247.1	97 Bk 247.1	98 Cf 251.1	99 Es 252.1	100 Fm 257.1	101 Md 258.1	102 No 259.1	103 Lr 262.1

metals

nonmetals

metalloids